SCIENCE

KEY STAGE TWO
SCOTTISH LEVELS C-E

PHYSICAL PROCESSES

FRANCES MACKAY

Published by Scholastic Ltd,
Villiers House,
Clarendon Avenue,
Leamington Spa,
Warwickshire CV32 5PR

7890 901234

AUTHOR
FRANCES MACKAY

EDITORS
NOEL PRITCHARD AND JOEL LANE

ASSISTANT EDITOR
LIBBY WEAVER

SERIES DESIGNER
LYNNE JOESBURY

DESIGNER
TOBY LONG

ILLUSTRATIONS
JEREMY BAYS AND
CHARLIE ANNE TURNER

COVER ILLUSTRATION
JONATHAN BENTLEY

INFORMATION TECHNOLOGY CONSULTANT
MARTIN BLOWS

SCOTTISH 5–14 LINKS
MARGARET SCOTT AND SUSAN GOW

Designed using Aldus Pagemaker

British Library Cataloguing-in-Publication Data
A catalogue record for this book is available from the British Library.

ISBN 0-590-53369-X

Contents

Introduction

Scholastic Curriculum Bank is a series for all primary teachers, providing an essential planning tool for devising comprehensive schemes of work as well as an easily accessible and varied bank of practical, classroom-tested activities with photocopiable resources.

Designed to help planning for and implementation of progression, differentiation and assessment, *Scholastic Curriculum Bank* offers a structured range of stimulating activities with clearly-stated learning objectives that reflect the programmes of study, and detailed lesson plans that allow busy teachers to put ideas into practice with the minimum amount of preparation time. The photocopiable sheets that accompany many of the activities provide ways of integrating purposeful application of knowledge and skills, differentiation, assessment and record-keeping.

Opportunities for formative assessment are highlighted where appropriate within the activities, while separate summative assessment activities give guidelines for analysis and subsequent action. Ways of using information technology for different purposes and within different contexts, as a tool for communicating and handling information and as a method for investigating, are integrated into the activities where appropriate, and more explicit guidance is provided at the end of the book.

The series covers all the primary curriculum subjects with separate books for Key Stages 1 and 2 or Scottish Levels A–B and C–E. It can be used as a flexible resource with any scheme, to fulfil National Curriculum and Scottish 5–14 requirements and to provide children with a variety of different learning experiences that will lead to effective acquisition of skills and knowledge.

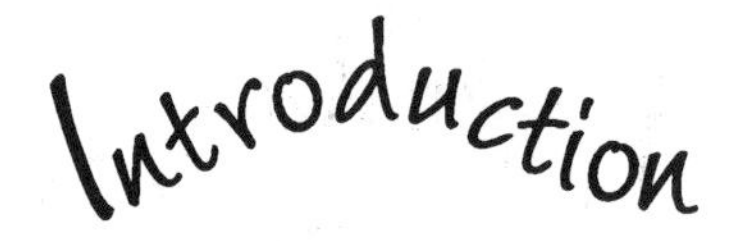

SCHOLASTIC CURRICULUM BANK SCIENCE

The *Scholastic Curriculum Bank Science* books enable teachers to plan comprehensive and structured coverage of the primary science curriculum and pupils to develop the required skills, knowledge and understanding through activities that promote scientific thinking and ways of working.

Each book covers one key stage. At Key Stage 1/Scottish levels A–B, all areas of science are covered in one book. At Key Stage 2, there are three books which reflect the sections of the programme of study (Life Processes and Living Things, Materials and their Properties and Physical Processes). Experimental and Investigative science is integrated into the three Key Stage 2/Scottish levels C–E books, so that it is tackled in context.

Bank of activities

This book provides a bank of activities that can be used in many different ways – to form a framework for a scheme of work; to add breadth and variety to an existing scheme; or to supplement a particular topic. The activities are designed to address a number of important areas of study.

Systematic enquiry

A wide range of activities has been presented, to create opportunities for focused exploration and investigation to acquire scientific knowledge, understanding and skills. The activities involve both firsthand experience and the use of other sources of information. Opportunities for the use of IT for storing, retrieving and presenting information, and for investigative purposes, are suggested throughout.

Communication skills

The activities aim to develop children's communication skills by encouraging them to:

▲ ask questions;
▲ learn and use scientific vocabulary;
▲ use standard measures;
▲ discuss findings with others;
▲ present data in a variety of different ways.

Science in everyday life

Through a variety of domestic and environmental contexts, pupils are able to acquire an awareness of the importance of science in everyday life, of the part science has played in the development of many of the things they use, and of the need to treat their environment with care and sensitivity.

The nature of scientific ideas

The activities will help children to understand that scientific knowledge and understanding rely on evidence, and that scientific evidence can be obtained in a number of ways. They will also help children to realise that science can provide explanations for many of the things that happen around them.

Health and safety

The activities encourage children to develop their knowledge and understanding of health and safety when working with living things and with materials. They will help pupils to recognise potential hazards to themselves and others, assess the risks to themselves and others, and take action to help control the risks.

Lesson plans

Detailed lesson plans, under clear headings, are given for each activity and provide material for immediate implementation in the classroom. The structure for each activity is as follows:

Activity title box

The information contained in the box at the beginning of each activity outlines the following key aspects:

▲ *Activity title and learning objective* – For each activity, a clearly-stated learning objective is given in bold italics. These learning objectives break down aspects of the programmes of study into manageable, hierarchical teaching and learning chunks, and their purpose is to aid planning for progression. These objectives can be easily referenced to the National Curriculum and Scottish 5–14 requirements by using the overview grids at the end of this chapter (pages 9 to 12).

▲ *Class organisation/Likely duration* – Icons 👥 and 🕒 signpost the suggested group sizes for each activity and the approximate amount of time required to complete it.

▲ *Safety* – Where necessary, safety considerations are flagged with the ⚠ icon.

Introduction

Previous skills/knowledge needed
Information is given here when it is necessary for the children to have acquired specific knowledge or skills prior to carrying out the activity.

Key background information
The information in this section is intended to help the teacher to understand the scientific concepts and ideas covered in each activity. It generally goes beyond the level of understanding expected of most children, but will help to give the teacher confidence to ask and answer questions and to guide the children in their investigations.

Preparation
Advice is given for those occasions where it is necessary for the teacher to prime the pupils for the activity or to prepare materials, or to set up a display or activity ahead of time.

Resources needed
All of the materials needed to carry out the activity are listed, so that either the pupils or the teacher can gather them together easily before the beginning of the teaching session.

What to do
Easy-to-follow, step-by-step instructions are given for carrying out the activity, including (where appropriate) suggested questions for the teacher to ask the pupils to help instigate discussion and stimulate investigation.

Suggestion(s) for extension/support
Ideas are given for ways of providing for easy differentiation where activities lend themselves to this purpose. In all cases, suggestions are provided as to how each activity can be modified for the less able or extended for the more able.

Assessment opportunities
Where appropriate, opportunities for formative assessment of the children's work during or after a specific activity are highlighted.

Opportunities for IT
Where opportunities for IT present themselves, these are briefly outlined with reference to particularly suitable types of program. The chart on page 158 presents specific areas of IT covered in the activities, together with more detailed support on how to apply particular types of program. Selected lesson plans serve as models for other activities by providing more comprehensive guidance on the application of IT, and these are indicated by the bold page numbers on the grid and the 🖳 icon at the start of an activity.

Display ideas
Where they are relevant and innovative, display ideas are incorporated into activity plans and illustrated with examples.

Other aspects of the Science PoS covered
Inevitably, activities will cover aspects of the programmes of study in other areas of the science curriculum; and in particular, Experimental and Investigative Science will be a feature of many of them. These links are highlighted under this heading.

Reference to photocopiable sheets
Where activities include photocopiable activity sheets, small reproductions of these are included in the lesson plans, together with guidance notes for their use and, where appropriate, suggested answers.

Investigations
Although aspects of Experimental and Investigative Science will be integral to most activities, each book includes a separate section of investigations and real-life problem-solving activities. These activities are more open-ended than those elsewhere in the book, and provide opportunities to test ideas and carry out whole investigations, utilising and building on content knowledge. Guidance for the teacher on concepts likely to emerge from such investigations is given. Activities suitable for investigations are flagged by the ◈ icon.

Assessment

This chapter provides a range of tasks related to the main areas of study covered elsewhere in the book that can be used for summative assessment purposes. The activities have been designed so that they can either be used as individual tasks to provide the teacher with an ongoing evaluation of the children's progress or, alternatively, be presented together as a form of summative assessment at the end of a whole unit or at the end of Key Stage 2. The worksheets that make up the tasks can be found at the end of the Photocopiable section (pages 139 to 157). Activities intended for assessment purposes are flagged by the ✍ icon.

Photocopiable activity sheets

Many of the activities are accompanied by photocopiable activity sheets. There may be more than one version of some activities; or an activity sheet may be 'generic', with a facility for the teacher to fill in the appropriate task in order to provide differentiation by task. Other sheets may be more open-ended, to provide differentiation by outcome.

Cross-curricular links

Cross-curricular links are identified on a simple grid which cross-references the particular areas of study in science to the programmes of study for other subjects in the curriculum, and where appropriate provides suggestions for activities. (See page 160.)

PHYSICAL PROCESSES

A study of physical processes will enable children to enhance their understanding of how things work as well as to develop a greater awareness of the reasons behind everyday phenomena, such as the effects of light, sound and motion and the daily and seasonal changes which occur on Earth.

The science of physical processes offers a wealth of opportunities for investigations which involve first hand experience and will help to develop skills of observation, prediction, testing and recording. Many aspects of this study will involve the designing, making and trialling of machines and devices to test ideas about physical processes. Such experiences will enable the children to develop a greater understanding of the way things work and of the forces involved in the devices they are exploring and trialling.

This book aims to develop the children's knowledge of and natural curiosity about the physical world through a wide variety of scientific activities designed to cater for the broad range of abilities and interests in the primary classroom. Specifically, it aims to provide the children with experience in all aspects of the Physical Processes section of the Key Stage 2 Programme of Study.

The activities themselves aim to provide the teacher with enough information and guidance to enable even the most inexperienced and unconfident teacher to make an attempt. The activities are focused on specific learning objectives, and are designed to be used as a structured lesson plan or as a broad guide for the teacher to develop her own lesson plans. There are photocopiable sheets, ideas for formative and summative assessment, IT applications, display ideas and detailed guidance on possible investigations.

In all, the book aims to provide the teacher with the maximum support and encouragement needed to teach children about physical processes. All that remains to be supplied is curiosity and enthusiasm, qualities that the children will (hopefully) possess already.

Learning objective	PoS/AO	Content	Type of activity	Page
Electricity				
Many everyday appliances use electricity.	1a, KS1/*Energy and forces: Properties and uses of energy, Level B*	Introduction to electricity – how it can be used. Research on how electricity can be generated.	Whole class, then small groups or pairs. Photocopiable page used as discussion starter. Research using reference books.	14
Electricity can be dangerous.	Health & safety, 5a, b/*As above, Level B*	Discussion about safety aspects of using electricity. Designing a safety poster.	Pairs or small groups. Photocopiable page. Whole-class discussion.	15
A complete circuit is needed to make electrical devices to work.	1a/*As above, Level C*	Investigation – making a bulb light up in a circuit.	Individuals or pairs. Photocopiable page. Investigation.	16
Electricity can be switched on and off.	1b/*As above, Level C*	Making and using switches in models.	Individuals or pairs. Investigation. Discussion of results.	18
Switches can be used to control electrical devices.	1b, 1d/*As above, Level C*	Making circuits with two switches.	Individuals or pairs. Photocopiable page as instruction sheet. Own investigation. Class discussion.	20
Some things conduct electricity.	AT3, 1c/*As above, Level C*	Investigating materials to see if they conduct electricity.	Pairs or small groups. Photocopiable page to record results. Investigation.	21
Electricity in a circuit flows in one direction only.	1a, 1d/*As above, Level D*	Discussion and investigation of current flow.	Individuals or pairs. Investigation. Drawing circuits.	23
The current in a circuit can be varied.	1c/*As above, level E*	Discussion and investigation of resistance.	Individuals or pairs. Investigation. Class discussion.	24
A motor can make electrical devices work.	1a, 1b/*As above, Level E*	Investigating motors. Making an electric winch.	Pairs or small groups. Photocopiable page as instruction sheet. Class discussion.	26
Circuits can be represented by drawings and diagrams.	1d/*As above, Level E*	Discussion and representation of circuits using drawings and diagrams.	Whole class or small groups. Photocopiable sheet. Class discussion.	28
Diagrams can be used to construct circuits.	1d/*As above, Level E*	Constructing circuits from diagrams.	Pairs or small groups. Photocopiable sheet. Class/group discussion.	29
Forces and motion				
Many things are able to move.	2a, KS1/*Energy and Forces: Forces and their effect, Level B*	Testing out objects to see if they roll, slide. Looking at ways things move.	Small groups. Using a collection. Investigation. Class discussion.	32
A force is a push or a pull.	2b, KS1; 2f, KS2/ *As above, Level B*	Sorting objects into pushes or pulls to make them work. Pushing and pulling objects.	Pairs or small groups. Photocopiable page. Investigation. Recording. Class discussion.	33

Learning objective	PoS/AO	Content	Type of activity	Page
Forces can change the shape of objects.	2d, KS1/*As above, Level B*	Finding out if objects can change shape.	Pairs or small groups. Using a collection. Investigation. Recording. Group discussion.	34
The shape of an object can have an effect on the forces needed to change that object.	2g, 2h/*As above, Level B*	Investigating the strength of shapes.	Individuals or pairs. Photocopiable page. Investigation. Recording. Class discussion.	35
There are forces of attraction and repulsion between magnets.	2a/*As above, Level C*	Investigating properties of magnets.	Pairs or small groups. Investigation. Group discussion.	37
Magnets are attracted to some materials.	2a/*As above, Level C*	Investigating whether objects are magnetic.	Pairs or small groups. Photocopiable page. Investigation. Class discussion.	39
Magnetic force will pass through some materials.	2a/*As above, Level D*	Investigating whether magnets will work through materials. Testing the strength of magnets.	Pairs or small groups. Photocopiable page. Investigation. Recording. Class discussion.	40
Friction can slow a moving object.	2c/*As above, Level C*	Investigating the effect of friction on a moving object.	Small groups. Photocopiable page. Investigation. Measuring and recording. Class discussion.	41
Gravity is a force.	2b/*As above, Level D*	Dropping objects to see which ones land first. Investigating what happens.	Pairs or small groups. Investigation. Recording. Class discussion.	44
Objects have weight due to the pull of gravity.	2b/*As above, Level E*	Measuring the weight of objects using a newton meter.	Small groups. Measuring and recording. Group discussion.	45
Air resistance can slow a moving object.	2c/*As above, Level D*	Making and testing parachutes.	Pairs or small groups. Photocopiable sheet. Investigation. Recording. Class discussion.	46
When elastic bands are stretched they exert a force on whatever is stretching them.	2d/*As above, Level D*	Making and testing an elastic-powered buggy.	Pairs or small groups. Photocopiable page. Using instructions. Investigation. Measuring and recording. Discussion.	48
When a spring is compressed it exerts a force on whatever is compressing it.	2d/*As above, Level D*	Making a spring tester to test the reactions of different springs.	Pairs or small groups. Investigation. Recording. Discussion.	50
Forces act in particular directions.	2f/*As above, Level D*	Discussion of the forces involved in stationary and moving objects. Using arrows to show direction and strength.	Small groups or whole class. Photocopiable page. Teacher-directed lesson. Discussion.	51

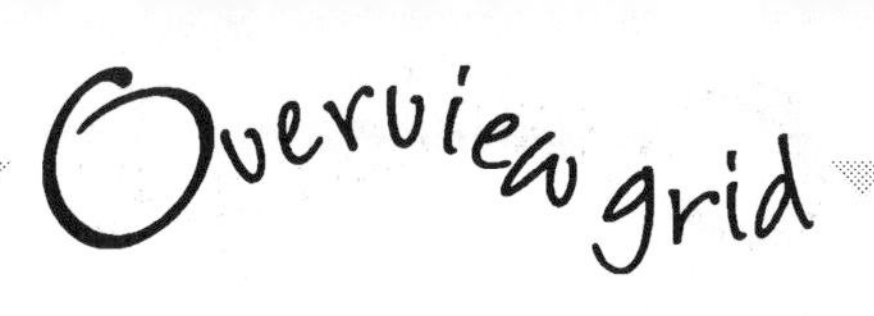

Learning objective	PoS/AO	Content	Type of activity	Page
Forces can be balanced or unbalanced.	2g, 2h/*As above, Level D*	Exploring floating and sinking.	Pairs or small groups. Observation. Investigation. Recording. Discussion.	53
Light				
Light travels from a variety of sources.	3a/*Energy and Forces: Forms and sources of energy, Level B*	Discussion and observation of light sources.	Whole class, then small groups. Photocopiable page. Observation. Discussion.	56
Light travels in a straight line from a source.	3a/*Properties and uses of energy, Level C*	Observation of how light behaves. Use of ray box.	Pairs or small groups. Investigation. Observation. Discussion.	57
Light can travel through some materials.	3b/*As above, Level C*	Testing objects to see if light will pass through them.	Small groups. Investigation. Sorting. Recording. Discussion.	58
Shadows are formed when light cannot pass through materials.	3b/*As above, Level C*	Predicting the shape of shadows made by objects. Testing out the predictions.	Pairs or small groups. Photocopiable page. Investigation. Recording. Discussion.	59
The shape of a shadow is affected by the object and the position of the light source.	3b/*As above, Level C*	Investigating the factors which affect the shape of a shadow.	Pairs or small groups. Investigation. Recording. Discussion.	61
The size of a shadow is affected by the position of the object and the light source.	3b/*As above, Level C*	Investigating the factors which affect the size of a shadow.	Pairs or small groups. Investigation. Measuring. Recording. Discussion.	62
Light can be reflected.	3c/*As above, Level C*	Using a collection of shiny objects. Carrying out an investigation on reflection.	Pairs or small groups. Observation. Initiating an investigation. Recording. Discussion.	63
The image seen in a mirror is reversed.	3c/*As above, Level C*	Exploring how to see things using a mirror.	Pairs. Photocopiable page. Observation. Discussion.	64
Light reflects off mirrors at the same angle as that at which it arrives.	3c/*As above, Level C*	Observing how light is reflected off mirrors.	Pairs or small groups. Investigation. Observation. Discussion.	66
Objects can be seen when light reflects off them into our eyes.	3d/*As above, Level C*	Learning about the parts of the eye and how we see things.	Whole class. Observation. Discussion.	67
Sound				
Sounds are all around us. Sounds travel away from sources and get fainter as they do so.	KS1, 3c, 3d/*Energy and Forces: Forms and sources of energy, Level B*	Listening to sounds in school. Recording distances when sounds can no longer be heard.	Pairs. Photocopiable page. Observation, measurement, recording. Class discussion.	70

Learning objective	PoS/AO	Content	Type of activity	Page
Sounds can be made in many ways.	3e/*As above, Level B*	Making different sounds using junk materials.	Individuals, pairs or small groups. Investigation. Recording. Class discussion.	71
Sounds are made when things vibrate.	3e/*As above, Level B*	Making objects vibrate. Making a musical instrument.	Small groups. Observation. Investigation. Class discussion.	72
Sounds vary in loudness.	3f/*Properties and uses of energy, Level C*	Exploring soft and loud sounds. Making musical instruments.	Small groups. Observation. Investigation. Class discussion.	74
Sounds vary in pitch.	3f/*As above, Level C*	Making instruments using instruction cards.	Small groups. Photocopiable cards. Class discussion.	76
Vibrations from sound sources can travel through some materials to the ear.	3g/*As above, Level C*	Testing how well sound travels through different materials.	Small groups. Investigation. Recording.	77
Our ears are used to detect sounds.	3g/*As above, Level C*	Testing our hearing. Judging direction of sound using two and one ear.	Pairs. Investigation. Recording. Class discussion.	79
The Earth and beyond				
The Earth, Moon and Sun are separate, spherical bodies.	4a/*Earth and Space: Earth in Space, Level A*	Discussion about shape and sizes of Sun, Earth and Moon. Distance of Earth from Sun.	Whole class. Measuring. Observation. Discussion.	82
The position of the Sun appears to change throughout the day.	4b/*As above, Level A*	Recording the position of the Sun during the day.	Small groups or whole class. Observation. Recording. Discussion.	83
Shadows change as the position of the Sun appears to change throughout the day.	4b/*As above, Level D*	Using a shadow stick to track shadows during the day.	Small groups or whole class. Observation. Measuring. Recording. Discussion.	84
Day and night are caused by the Earth spinning on its axis.	4c/*As above, Level D*	Discussion about how day and night are caused using a globe to demonstrate.	Whole class. Observation. Photocopiable page. Discussion.	86
The Earth's rotation causes time differences in different parts of the world.	4c/*As above, Level D*	Observing lengths of shadows in different parts of a model world. Discussion about world time zones.	Small groups. Photocopiable page. Observation. Discussion.	88
Day length varies according to the time of year and position on the Earth.	4d/*As above, Level D*	Using a model to show how seasons relate to the Earth's orbit of the Sun.	Whole class or small groups. Observation. Discussion.	89
The Moon orbits the Earth.	4d/*As above, Level D*	Using a model to demonstrate how the Moon orbits the Earth.	Whole class. Observation. Discussion.	91

Electricity

The activities in this section of the book encourage children to explore the properties and uses of electricity, looking in particular at simple circuits. In the course of carrying out the activities, the children will gain experience in questioning, observing, predicting, recording, measuring and drawing conclusions. They will also have opportunities to work co-operatively and to share their ideas with others.

Electricity is the movement of electrons in a particular direction, from one atom to another. Electricity has a number of properties:

▲ Electricity can flow or move.
▲ Electricity travels in a continuous path or circuit.
▲ Some materials allow electricity to flow through them (*conductors*) and some do not (*insulators*).
▲ Electricity cannot be created. All matter contains electrons and electricity involves a flow of these electrons. All that is needed is something, such as a battery, dynamo or generator, that will set up an imbalance to 'push' the electrons along.

It is vital to discuss safety aspects before beginning practical work on electricity. *Mains electricity and electricity from car batteries are not safe to use, and under no circumstances should children play with mains electricity.* Show them how to hold a plug correctly when putting it into a socket (their fingers should be at the back of the plug). Inform the children that they could receive an electric shock if they use wet hands when touching a socket. Explain the dangers of cutting through cables when using electrical equipment, and the dangers of frayed leads on electrical appliances.

USES OF ELECTRICITY

Many everyday appliances use electricity.

Whole class, then pairs or small groups.

45–60 minutes.

See guidelines on page 13.

Previous skills/knowledge needed
None specifically required for this activity.

Key background information
Electricity is the movement of electrons in a particular direction, from one atom to another. It flows or moves in a continuous path or circuit and can be switched on and off. Electricity cannot be created. All matter contains electrons and electricity involves a flow of these electrons. A generator, dynamo or battery is used to 'push' the electrons along, thereby enabling us to use the electrical energy in some way.

Preparation
None specifically required for this activity.

Resources needed
One copy per child of photocopiable page 114, pencils, reference books on electricity that include information about how electricity is generated.

What to do
Explain to the children that they are going to begin some work on electricity by looking at how it can be used. Provide each child with photocopiable page 114, and ask them to complete both sections of it. Then ask the children to get into pairs or small groups to discuss their answers. Can the group agree? Are there some answers about which the children are uncertain?

Bring the whole class back together to compare the groups' results. Begin the discussion with the section on naming objects which use electricity. What do the torch, car and travel clock have in common? Were the children aware that batteries can be used to provide electricity? What other objects can they name which use batteries?

Discuss each statement in turn. Ask the children to give examples of electrical appliances which produce heat and/or light. Explain that not all people in the world have access to electricity. Can the children suggest countries where it may not be used in all homes? How do people with no electricity cook their food and obtain light? Ask the children to imagine what their lives would be like without electricity. What things would change? What would they miss most if there were no electricity? Why? How would they cook food and get light?

Why does a car need electricity? Discuss how a car battery is used to provide power for the starter motor, which in turn starts the engine.

Ask the children to tell you what they think happens when the switch in a socket is turned off. What happens to the electricity; is it still there? Explain that electricity is capable of moving through certain things, such as wires. Can the children explain how they think electricity reaches their homes? Ask the children to tell you how they think water, coal and wind are used to generate electricity.

The lesson could be completed by asking the children to use the reference books to find the answers to some of the questions raised during the discussion. They could find out how electricity is generated in power stations and how it travels to our homes.

Suggestion(s) for extension
Ask the children to write down or prepare a five-minute talk on what they have learned about electricity from their discussions and research.

Suggestion(s) for support
If necessary, read the instructions and statements on photocopiable page 114 to the children. Help the children feel confident about participating in the group and whole-class discussions. Explain at the outset that you do not expect them to know the answers to all the questions on the worksheet or the questions raised through discussion, and that the purpose of the lesson is to help them find out more about electricity.

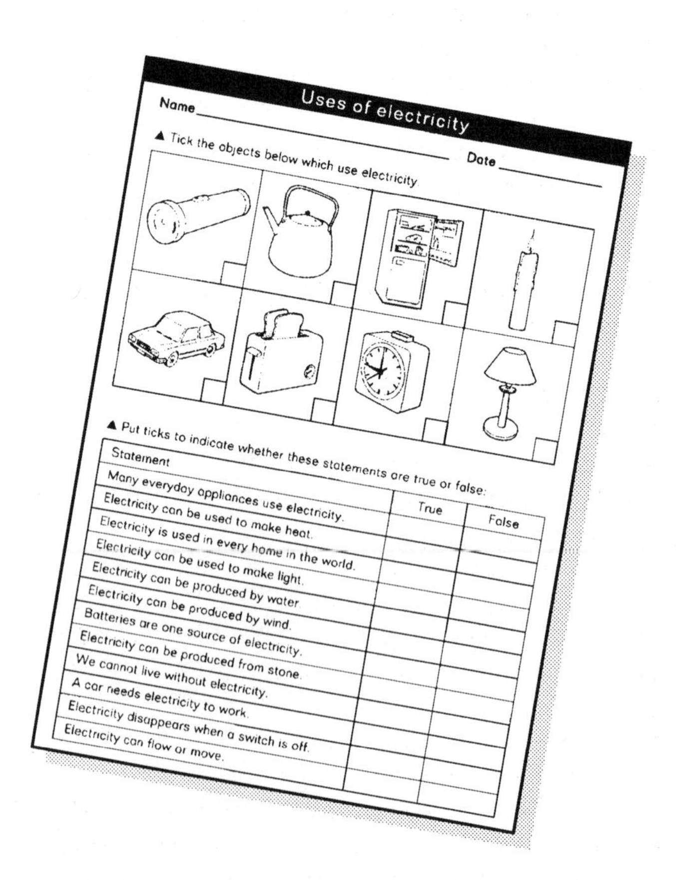
Uses of electricity

Name ______ Date ______

▲ Tick the objects below which use electricity

▲ Put ticks to indicate whether these statements are true or false:

Statement	True	False
Many everyday appliances use electricity.		
Electricity can be used to make heat.		
Electricity is used in every home in the world.		
Electricity can be used to make light.		
Electricity can be produced by water.		
Electricity can be produced by wind.		
Batteries are one source of electricity.		
Electricity can be produced from stone.		
We cannot live without electricity.		
A car needs electricity to work.		
Electricity disappears when a switch is off.		
Electricity can flow or move.		

Assessment opportunities

The children's answers to the questions on photocopiable sheet 114 will enable you to assess how much the children already know about the uses and production of electricity. The whole-class discussion will further highlight those areas that the children understand or are confused about. It will provide a good starting-point for directing the children's experiences further.

Opportunities for IT

Children could use graphing software to display the results of a survey of the number of electrical sockets in each room in the school. They might conduct a similar survey of their own home. This could lead to questions about why there are more sockets in some rooms than in others. The survey results might also be linked to the work on electrical appliances – more being found in the kitchen or lounge than in the dining room, for example.

Children could also create a simple database of electrical examples. This could include fields such as:

Appliance	kettle
Source	mains
Location	kitchen
Heat	yes
Light	no
Sound	no
Movement	no

Children could then use the database to find answers to the following questions.

▲ Which appliances create heat? (Search for *heat* and print *appliances*.)

▲ Which appliances create heat and movement? (Search for *heat* and *movement* and print *appliances*.)

▲ Which appliances run from batteries? (Search for *source* and print *appliances*.)

▲ Which appliances create heat but not light, or create sound but not heat?

Display ideas

Ask the children to draw pictures of things in the school which use electricity. Mount the pictures and put them on the wall. Conduct a survey of the number of sockets in each classroom and make graphs of the results. Add these to the display. Place some items which use electricity on a table in front of the display, together with a set of question cards and reference books on electricity. Encourage the children to find out the answers to these questions.

Reference to photocopiable sheet

The objects which should be ticked are: torch, fridge, car, toaster, travel clock and lamp. The statements which are false are: electricity is used in every home in the world, electricity can be produced from stone, we cannot live without electricity, electricity disappears when a switch is off.

ELECTRICAL SAFETY

Electricity can be dangerous.

Pairs or small groups.

45–60 minutes.

See guidelines on page 13.

Previous skills/knowledge needed

Electricity is used in many everyday appliances.

Key background information

Mains electricity and electricity from car batteries can be very dangerous and can kill. This point must be made very clear to the children. Children need to know how to hold a plug correctly when putting it into a socket (fingers should be at the back of the plug). They need to know that they could receive an electric shock if they use wet hands when touching a socket, if they cut through an electrical cable and if they touch frayed leads on electrical appliances.

Preparation

None specifically required for this activity.

Resources needed

One copy per pair/group of photocopiable page 115, pencils, paper, colouring pencils, an electrical lead.

What to do

Explain to the children that they are going to find out about safety with electricity. Divide the children into pairs or small

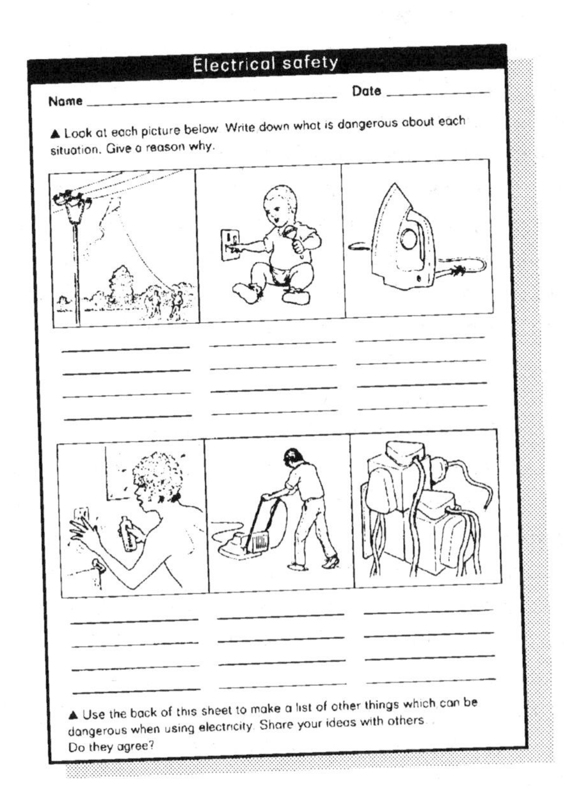

Electrical safety

Name ______ Date ______

▲ Look at each picture below. Write down what is dangerous about each situation. Give a reason why.

▲ Use the back of this sheet to make a list of other things which can be dangerous when using electricity. Share your ideas with others. Do they agree?

groups and provide them with copies of photocopiable page 115. Ask them to look at the pictures and decide what is dangerous about each one. Allow about five to ten minutes for this, then bring the whole class back together. Talk about each picture in turn to share the children's ideas about the dangers involved.

Explain that mains electricity and electricity from car batteries are very dangerous and that electricity can kill. Tell the children that the electricity from small torch batteries is quite safe and will not harm them. Show them an electrical lead and ask them to tell you how they think they should hold it when they are putting it in a socket. Ensure that the children know how to hold the plug correctly, and explain what can happen if their fingers touch the exposed metal in the plug.

Ask the children to look at photocopiable page 115 again and complete the written section under each picture. They could then make a list, in pairs or small groups, of other safety issues to consider when using electricity. Discuss these lists with each group in turn or together as a whole class.

The children could then design and make a poster which tells others how to keep safe when using electricity.

Suggestion(s) for extension

Conduct a safety survey of electrical appliances and sockets in the classroom. Are any sockets too near a sink? Are any electrical leads frayed? Have the electrical appliances had a recent safety check? Alert the headteacher to any things which may need attention.

Suggestion(s) for support

Pair up more able writers with less able ones, or act as scribe when the children are completing the written section of photocopiable sheet 115.

Assessment opportunities

The group and whole-class discussions will enable you to assess how aware the children are of the dangers of electricity generally. Opportunities will also arise, as the teacher moves from group to group, for more in-depth discussions with individual children.

Opportunities for IT

Children could use an art or graphics package to design a poster about electrical safety. This might involve using the software to combine text and graphics. If the children have access to a scanner, they could scan in pictures of different electrical appliances for the poster. Alternatively, selections of clipart might have pictures, signs or symbols that children could use.

Children could use a word processor or desktop publishing package to write electrical safety instructions for display in the classroom or around the school. Children could also make labels for a display of electrical items in the classroom.

Display ideas

Make a large red danger sign and mount it on the wall. Display the children's posters around the sign. Place a table near the display and put a collection of electrical items on the table, such as a frayed lead, a plug, a broken wall socket and so on. Make signs to match each item with information about safety issues, such as why frayed leads are dangerous, how to hold a plug correctly, and so on.

Reference to photocopiable sheet

Less able children could be paired with more able ones to complete photocopiable sheet 115. The pictures could also be cut out to be used in the safety posters, if the children's drawing skills are limited.

MAKING A CIRCUIT

A complete circuit is needed to make electrical devices work.

Individuals or pairs.

30–45 minutes.

See guidelines on page 13.

Previous skills/knowledge needed

Batteries provide electricity, as well as mains. Small-battery electricity is safe to handle.

Key background information

Electricity is the movement of electrons in a particular direction, from one atom to another. Electricity can flow or move. It travels in a continuous path or circuit. It will only keep moving and light a bulb if this path is unbroken.

When the flow of electricity was first investigated by the scientist André Ampère, it was thought that electricity flowed from *positive* to *negative*. This idea was accepted generally and is still recognised in many parts of the world. More recently, however, scientists have discovered that this is incorrect and that electricity actually flows from negative to positive!

Electricity flows in one direction only. As it passes through a light bulb, it meets a thinner wire in the filament and has to 'work harder' to get through, due to the wire's *resistance*. Because the wire is thin and coiled and the electricity is 'working harder', the electrical energy is changed to heat and light energy and so the filament lights up. An inert gas in the bulb prevents it from bursting into flames.

Preparation

Try out the activity yourself before asking the children to do the task. This will help you to discover some of the difficulties the children may experience, and will also ensure that the bulbs and batteries are functioning correctly. Figure 1 shows how the circuit could be constructed.

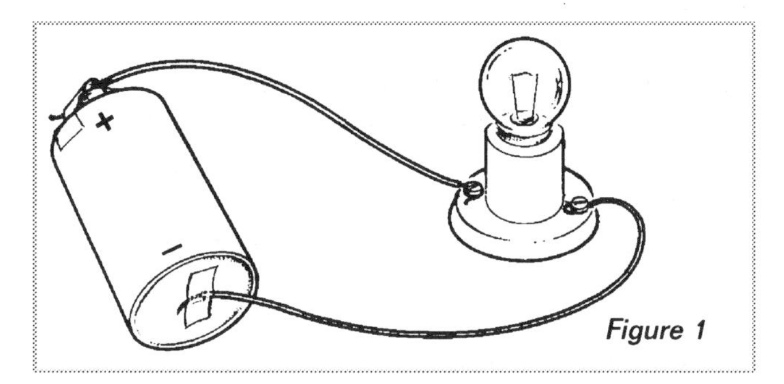

Figure 1

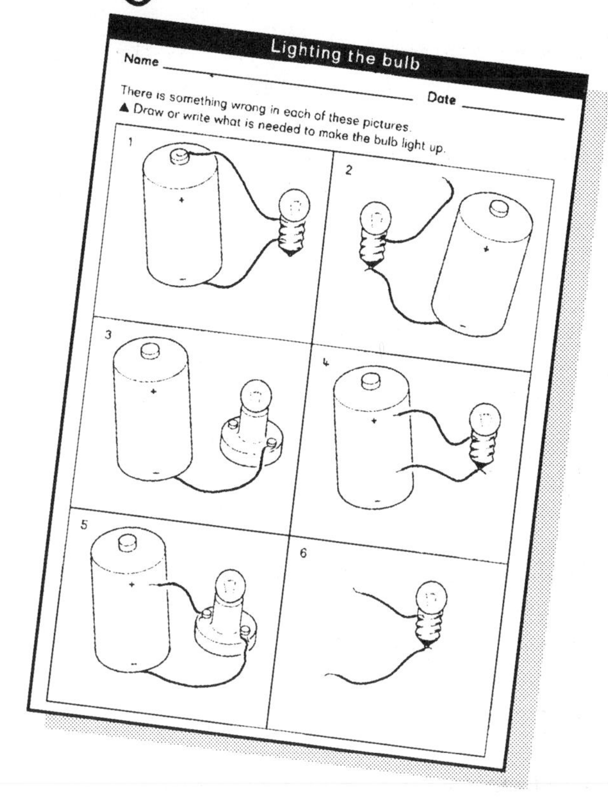

Resources needed

A 1.5V battery, a 1.5V bulb, a bulb holder, a small screwdriver, two insulated wires with the ends bare, adhesive tape, one copy per child (or pair) of photocopiable page 116, pencils.

What to do

Explain to the children that they are going to do some work on electricity. Remind them that mains electricity is dangerous, but that small-battery electricity is safe to handle. Provide the children with all the equipment and ask them the following question: Can you make the bulb light up? Allow them time to explore and try out different things. If they are struggling, ask questions such as: Where do you think the wires should go? Why does the bulb holder have two screws on it? How can you use the screwdriver to help you attach the wires? Where do you think the bulb should go? Where do you think the wires should join on to the battery?

Help the children join the wires to the bulb holder if they become frustrated. Then allow them more time to see how the wires might be attached to the battery. If the children still cannot get the bulb to light, ask them to try the wires in different places on the battery – both at one end, then both at the other end, then one at each side, then one wire on the negative end and one wire on the positive end. The bulb should now light up. Use adhesive tape to secure the wires to the battery.

Ask the children to consider the following: What happens if one of the wires is removed from the battery? What happens if one wire is removed from the bulb holder? Why does the bulb not light up? What does this tell us about making a circuit with batteries and bulbs?

Ask the children to make a circuit without using the bulb holder. This will help them to understand where the wires need to go on the bulb to make it light up. Encourage them to look at the bulb holder itself to see where the connections go. What parts of the bulb do they touch? Can the children explain why they need to touch the bulb on the side and the bottom? (One of the wires going to the filament is connected to the metal screw thread of the bulb and the other wire is connected to the stud at the bottom of the bulb. The wires are kept apart by insulating materials inside the base of the bulb. See Figure 2.)

filament
insulating material
wires
metal screw thread
insulator
stud

Figure 2

Provide the children with a copy of photocopiable sheet 116 and ask them to complete it individually or in pairs. Discuss the results to make sure the children know that a complete circuit is needed in each example on the sheet.

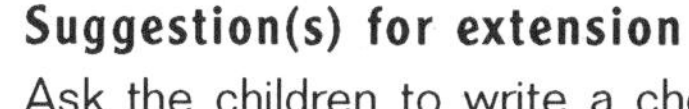

Suggestion(s) for extension

Ask the children to write a checklist of possible faults if the circuit appeared to be joined up correctly, but the bulb did not light up. The checklist could include: one of the wires might not be joined securely enough to the battery; the bulb might have 'blown'; the battery could be 'dead'; the wire may not be attached correctly to the bulb holder; and so on.

Suggestion(s) for support

Provide the children with a bulb holder with the wires already attached. Work closely with the children, asking the questions given in the 'What to do' section to help them find the right solution. Encourage trial-and-error methods. Show the children how to make the circuit if necessary, and then ask them to try it again themselves.

Assessment opportunities

The discussions you have with the children when they are making the circuit will enable you to assess how much the children know about circuits already. Photocopiable page 116 can be used at the end of the activity to assess whether or not a child has understood about the need for a complete circuit; or it could be used later as a form of summative assessment.

Display ideas

Make a large three-dimensional model of a simple circuit, with wires, battery and bulb, to display on the wall. Add labels naming each part and a larger heading entitled 'Making a circuit'. Add drawings of circuits which would not light up the bulb because some part of them was incorrect. (Some examples are given in photocopiable sheet 116.) Challenge the children to say what is wrong with each picture.

Other aspects of the Science PoS covered

Experimental and Investigative Science – 1a; 2a, b, c; 3c, e.

Reference to photocopiable sheet

This sheet is used as part of the lesson, but could also be used later to assess retention of knowledge. The corrections for each picture are: 1 – the wire from the negative end of the battery needs to touch the bottom of the bulb; 2 – the wire at the positive end of the battery needs to touch the top of the battery; 3 – a wire needs to join the top of the battery to the other bulb holder screw; 4 – the wires need to touch the top and base of the battery; 5 – the wire needs to touch the positive end of the battery; 6 – a battery needs to be included with the wires touching the top and base of it.

SWITCHES

Electricity can be switched on and off.

Individuals or pairs.

60–120 minutes.

See guidelines on page 13.

Previous skills/knowledge needed

A complete circuit is needed to make electrical devices work.

Key background information

Electricity is a flow of electrons. The movement of electrons through a wire is called an electric current. Electricity travels in a continuous path or circuit. When a switch is on, it acts as a 'bridge', completing the path for the electrons to pass along. When the switch is off, the bridge is 'lifted' and the electrons can no longer pass through.

Preparation

Ensure that the various electrical components (bulbs, batteries and so on) are functioning properly before starting this activity.

Resources needed

For switch: a paper-clip, two paper-fasteners, a piece of card, three pieces of insulated wire with the ends bare, a 1.5V bulb, a 1.5V battery, a bulb holder, a small screwdriver, adhesive tape.

For house: a small cardboard box, card, scissors, two or three 1.5V bulbs, bulb holders, a 1.5V battery, a small screwdriver, wire, switches (as made in the activity).

For traffic lights: red, green and orange cellophane, card, scissors, three 1.5V bulbs, bulb holders, three 1.5V batteries, wire, switches (as made in the activity), a collection of old switches (optional).

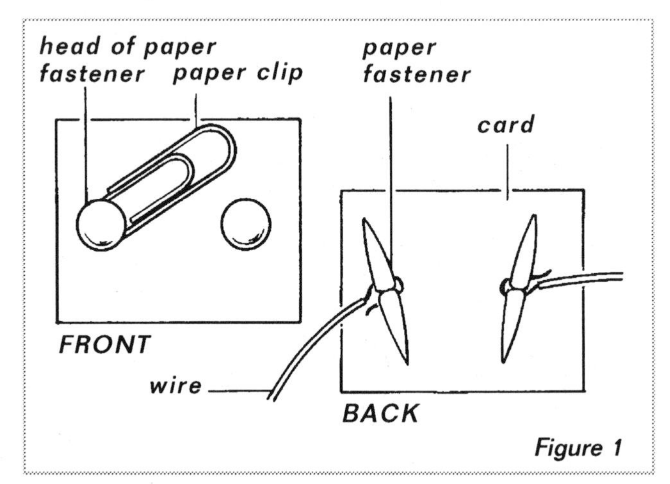

Figure 1

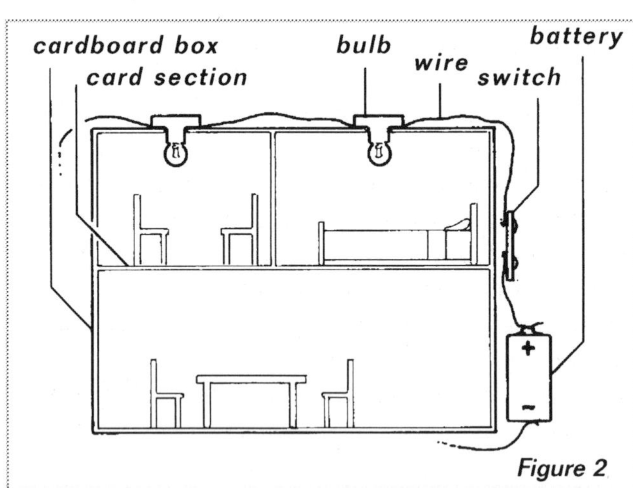

Figure 2

What to do

If possible, show a collection of switches to the children. Ask them to tell you why they think switches are used. What might happen if we could not turn off the electricity? Why are switches not used in bathrooms? Why is a pull-switch safer in places where there is water?

Allow the children to look at the collection of switches to see if they can work out how these switches might operate. Why is the electricity not on when the switch is off? What happens to the electricity? Is it still there? Why won't it flow?

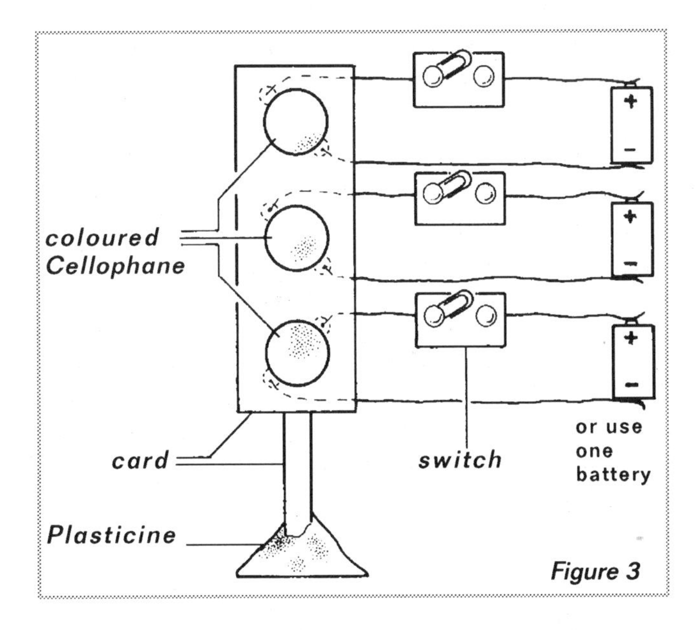

Figure 3

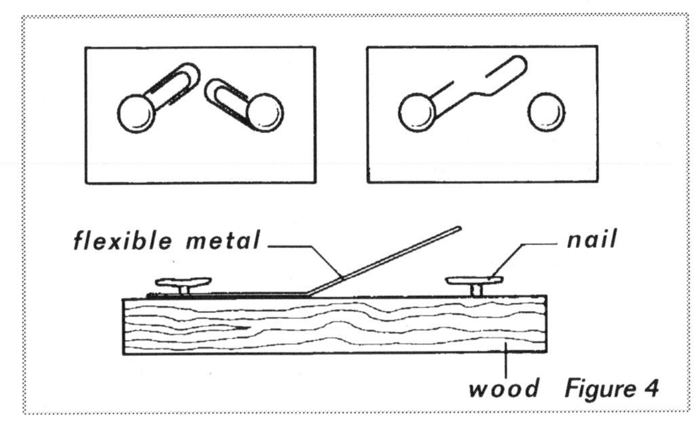

Figure 4

Relate the children back to work which they may already have done on making circuits (see the activity on page 16). Remind them that a complete circuit is needed to make an electrical device work.

Ask the children to make a circuit and then challenge them to find a way to turn the bulb on and off. They could do this by lifting a wire on and off one end of the battery. Explain to them that this is how a switch works, and that in order for the electricity to flow around the circuit, it must have a complete path with no breaks in it.

Provide each child with a paper-clip, two paper-fasteners, some card and wire and challenge them to make a more permanent switch, one they could use on a model to turn a light on and off without having to lift the wire from the battery.

If the children have difficulty making the switch, help them by pushing the paper-fasteners through the card and adding the paper-clip. Show them how to move the paper-clip so that it touches the fastener. Ask the children to work out where they think the wires should join on to the switch. Tell them to attach the wires to the back of the switch, so that the wires would not show if they were putting the switch on a model (see Figure 1).

If the bulb lights up even when the switch is off, check the back of the switch. If the arms of the paper fasteners meet they will make a complete circuit all the time, so make sure they are apart. If the bulb does not light up at all, encourage the children to look for areas where there may be a possible fault in the circuit. Are the wires attached securely to the battery? Does the same bulb work in someone else's circuit, or has it blown? Are the wires attached securely to the switch?

Next, challenge the children to make a model house with lights that can be turned on and off, or a model set of traffic lights. (A solution for each is given in Figures 2 and 3.)

Suggestion(s) for extension

Challenge the children to make other types of switches (some examples are shown in Figure 4). Can the children make a set of switches for a long flight of stairs where the light can be turned on and off at the top of the stairs as well as at the bottom?

Suggestion(s) for support

Help the children to make the switch if they become frustrated. Help them to look for any faults in the circuit to ensure that the bulb lights up. Discuss their ideas about how they might make the house or the traffic lights. Encourage them to draw a plan. Talk through the plan with them. Will the switch work in each case? How many switches will they need? Will all the switches work off one battery? Allow them to make mistakes when making the models, so that they can be encouraged to look for possible faults and find ways to correct them.

Assessment opportunities

Assess how well the children have understood the concept of a switch by looking at the models they build. Asking the children to look for possible faults will help you to assess how well they understand the need for a complete circuit.

Opportunities for IT

Once children have understood the use of switches and built a model, the work could be extended to the use of a computer to control the traffic lights or the lighting in the model house. This would require the use of a control interface linking the computer to the electrical circuit to be controlled. The children could use control software to change the traffic lights automatically in the correct sequence, allowing for a pause at each stage. The children could define a procedure for the correct sequence, which could be saved and then be retrieved for use at a later time.

More adventurous children could set up two sets of traffic lights and model the sequence at a junction, to make sure that when one set was on red the other set was on green, and there was no time when both sets were on green.

Children working with a model house could also set up a light cell to sense when the level of outside light was reduced and to turn on the house lights.

This work should also be discussed with children so that they can look for other examples in everyday life where computers are used to control events, particularly where safety is important (level crossing gates, airport control systems, street lighting, burglar alarms, and so on).

Display ideas

Use a collection of switches or drawings and photographs of switches to make a display of different switch types. Place a table near the collection to display the children's drawings and models of houses and traffic lights.

Other aspects of the Science PoS covered

Experimental and Investigative Science – 1a, e; 2a, b; 3c.

ELECTRICAL DEVICES

Switches can be used to control electrical devices.

Individuals or pairs.

60–80 minutes.

See guidelines on page 13.

Previous skills/knowledge needed

Electricity can be turned on and off. How to make a simple switch.

Key background information

Switches can be used to open and close electrical circuits. They act as 'gates'. A circuit with two switches in it can be used in two different ways to make an electrical device such as a bulb work. Both switches can be turned on to make the bulb work (AND gate), or either one of the two switches can be turned on to make the bulb work (OR gate).

Preparation

It is very useful to try this activity before presenting it to the children. This will enable you to appreciate some of the problems the children may encounter during the lesson, allowing you to be more fully prepared. It also gives you the opportunity to test the various electrical components to make sure they are all working properly.

Resources needed

A 1.5V battery, a 1.5V or 2.5V bulb, a bulb holder, a small screwdriver, seven pieces of insulated wire with the ends bare, two pieces of card (7cm x 3cm), four paper-clips, four paper-fasteners, adhesive tape, one copy per child of photocopiable page 117, pencils, paper.

What to do

Explain to the children that you want them to find out more about how switches can be used to make things work in an electrical circuit, and that you have a worksheet for them to follow for the first part of the session. Hand out photocopiable sheet 117 to the children and make sure they understand what to do. (Remind the children how to make a switch using paper-clips, if necessary.)

To help the children focus on their task, ask them questions as they make the circuit: What do you think will happen if only one switch is on? Can you explain why? What do you think will happen if both switches are on? Can you explain why? Why won't the bulb light up if both switches are off? Where is the electricity coming from? Where is it going to? What would happen if you unscrewed the bulb when it was working? Can you explain why? When would it be useful to have a circuit like this one (on stairs or along corridors)?

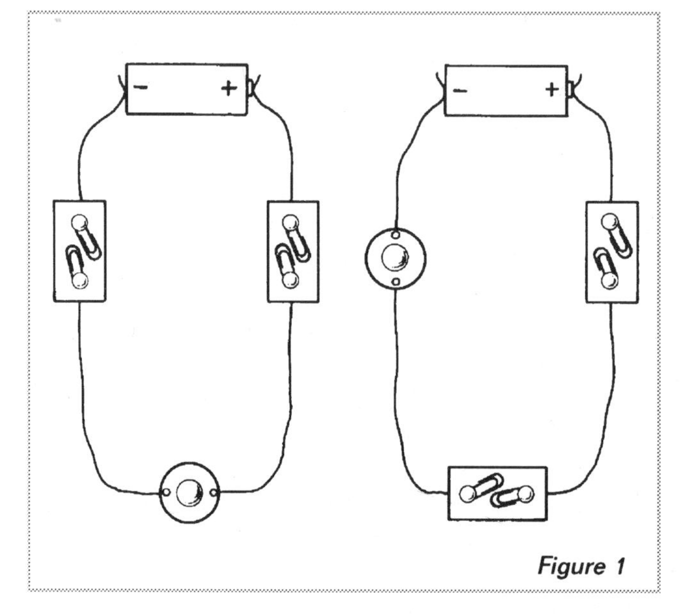

Figure 1

When all the children have completed the circuit, bring the whole class together to discuss what they found out. Make sure they understand that when either switch is closed there is a complete circuit from the battery to the bulb, to the switch and back to the battery.

Next, challenge the children to make another circuit using two switches; but this time, tell them that both switches must be on to make the bulb light up (this will be an AND gate). Ask the children to record how they made the circuit. Two possible solutions are shown in Figure 1.

When the children have completed their circuits, discuss their solutions with them and compare the two types of circuit. Discuss why we might need each type of circuit. (For example, AND gate in a tumble-drier: the drier must be switched on *and* the door closed before the motor will work. OR gate in a car: *either* car door can be opened to make the interior light work.)

Suggestion(s) for extension

Challenge the children to design and make a burglar alarm (buzzer) which works when either of two doors on a model house is opened.

Suggestion(s) for support

Some children may have difficulty making the circuit. Help them to attach the wires to the bulb holder if necessary. Make sure the bare sections of the wires are long enough to attach the wires going to the switches. If the bulb lights up even when the switches are off, the paper fasteners or wires may be touching at the back of the switch, making the circuit complete. Help the children to find possible faults in their circuits if the bulb does not light – are the wires attached securely to each component? Does the same bulb work in someone else's circuit? Is the battery working?

Assessment opportunities

This activity will enable you to assess how well the children understand the need for a complete circuit to make electrical devices work. It will also enable you to assess how well the children can follow instructions in the form of diagrams and how well they can record their own circuits.

Opportunities for IT

This work could be an extension of the activity on page 18, with the children creating more complex circuits and using switches to control the flow of electricity in a circuit. They could use a control interface linked to the computer to make a simple circuit which mirrors the action of a tumble-drier or car doors. Children might look for other examples of AND gates and OR gates.

There are also direct links in this work to the use of databases, with questions that reduce the search criteria (AND) or widen the search criteria (OR).

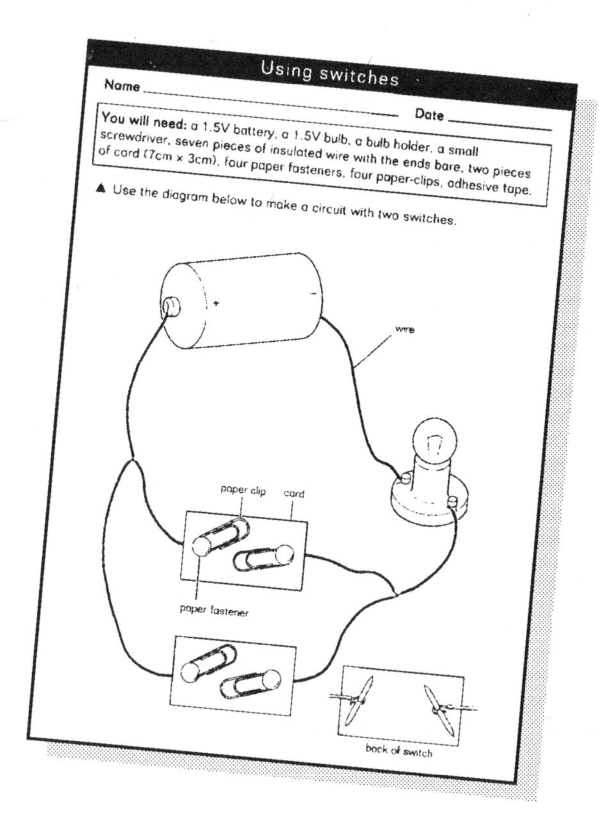

Using switches

Name ________ Date ________

You will need: a 1.5V battery, a 1.5V bulb, a bulb holder, a small screwdriver, seven pieces of insulated wire with the ends bare, two pieces of card (7cm x 3cm), four paper fasteners, four paper-clips, adhesive tape.

▲ Use the diagram below to make a circuit with two switches.

Display ideas

Ask the children to draw pictures of electrical devices which use switches. Display these on a wall together with the children's own recording of the circuits they have made using switches.

Other aspects of the Science PoS covered

Experimental and Investigative Science – 1a; 2a, b, c; 3b, c, e.

Reference to photocopiable sheet

Photocopiable sheet 117 is used as a reference guide in the first part of the lesson. If you prefer to challenge some children to make the circuit without using the guide, the sheet could be used as a solution sheet.

CONDUCTORS

Some things conduct electricity.

Pairs or small groups.

45–60 minutes.

▲ *See guidelines on page 13.*

Previous skills/knowledge needed

A complete circuit is needed to make electrical devices work.

Key background information

Conductors are materials which allow electricity to flow through them. All metals are conductors of electricity. Wires are used in electrical circuits because the electricity flows easily along the metal. *Insulators* do not allow electricity to flow through them. Most non-metals are poor conductors. Rubber is one of the best insulators. Insulators can be used to prevent the flow of electricity. This is why electrical wire is coated with plastic, and why electricians might wear rubber gloves.

Preparation

Ensure that the various electrical components are functioning properly before starting the activity.

Resources needed

A 1.5V battery, a 1.5V bulb, a bulb holder, three pieces of insulated wire with the ends bare, two crocodile clips, adhesive tape, one copy per pair/group of photocopiable page 118, pencils, a small screwdriver, a metal spoon, a plastic spoon, a wooden ruler, glass, paper, cotton fabric, a brass weight.

What to do

Ask the children to make a circuit using the bulb and holder, battery and wires. Make sure that the bulb lights up and that any faults in the circuit have been corrected. Ask the children to connect two wires in series within the circuit, using the two crocodile clips. By separating the two crocodile clips, they can create a gap in the circuit. Why won't the bulb light up now? What could you do to make it light? Try touching the crocodile clips together. Why does the bulb light up now?

Ask the children to tell you why they think the wire in their circuit is coated in plastic. Explain that some materials allow electricity to flow through them and others do not. Tell them that materials which prevent electricity from flowing through them are called insulators and materials which let electricity through are called conductors. Explain that the plastic coating on the wire is an insulator. Why is this a safety feature? Why do the ends of the wire in the circuit need to be bare? What other electrical things in the home and at school are covered in plastic?

Next, challenge the children to find out the names of other conductors and insulators. Provide them with a copy of photocopiable page 118 and ask them to predict which of the objects listed will act as conductors. Explain that they need to place the items in between the crocodile clips, so that a complete circuit is made. If the bulb lights up, the material tested is a conductor. After they have tried the items listed on the sheet, tell them they can test other objects in the room. Remind them to make a prediction first before testing it out.

After the children have completed the testing, bring the groups together for a discussion of the results.

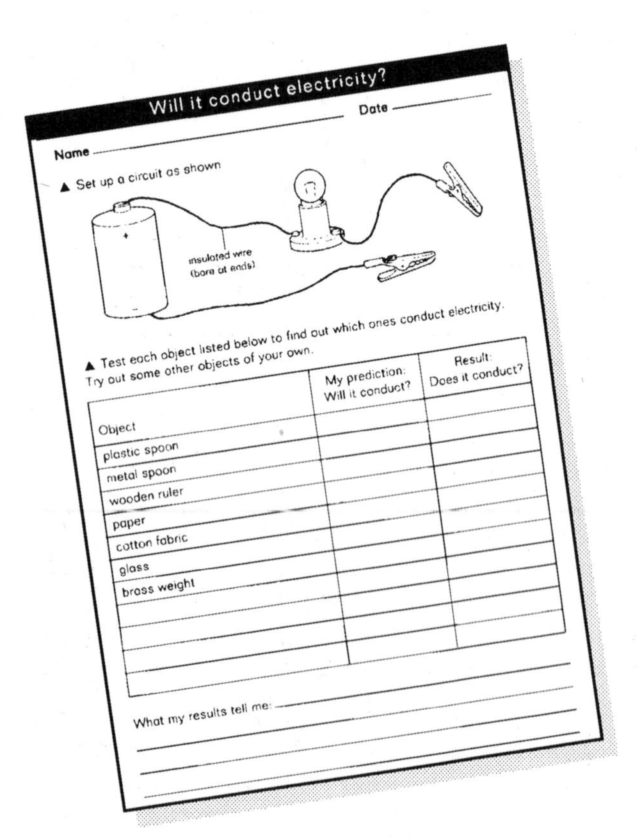

Will it conduct electricity?

Name ______ Date ______

▲ Set up a circuit as shown

▲ Test each object listed below to find out which ones conduct electricity.
Try out some other objects of your own.

Object	My prediction: Will it conduct?	Result: Does it conduct?
plastic spoon		
metal spoon		
wooden ruler		
paper		
cotton fabric		
glass		
brass weight		

What my results tell me: ______

▲ Were their predictions correct?
▲ Which materials were good conductors?
▲ What problems did they have while they were testing? How did they overcome them?
▲ Which materials acted as insulators?
▲ Were they surprised by any of the results? Can they explain them?

Suggestion(s) for extension
Challenge the children to join up as many conductors as they can and still make the bulb light up. This will show the children how important it is to have good connections in the circuit, and will give them experience in finding faults in the circuit. They may suggest connecting elements in parallel.

Suggestion(s) for support
Help the children to make the initial circuit, with the crocodile clips if necessary, to ensure that there are no faults in the circuit and that the bulb will light up. Show them how to fasten the objects being tested in the 'jaws' of the crocodile clips, so that all parts of the circuit are linked.

Assessment opportunities
A discussion of the results will enable you to ask individuals about the terms 'conductor' and 'insulator', thereby ascertaining how well they understand the difference between the two.

Display ideas
Draw two large circles on card, and draw the items which are conductors inside one of the circles and items which are insulators inside the other. Mount the circles on the wall with a large heading, 'Conductors or insulators?', written above it. Place the testing kit of bulb and holder, battery and crocodile clips on a table in front of the wall display and add a box containing the items drawn in the circles. Make a sign challenging the children to decide which circle shows the insulators and which one shows the conductors by testing the items. If other items are tested, add drawings of these to the circles.

Other aspects of the Science PoS covered
Experimental and Investigative Science – 1a, b; 2a, b; 3a, b, c, d, e.

Reference to photocopiable sheet
The metal objects will conduct electricity. Be aware that some metals (for example, some types of copper wire) have a clear plastic coating on them and this may need to be scratched off before they can conduct. Coins may also need to have their surfaces scratched to remove any dirt covering the metal. Encourage the children to test different kinds of metals. They could use another piece of paper if they wish to record more items.

CURRENT FLOW

Electricity in a circuit flows in one direction only.

Individuals or pairs.

30–45 minutes.

See guidelines on page 13.

Previous skills/knowledge needed

A complete circuit is needed to make electrical devices work.

Key background information

Electricity flows in one direction only in a given circuit. It flows from the negative end of the battery to the positive end. Initially, scientists thought that the flow was from positive to negative, and unfortunately this convention is still used when drawing circuit diagrams. The amount of current in a series circuit is the same in both the outgoing and the returning wire. This can be measured using an ammeter.

Children may have several misconceptions about the flow of electricity in a circuit, such as:

▲ The current flows along only one of the wires.

▲ The current flows from both ends of the battery and meets in the bulb in the middle ('the clashing currents' model).

▲ The current will be less in the wire coming from the bulb, because some of the electricity will have been 'used up'.

Preparation

Ensure that the buzzers and other electrical components are working before carrying out the activity.

Resources needed

A 1.5V battery, a 1.5V bulb, insulated wires with the ends bare, a small screwdriver, a bulb holder, adhesive tape, a buzzer, paper, pencils, an ammeter (optional).

What to do

Ask the children to make the bulb light up using the battery, bulb and holder, and wires. Then ask them to draw a picture of their circuit, using arrows to show which way they think the electricity is flowing in the circuit. Where does it come from and where does it travel to?

Discuss their drawings. Some of the children may think that the electricity flows from both ends of the battery and meets in the bulb. Others may think that the electricity flows in only one of the wires. Explain to the children that the current actually flows from one end of the battery, through the wire to the bulb, and then through the other wire back to the battery. Demonstrate this by removing one of the wires. What happens?

Many children may then ask why the battery 'runs out' if the electricity keeps flowing back into it. Explain to them that a battery contains chemicals which react together to make the electricity flow. Eventually, the chemicals stop working and the battery no longer works. The electricity only flows when the battery is using up energy to make it flow: it is not the *electricity* that runs out, but the power to drive an electric current.

Some children may still find the idea of current flow difficult to grasp, so an analogy may be useful (though all analogies have their limitations). Tell them to imagine that the wires are water pipes, the battery is a water pump and the bulb is a water wheel. If water is pumped along the pipes to the wheel, it will continue to flow round and round the circuit until the pump is switched off or breaks down.

Tell the children that the idea of current flow can also be shown by using a buzzer. Ask them to try and make the buzzer work by attaching the buzzer's wires to a battery. Some buzzers will only work if the red wire is attached to the positive end and the black wire is attached to the negative end. If the current were flowing from both ends of the battery, as some children may have thought, then the buzzer would work no matter which way round the wires were.

Next, ask the children to tell you what they think is happening to the current as it flows around the circuit. Is the current the same all the way round? Many children will suggest that some of the electricity is 'used up' in the bulb, and so less electricity must be present in the returning wire. In fact, the current stays the same all the way round the

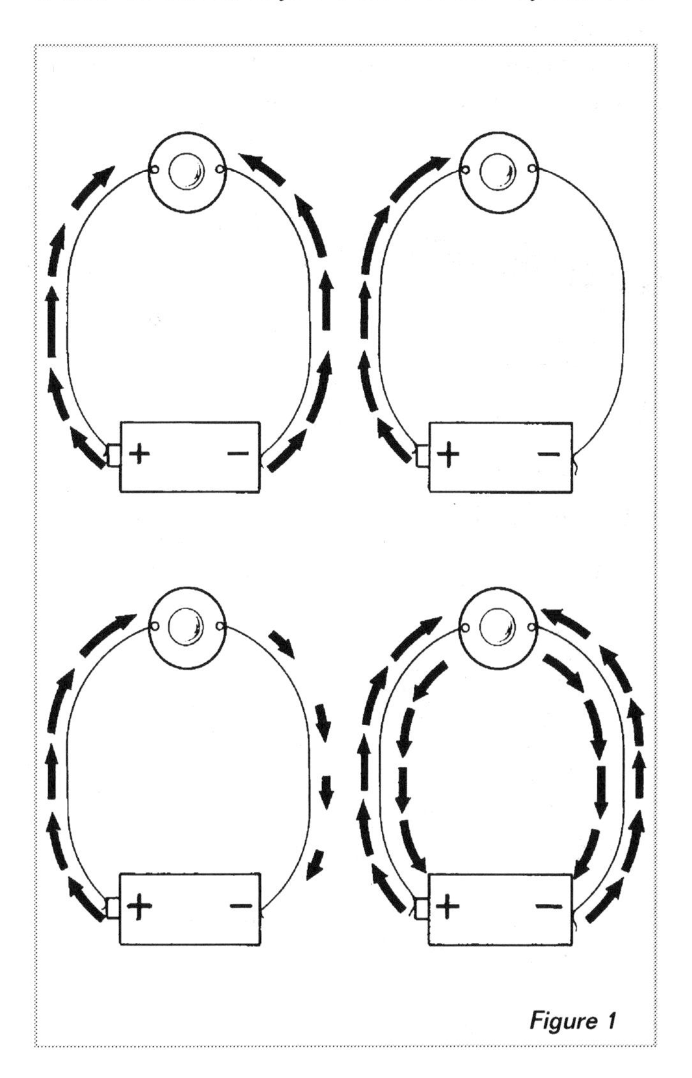

Figure 1

circuit. If an ammeter is available, the current in both wires can be measured to demonstrate this (make sure the red [+] terminal of the ammeter is always nearer to the positive end of the battery than to the negative end, because otherwise the pointer will be moved the wrong way). *Electrical energy carried by the current* is converted to light and heat in the filament of the bulb, but the current itself stays the same.

At the end of the discussion, ask the children to tell you what they think they have learned about electricity in a circuit. Use this opportunity to assess whether or not the children have grasped the main ideas presented to them.

Suggestion(s) for extension

Copy the diagrams shown in Figure 1. Ask the children to write down or explain what is wrong with each one and why.

Suggestion(s) for support

Help the children to make the circuit if necessary. If they are not sure what you mean by 'the flow of electricity', ask the following questions to help them develop their ideas: What part of the circuit produces the electricity? How do we know the electricity is working? [the bulb lights up] How does the electricity get to the bulb? How does it get from the bulb to the battery?

Assessment opportunities

Use the discussion time at the end of the activity to find out what the children have understood, or ask the children to write and/or draw what they have learned from the task. This work could be used as a starting-point for further discussion with the children about the nature of the flow of electricity.

Display ideas

Draw a large picture of a series circuit with labels naming the parts. Mount this on the wall, together with the children's drawings of and writing about current flow in a circuit.

Other aspects of the Science PoS covered

Experimental and Investigative Science – 1a; 2a, b, c; 3b, e.

RESISTANCE

The current in a circuit can be varied.

Individuals or pairs.

30–45 minutes.

See guidelines on page 13.

Previous skills/knowledge needed

A complete circuit is needed to make electrical devices work.

Key background information

Resistance determines how easily electricity can flow in a circuit. Good conductors, such as metals (and graphite as used in 'lead' pencils), have a low electrical resistance – that is, they allow electricity to flow through them easily. Most non-metals have a high electrical resistance. Resistance also depends on the size and shape, as well as the type, of the material. Resistance increases as length increases, thus longer wires offer more resistance than shorter wires. Thick wires offer less resistance than thin wires.

When light bulbs are connected in a line, one after the other, it is called a *series circuit*. If a connection in this line is broken, the current cannot flow and all the bulbs will go out. The bulbs offer *resistance* to the current. The same current goes through each bulb in turn, but two bulbs in a series circuit will be brighter than three or four bulbs in a series circuit because they offer less resistance. Thus the more bulbs are connected in a series, the greater the resistance is and the dimmer the bulbs will be.

Preparation

Ensure that all the electrical components are working before starting the activity.

Resources needed

Two 1.5V batteries, four or five 3.5V bulbs, bulb holders, insulated wires with the ends bare, adhesive tape or a twin battery holder, a small screwdriver, two lead pencils (or two pieces of lead removed from one or two pencils) of the same length but different thickness and with both ends sharpened, two lead pencils (or pieces of lead) of the same thickness but different length and with both ends sharpened, a rheostat (optional).

What to do

Ask the children to make a circuit using one bulb and a holder. Make sure it works by checking that the bulb lights up. Then ask them to add another bulb and holder to the circuit, so the bulbs are in line with each other in a series. What can the children say about the brightness of the bulbs compared with the first circuit? Has it changed? What happens if one of the bulbs is unscrewed? Can the children suggest why?

Ask the children to add another bulb to the circuit, then another, until they have four or five bulbs in a line. Ask them to note what happens to the brightness of the bulbs each time. Can the children suggest why this is happening? Unscrew one of the bulbs. What happens? Compare this to Christmas tree lights: what happens when one of the bulbs has blown?

Explain to the children that a circuit containing a row of bulbs in a line is called a *series circuit*. Confirm, from the children's work with the circuits, that the more bulbs there are in a line, the less bright the bulbs are. Explain that this is because the bulbs offer resistance to the electrical current.

Ask the children to look more closely at the light bulb itself. What part of the bulb lights up? Tell them that this is called the *filament*. What do they think it is made of? Explain that resistance determines how easily electricity can flow in a circuit. Metal objects, such as wires, allow electricity to flow through them easily; but thin wires like the filament in a bulb make it harder for the electricity to flow (more resistance) than thick wires. (Though all analogies have their limitations, this could be linked to a child trying to wriggle through a thin pipe and a wider pipe. It would be harder in the thin pipe: there would be more resistance to movement.) When electricity flows through a metal, electrons bump into particles in the metal. Each collision makes the particles vibrate. In a thin wire, the electrons bump into the particles more often, causing the wire to heat up. The filament in a bulb heats up so much that it glows and gives off light.

Tell the children that the filament is a special wire made of *tungsten*, which has a very high melting point, and that there is a special (*inert*) gas inside the bulb which prevents the wire from catching fire.

The filament in the bulb thus restricts the flow of current in the circuit. In a series circuit with two bulbs, the current flow is reduced further because there are two filaments offering resistance. Both bulbs are dimmer than in the circuit with only one bulb, because in a series circuit, the current is the same everywhere in the circuit – so any increase in resistance has the same effect on all parts of the circuit. If you want to increase the current, you would need to increase the 'push' supplied by the battery by adding an extra or stronger battery.

Talk to the children about the use of dimmer switches. Explain that they are used to make lights brighter or dimmer. Tell them that they can make a dimmer switch of their own by using the lead from a pencil. Make up a circuit with one bulb and two batteries, as shown in Figure 1.

Attach the wires to both ends of the shorter pencil or lead and observe the brightness of the bulb. Then attach the wires to the longer pencil or lead. What has happened to the brightness of the bulb? If you are using a lead removed from a pencil, the wires can be moved up and down the lead to alter the brightness of the bulb. Can the children suggest why this is happening? (Resistance increases as length increases.)

Next, try two pencils or leads of the same length but different thicknesses. What happens to the brightness of the bulb this time? Does the electricity travel more easily through the thicker graphite or the thinner graphite? (This can be compared to the thin wire in a light bulb: the electricity has to 'work harder' to move through the thin wire.)

If a rheostat is available, use this to demonstrate how a dimmer switch works. Attach the rheostat to a circuit with one bulb and move the sliding contact to make the bulb brighter and dimmer. Can the children suggest why this happens? (The wire in the rheostat is coiled, and if the slide is at the beginning of the coil, there is more resistance than if the slide were at the end because there is a greater length of coiled wire in the circuit.)

Suggestion(s) for extension

Investigate other resistors in a series circuit, such as variable resistors, LEDs, LDRs and thermistors, to observe the effects of temperature and light changes.

Suggestion(s) for support

Help the children to connect the components in the circuits, if necessary. Make sure the connections are secure, so that the current can flow. Sometimes one bulb in a series circuit will appear to be brighter than the others. This can cause confusion, because it appears that one bulb is receiving more current than the others. If this happens, swap the brighter bulb with another one in the circuit to show that the brighter bulb has now moved position. One reason why the bulbs may vary is that they have different resistances. Check the metal thread on the bulbs for the specified voltage and current to make sure they are all the same. There may also be variations in the manufacturing process which can produce bulbs of different brightnesses.

Assessment opportunities

Ask the children to write down or tell you what they have learned from the activities. Use this to assess how much the children have understood about resistance, and hence to decide how to plan for future activities.

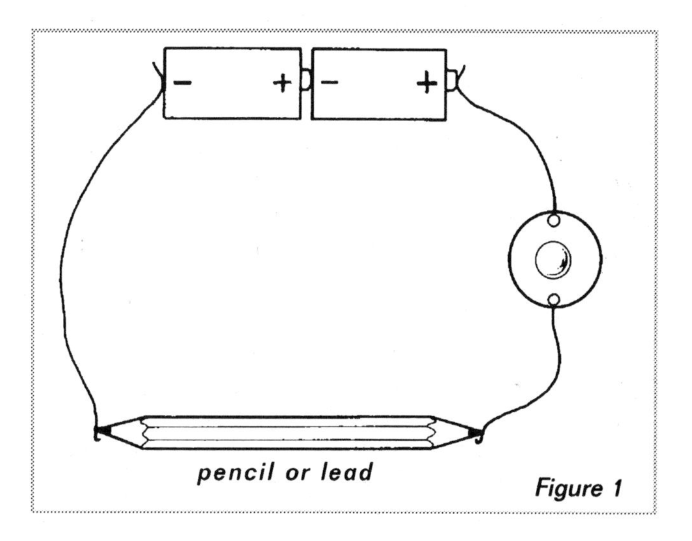

Figure 1

Opportunities for IT

Children could use a simple temperature sensor, which changes the resistance in a circuit in relation to the temperature, and link this to a computer to monitor the changes in temperature in a particular place over a period of time; the classroom, a fridge or an outside location might be possible places to try. The results can be displayed on a graph showing the changes in temperature during the day. Similar work could be undertaken using a light sensor.

Display ideas

Ask the children to write about and draw what is happening inside a light bulb when it lights up. Mount this work on the wall, together with a large diagram of a light bulb with all the parts labelled. Make a model house with lights in each room. Incorporate a dimmer switch using the lead from a pencil, so the lights can be dimmed. Place the model on a table in front of the wall display, with a sign encouraging the children to try and dim the lights.

Other aspects of the Science PoS covered

Experimental and Investigative Science – 1a; 2a, b, c; 3b, c, e.

MOTORS

A motor can make electrical devices work.

Pairs or small groups.

60–90 minutes.

See guidelines on page 13.

Previous skills/knowledge needed

A complete circuit is needed to make electrical devices work. The current in a circuit can be varied.

Key background information

Electric motors are used in a wide variety of machines and devices. Inside the motor is a wheel called a *rotor.* Near the rotor is a coil of wire through which electricity flows. This causes the wire to become an *electromagnet.* It magnetises the metal that surrounds the rotor, and the magnetic forces in this metal 'pull' on the rotor, causing it to turn at right angles to the magnetic field. The rotor would stay there if it were not for a special contact system, called a *commutator.* This causes the direction of the current to be reversed whenever the coil is at right angles to the magnetic field. The result is that the rotor keeps rotating in the same direction. (See Figure 1.)

Preparation

Make sure that the various electrical components that the children will use are working properly before they start the activity.

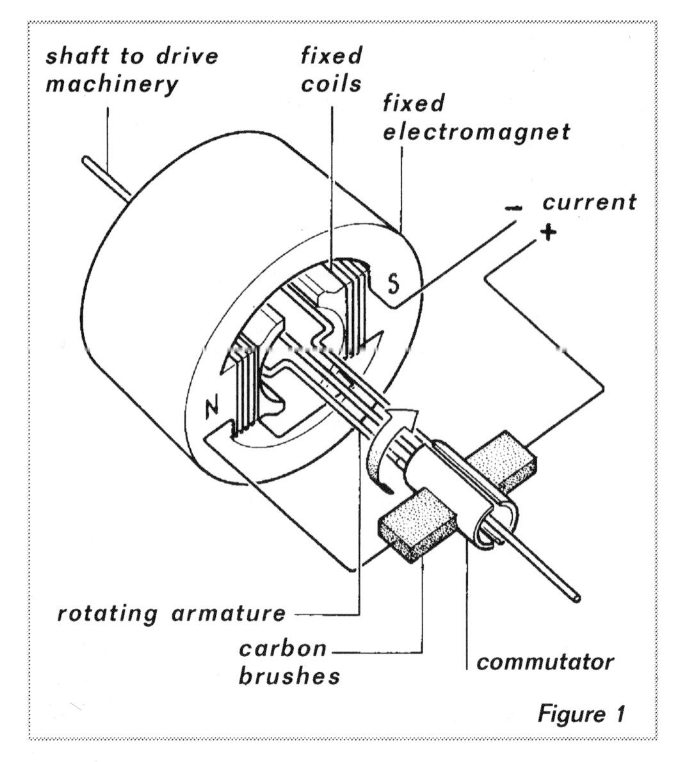

Figure 1

Resources needed

One copy per pair/group of photocopiable page 119, a small electric motor (plus an old motor which could be taken apart, if one is available), a motor pulley, cotton thread, scissors, adhesive tape, two 1.5V batteries, three pieces of insulated wire with the ends bare, the lead from a pencil, a shoe box, a wooden board or large book, two bar magnets, a toy car, a motor mount (optional).

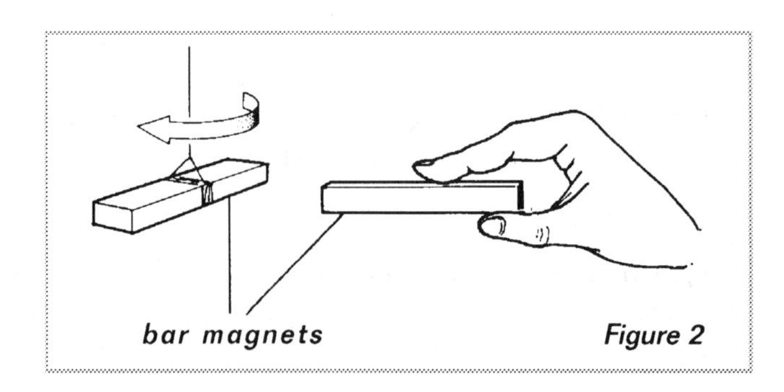

Figure 2

What to do

Talk to the children about where motors might be used. Can they name some household appliances which use motors? Do they know what the motor does in some of these devices? If possible, take apart an old motor to show the children what is inside it. Briefly explain how the motor works, and tell the children that this can be demonstrated by using two bar magnets.

Suspend one of the magnets on a thread and hold the other one near one end of the magnet. The suspended magnet will begin to turn. Keep changing the ends of the magnet held in the hand, so that first one pole and then the other is facing the suspended magnet. The magnet will spin.

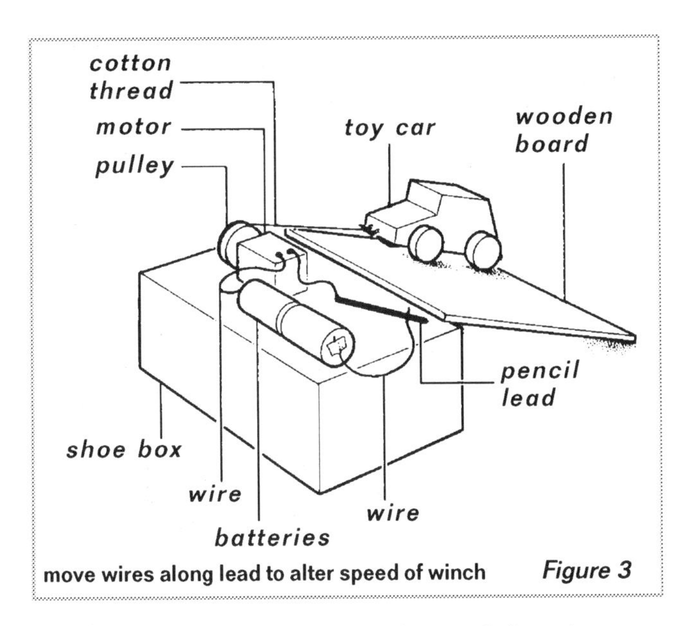

move wires along lead to alter speed of winch *Figure 3*

Explain that this is how the arm which extends from the motor is made to spin continuously. If a pulley is attached to the arm, then the motor can make things attached to the pulley move. (See Figure 2.)

Tell the children that they are going to try using the 'motor' by making an electric winch to move a toy car up a ramp. Provide the children with photocopiable page 119, explaining what to do, if necessary.

As the children are making the winch, discuss what they are doing with them. Why does the car move so fast? What would happen if we used only one battery? Try it. What might happen if we used a heavier car, or a longer ramp? Challenge the children to think of a way to make the winch move more slowly. One solution is shown in Figure 3.

After the children have completed their models, bring the whole class together to discuss what they have found out. What problems did they have? How did they solve them? What other uses could this device have? What could they try next?

Suggestion(s) for extension

Challenge the children to make a motorised model of their own design, using the knowledge gained from making the winch.

Suggestion(s) for support

Pair up more able children with less able ones if they are having difficulty working from photocopiable page 119, or be available to help the less able children yourself. The winch will not work successfully if the connections are not secure, so make sure that the children join the wires to each component very carefully. It is not necessary for the children to understand fully how the motor works, as long as they know that the motor can make other things move.

Assessment opportunities

Ask the children to draw and write about how the winch works. Use this information to discuss the ideas more fully with individual children. An extension of this could be to ask the children to apply this knowledge to how they think a hair-drier might work. This will enable you to assess the children's knowledge and understanding of circuits, switches and motors.

Opportunities for IT

Children might extend the work with motors to control technology, using a computer and an interface to control the motor. When making the winch, they could use the computer to control the raising or lowering of the toy car. They would need to work out how many seconds it took the winch to raise the car. This information could then be used within the sequence of instructions, which would turn on the winch for the correct amount of time and then wait for ten seconds before lowering the car again.

More able children might explore the use of a sensor to decide when the car had reached the end of the run, which would automatically turn off the motor. The sensor could be a pressure pad which sends a message to the computer when the car runs over it, or a light sensor such that the car breaks the circuit when it passes through the sensor.

The children could use a word processor to write about their work. In particular, the children would need to organise their work carefully so that they describe the correct sequence of events. This might involve them in using the cut and paste or drag and drop facilities of the word processor to move their work into the correct sequence.

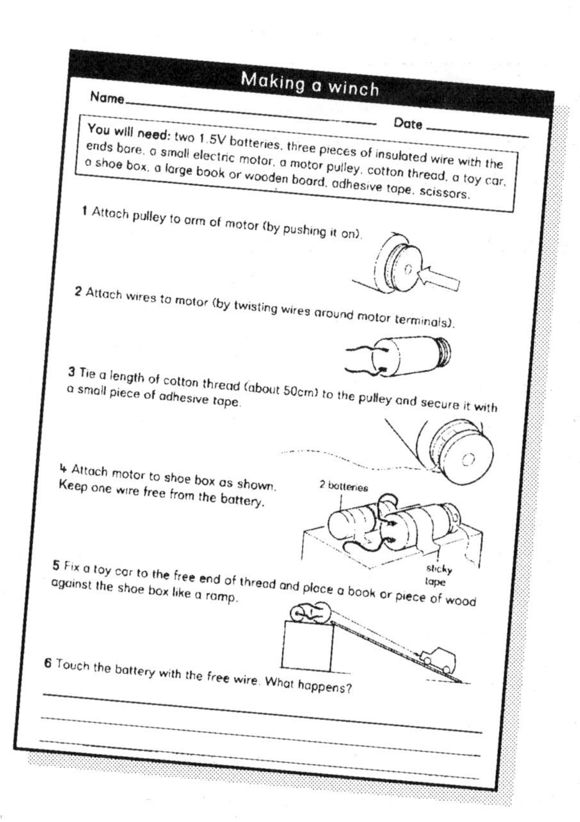

Making a winch

Name ______________________ Date __________

You will need: two 1.5V batteries, three pieces of insulated wire with the ends bare, a small electric motor, a motor pulley, cotton thread, a toy car, a shoe box, a large book or wooden board, adhesive tape, scissors.

1 Attach pulley to arm of motor (by pushing it on).

2 Attach wires to motor (by twisting wires around motor terminals).

3 Tie a length of cotton thread (about 50cm) to the pulley and secure it with a small piece of adhesive tape.

4 Attach motor to shoe box as shown. Keep one wire free from the battery.

2 batteries

sticky tape

5 Fix a toy car to the free end of thread and place a book or piece of wood against the shoe box like a ramp.

6 Touch the battery with the free wire. What happens?

Display ideas

Mount pictures or drawings of things which use motors on the wall. Add the children's own drawings of and writing about their investigation of winches. Display some old motors on a table in front of the wall display. Use labels to name the parts.

Other aspects of the Science PoS covered

Experimental and Investigative Science – 1a, b; 2a, b, c; 3b, c, e.

Reference to photocopiable sheet

Pair up more able children with less able ones if some children have difficulty in following the directions.

DRAWING CIRCUITS

Circuits can be represented by drawings and diagrams.

Whole class or small groups, then pairs.

30–45 minutes.

See guidelines on page 13.

Previous skills/knowledge needed

A complete circuit is needed to make electrical devices work. Switches can be used to control electrical devices. A series circuit is one in which the components are joined together in a line, one after the other.

Key background information

Circuits can be represented by drawings, but it is often helpful to have a quick and easy way to represent the components.

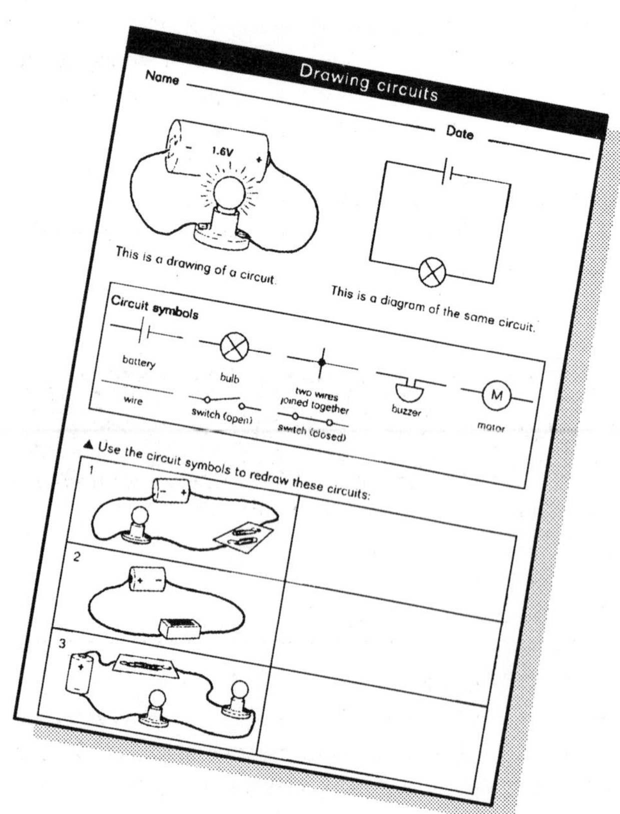

Drawing circuits

Name ______ Date ______

1.6V

This is a drawing of a circuit

This is a diagram of the same circuit.

Circuit symbols

battery, bulb, wire, switch (open), two wires joined together, switch (closed), buzzer, motor

Use the circuit symbols to redraw these circuits:

1

2

3

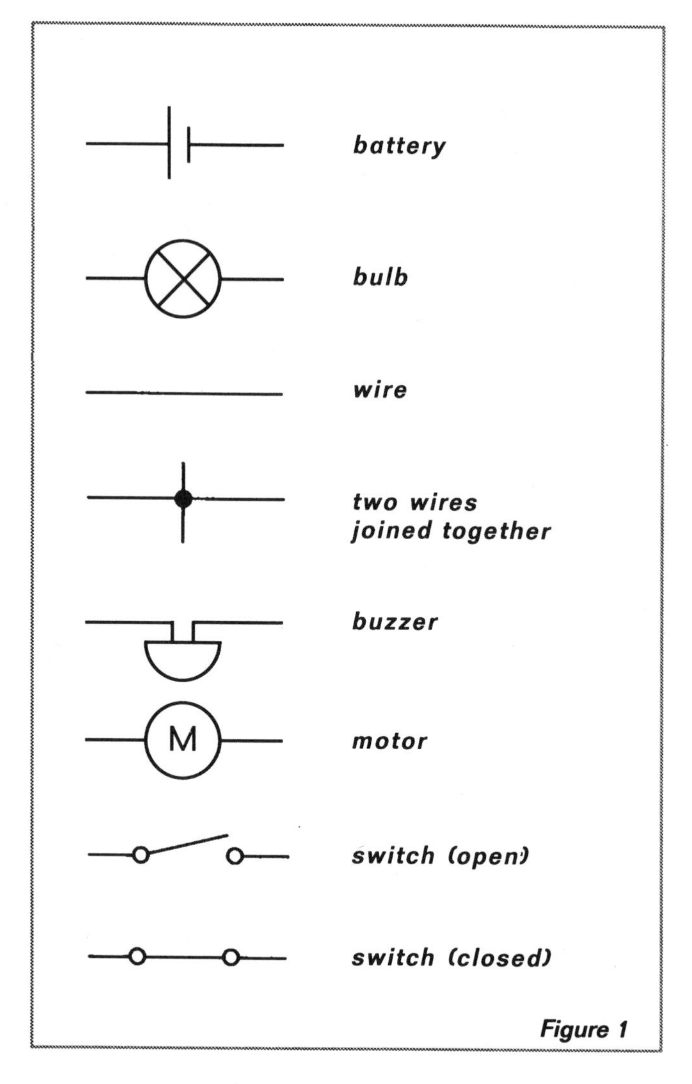

Figure 1

This is achieved by using formal diagrams with electrical circuit symbols. These reduce the need for accurate drawing skills and allow more complicated circuits to be drawn more quickly. Commonly used symbols include those shown in Figure 1.

Preparation

Ensure that the various electrical components are working properly before starting the activity.

Resources needed

One copy per child of photocopiable page 120, pencils, a 1.5V battery, insulated wires with the ends bare, a bulb, a bulb holder, a motor, a buzzer, switches (commercial ones and paper-clip ones made by the children), paper.

What to do

Provide the children with copies of photocopiable page 120 and draw their attention to the two pictures at the top of the page. Explain that one picture shows a circuit drawn in a similar way to the way they might draw their own circuits. Then explain that the other picture shows the same circuit represented as a diagram. What differences do the children notice between the two pictures?

Look at the symbols that are used in the circuit diagram. Hold up the real component as you say what each symbol represents. Point out the following things about the symbols: the positive end of the battery is shown by a longer, thinner line; a closed switch is shown by a line joining the two circles.

Ask the children why they think it is helpful to use symbols when drawing circuits. Mention that it is important for scientists to use the same symbols so that there is no confusion over what they mean, and to ensure that the symbols are used correctly. Ask the children if they would find it easier to use symbols or their own drawings. What are the disadvantages and advantages of each type of representation?

Ask the children to complete photocopiable page 120 by redrawing each circuit using symbols in a diagram. Show the children the correct answers when they have finished, and make sure they have drawn the battery and switch symbols correctly.

Next, working in pairs, ask each child to draw a series circuit to include *one* of the following components, with or without a switch:

- ▲ up to four bulbs;
- ▲ a buzzer;
- ▲ a motor.

When they have completed this, they can swap their drawings with their partner, who then has to draw the same circuit using a diagram with symbols. Help the children to check their diagrams.

Suggestion(s) for extension

Ask the children to make circuits using real electrical components, based on circuit diagrams which their partners have drawn.

Suggestion(s) for support

If necessary, help the children to find the symbol for each component in the circuits or pair up more able children with less able ones. Allow some time for the children to practise drawing the symbols separately, if necessary.

Assessment opportunities

The teacher can use the work the children do in the paired activity to assess how well they have understood the use of symbols and diagrams in circuit diagrams.

Opportunities for IT

Children could use a simple drawing package to make their circuit diagrams. They could either create the whole circuit using the drawing commands or select the various components from a clipart file, which could be purchased or created in advance by the teacher.

If prepared clipart is used, symbols for the various electrical components could be placed around the outside of the drawing area so that the children could duplicate each symbol needed and then drag the copy to where they wanted it to go. The connecting wires could then be added using the drawing commands. If a background grid is selected and a 'snap to grid' facility turned on, this will make it easier for children to line up the various parts of the circuit. The children should also save their work, so that they can continue it at a later date or return to a previously created file to modify it.

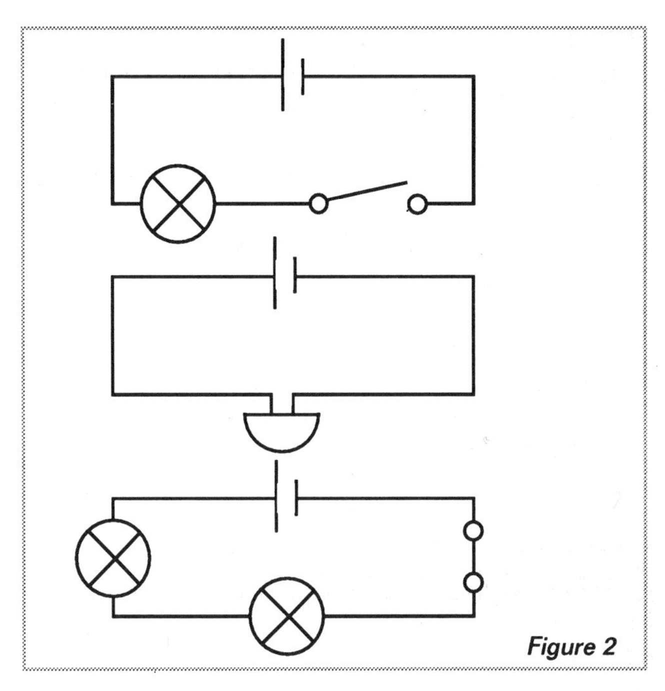

Figure 2

Display ideas

Draw some circuit symbols on separate pieces of card. Draw representational pictures of electrical components on other pieces of card. Join up the pictures of the components to make several different circuits. Make a sign challenging the children to make the circuits shown by joining up the cards with symbols on them. Display on a table.

Reference to photocopiable sheet

Pair up more able children with less able ones if necessary. The answers are shown in Figure 2.

CONSTRUCTING CIRCUITS FROM DIAGRAMS

Diagrams can be used to construct circuits.

Pairs or small groups.

45–60 minutes.

▲ *See guidelines on page 13.*

Previous skills/knowledge needed

A complete circuit is needed to make electrical devices work. Switches can be used to control electrical devices. Circuits can be represented by drawings and diagrams.

Key background information

Circuits can be represented by drawings and diagrams. These drawings and diagrams can be used to construct circuits. There are special symbols for each electrical component. Some common symbols are shown on page 28.

Preparation

Ensure the various electrical components are working properly before starting the activity.

Resources needed

One copy per pair/group of photocopiable page 121, two 1.5V batteries, three 3.5V bulbs, three bulb holders, a small screwdriver, insulated wires with the ends bare, a buzzer, a switch, adhesive tape.

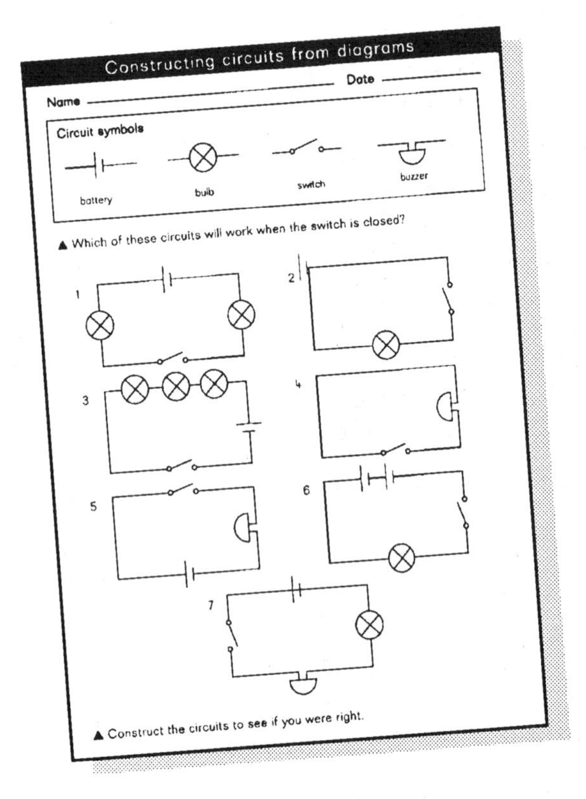
Constructing circuits from diagrams

Name ______ Date ______

Circuit symbols

battery bulb switch buzzer

▲ Which of these circuits will work when the switch is closed?

1 2 3 4 5 6 7

▲ Construct the circuits to see if you were right.

What to do

Remind the children of the symbols used in circuit diagrams if necessary. Provide them with photocopiable page 121 and the electrical components listed above. Explain the worksheet to the children and remind them that they should try to predict which circuits will work with the switch closed before they actually construct the circuits and see if they were correct.

As the children are constructing the circuits, ask them what their predictions are and ask them to tell you why they think the circuits will/will not work. Use this time to discuss various aspects of series circuits by asking such questions as: Where would you check for faults in the circuit if the bulb did not light up? Why is it important to attach wires to both ends of a battery/bulb/buzzer? Where is the electricity coming from? Where is it going to? How does a switch work? Which way round does the buzzer have to be before it will work in a circuit such as number 5 on the sheet?

When all the children have completed the task, bring the whole class together to discuss their findings. Were there any problems? How were these overcome? Were the results as expected? Use their experiences from making the circuits to discuss series circuits in more depth. Ask questions such as: In which circuit would the bulb(s) be brighter: 1, 3 or 6? Can you explain why? What would happen if you unscrewed one of the bulbs in circuit 3? Can you explain why? Why won't the bulb light up in number 2?

Suggestion(s) for extension

Working in pairs, ask the children to draw series circuits for their partners to construct.

Suggestion(s) for support

If some children have difficulty working from the diagrams, select the components for them and ask the children to match up each component to its symbol. Then help the children to construct the circuits, if necessary. Make sure the children understand that a secure connection is necessary for the current to flow, and help them to check their circuits for any possible faults.

Assessment opportunities

Use the time when the children are constructing the circuits to assess how well they can interpret the diagrams and how much they understand about the components in a series circuit.

Display ideas

Make large diagrams of circuits similar to those on photocopiable page 121. Mount these on the wall with a sign challenging the children to construct the circuits. Place the electrical components needed to make the circuits on a table near the wall display.

Other aspects of the Science PoS covered

Experimental and Investigative Science – 1a, b; 2a, b, c; 3b, c, d, e.

Reference to photocopiable sheet

The following circuits will work if the switch is closed: 1, 3, 5 and 6. In 7, the buzzer will sound, but the bulb will not light up. This is because the buzzer has a higher resistance than the bulb. Each component will work on its own in a circuit, but the buzzer will allow through a lower current than the bulb will. When the bulb and buzzer are in a circuit together, there is a high total resistance and therefore the current flowing through both components is low. It is enough to make the buzzer work, but not the bulb. Children might think of the buzzer as a 'bottleneck' for current, monopolising the power of the battery.

Forces & Motion

The activities in this section of the book encourage children to explore the properties of forces and motion. In the course of carrying out the activities, children will gain experience in questioning, observing, predicting, recording, measuring and drawing conclusions. They will also have the opportunity to work co-operatively and to share their ideas with others.

A force is a push or a pull. It affects the way things move. Forces can change the shape of objects and can make them speed up, slow down, stop or change direction. Forces can occur naturally, such as gravity; or they can be produced by people or machines, as in the use of levers, wheels and pulleys.

Forces act in particular directions, and they always act in pairs. For example, when an object such as a ball is stationary on the ground, there are two forces acting upon it: the downward force of gravity and the upward force of contact with the ground. Whenever an object pushes another, the other object also pushes back. If these forces are balanced, as in a floating object, then the object at rest will stay still. If the forces are unbalanced, the object can speed up, slow down or change direction. Forces are measured in newtons.

MOVEMENT

Many things are able to move.

Small groups.

45–60 minutes.

Children should take care when handling the scissors.

Previous skills/knowledge needed

None specifically required for this activity.

Key background information

Objects can move in many different ways. How an object moves depends on its shape, weight and texture and the surface on which it is moving. It also depends on the forces applied to that object. *Friction* is caused when two objects rub together. If the objects are rough or uneven, relative movement is more difficult. Smooth surfaces offer less resistance, so the objects move past each other more easily.

Preparation

None specifically required for this activity.

Resources needed

A tennis ball, a ping-pong ball, an empty square plastic bottle, an empty round plastic bottle, dice, a heavy book, a toy car, marbles, a large spring, scissors, an egg beater, five pencils, access to different floor surfaces such as carpet and planking.

What to do

Provide the children with the collection of objects and ask them to find out how they move. First, consider rolling the objects. Can they all be rolled? Do they all roll in the same way? Do the objects roll in a straight line? Do they roll in the same way on different floor surfaces? Do some objects roll longer distances than others? Does the square bottle roll differently from the round bottle? Do bottles curve when they roll? Why? Discuss the results of these observations.

What things can the children suggest that could make a difference to the way an object rolls? Does shape, weight or texture have an effect? What might explain any differences between the results on different floor surfaces? Is it easier to roll things on a smooth surface? Why? Mention the term 'friction' if this is appropriate, and discuss how this may have affected the results. Can the children think of other objects which roll easily?

Next, try sliding the objects. Are the results different on different floor surfaces? Which objects are difficult to slide? Can the children suggest why? Which objects are easy to slide? Does the amount of push make a difference to how far the object slides?

Discuss when we might need to slide an object. Consider moving heavy furniture. How can we make this task easier? Try sliding the heavy book on the carpet. Can the children suggest ways of making this movement easier? Try putting some marbles underneath the book. How does this help? Relate this to ball-bearings in machines or the sliding rails in drawers. Try putting some pencils underneath the book and slowly pushing the book along, bringing the back pencil to the front each time it is exposed. Tell the children that this was one way in which people used to move heavy objects (perhaps refer to the Ancient Egyptian pyramid builders). Can the children explain why this makes it easier to move the book?

Look at other types of movements, using the collection of objects. How do the scissors move when you use them? What other objects move in this way? Discuss the pivot point and compare it with a see-saw's movement. Look at the egg beater in more detail. What causes the beaters to turn? What other objects use cogs to make them work? How do springs move? What helps them to recover their shape after they have been pushed in?

Finally, ask the children to make a list of other objects in the classroom which move in particular ways – for example, things which roll, slide, pivot or use cogs.

Suggestion(s) for extension

Use the collection of objects to explore one aspect of movement in more detail. For example, what might affect whether an object rolls in a straight line?

Suggestion(s) for support

Work alongside the children as they are exploring the movement of the objects. Assure them that they cannot obtain a 'right' or 'wrong' answer to the questions, and that different people may obtain different results. These differences can be discussed when all the groups have completed the investigation; and this will probably lead to other questions being posed which could be investigated.

Assessment opportunities

Discussions with the children as they are carrying out the tasks will enable you to assess the children's ideas about movement, friction and forces, and will help to guide you in planning future activities.

Display ideas

Draw objects in the room which can move in the same way, such as those which can roll, slide or pivot, have cogs or have wheels. Mount these pictures on the wall with large signs saying what the type of movement is. Display a collection of objects on a table in front of the display. Write a sign which challenges the children to sort these objects according to the different types of movement illustrated in the wall display.

Other aspects of the Science PoS covered

Experimental and Investigative Science – 1a; 2b, c; 3b, c.

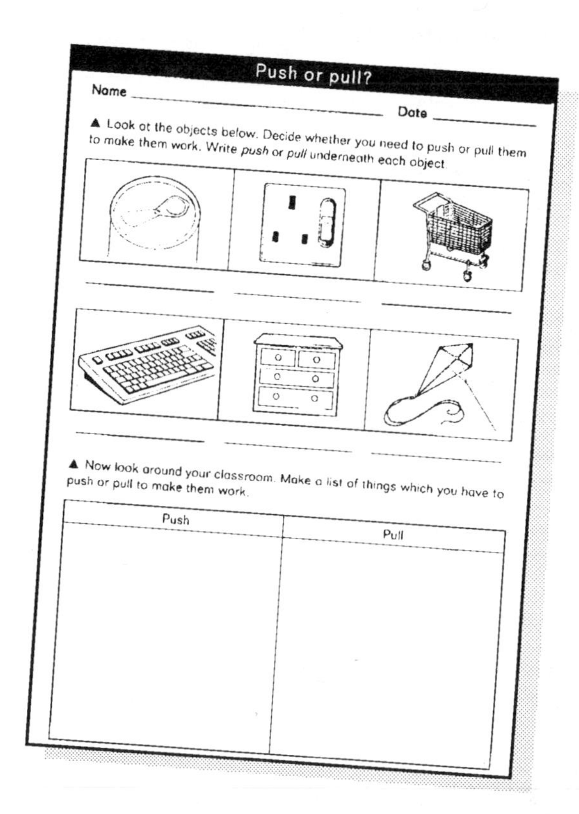

Push or pull?

Name ______________________ Date __________

▲ Look at the objects below. Decide whether you need to push or pull them to make them work. Write *push* or *pull* underneath each object.

▲ Now look around your classroom. Make a list of things which you have to push or pull to make them work.

Push	Pull

WHAT ARE FORCES?

A force is a push or a pull.

Individuals or pairs, then small groups.

60–90 minutes.

Previous skills/knowledge needed

Things move in a variety of ways.

Key background information

Objects cannot change their movement by themselves: they need a force to change their speed or direction of movement. A push or a pull is a force.

Preparation

None specifically required for this activity.

Resources needed

One copy per child (or pair) of photocopiable page 122, pencils, elastic bands, springs, collection of objects: a toy car, a full drink can, a book, a brick.

What to do

Ask the children either to write down or to tell you what they think a force is. How would they describe forces to someone else? What things can forces do? Discuss the children's answers and explain to them that scientists describe a force as a push or a pull. Tell them that a push or pull can make things start to move. Use some examples, such as a wheelbarrow, a toy car and a pull-down light switch. Explain that the actual push or pull causes the object to move, which in turn may cause other things to happen – for example, a light to go on when the cord is pulled.

Provide the children with copies of photocopiable sheet 122 and ask them to look at the pictures at the top of the sheet. Working individually or in pairs, ask them to complete this section, deciding whether each object needs to be pushed or pulled to make it work. Discuss their decisions. Do they all agree? Then ask the children to find five to ten items in the classroom which need to be pushed or pulled to make them work. Compare the answers of the whole class and make an agreed list of objects.

Next, provide the children with the collection of objects and ask them to push and pull each one along the floor to see which is the easier way to make the object move. Ask them to decide whether the force needed to move the object is small, medium or large. Could they find a way of measuring the force needed? (The amount of pull could be measured using an elastic band. The amount of push could be measured by using a compressed spring to push with.) Ask the children to record what happens in some way.

Discuss the children's ideas about pushing and pulling the objects and measuring or 'feeling' the force needed. Is it easier to push or to pull an object? Is the force needed to move an object different for different objects? How can forces make things move? Can forces act in different directions?

Suggestion(s) for extension

Use a newton meter to measure the force needed to pull the objects along the floor. Compare the results of this with the children's own measurements using an elastic band.

Suggestion(s) for support

Act as a scribe if necessary when the children are completing the photocopiable sheet, or pair up more able children with less able ones. Suggest the use of a spring and an elastic band as possible ways of measuring pushes and pulls respectively, if the children do not come up with any ideas of their own.

Assessment opportunities

The discussion about what forces are and what they can do will provide you with an insight into the children's perception and understanding of forces. This will enable you to decide what activities to do next, and assist with planning.

Display ideas

Make a large wall display of drawings, photographs and/or pictures of things which are pulled or pushed to make them work. Provide a collection of toys on a table in front of the display, and write a sign challenging the children to sort the objects into those which you pull and those which you push.

Other aspects of the Science PoS covered

Experimental and Investigative Science – 1a, e; 2a, b, 2c; 3a, c.

Reference to photocopiable sheet

Act as scribe if necessary when the children are completing the sheet, or pair up more able children with less able ones. The children could draw the objects rather than write their names.

CHANGING SHAPES

Forces can change the shapes of objects.
Pairs or small groups.
60–120 minutes.

Previous skills/knowledge needed

Forces are pushes and pulls.

Key background information

A force can make things change shape. Forces act in pairs. If the forces acting on an object are balanced, there is no change in shape; but if the forces are unbalanced, an object will change shape. Pushing, pulling, stretching, twisting and bending can cause objects to change shape.

Preparation

None specifically required for this activity.

Resources needed

Modelling clay, a balloon, an elastic band, an old pair of tights, an aluminium drink can, a drinking straw, a pipe cleaner, a small cardboard box, a plastic bottle, balsa wood, a sponge ball, wool, adhesive tape, paper, pencils.

What to do

Provide the children with the collection of objects listed above. Explain that they are going to find out if any of the objects can change shape by pushing, pulling, stretching, twisting or bending them. Demonstrate the idea by using the old tights as an example. Ask the children to predict whether they think the tights will change shape if they are stretched, twisted, bent or pushed. Try each idea and observe what happens. Were their predictions correct? Can the children suggest why the tights stretch easily?

Explain to the children that you want them to test the other objects in the same way. Encourage them to make a prediction each time and then to record what happens in some way, either as a written record or as a drawing.

After the children have completed the task, discuss their results with them. Did they get any unexpected results?

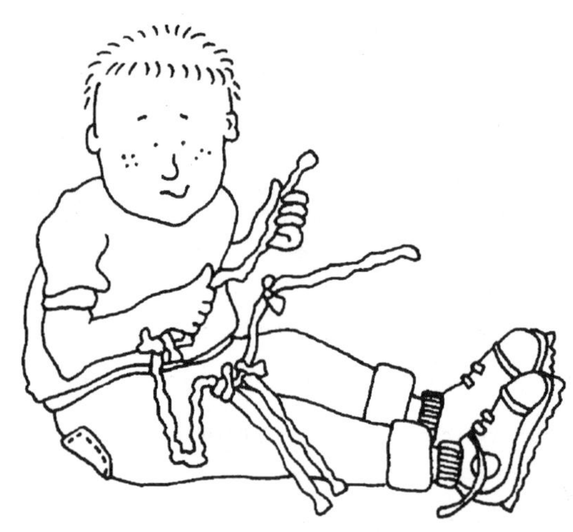

Which objects were difficult to change in shape? Can the children suggest why this is? Which objects changed shape easily? Why? Which objects could be changed back to their original shapes? Which ones could not be changed back? Which objects held their new shape easily? Can the children suggest why? What happened to the objects after they were changed – did some of them break, collapse or tear? What does this tell you about the materials they are made of? Which objects could change shape in *all* the ways tried?

What advantages and disadvantages are there in a material being able to change shape? Discuss examples of objects in which it is important for the material to change shape, such as a trampoline, and those things which need to retain their shape, such as a desk. How does this affect the choice of materials from which things are made?

Discuss the forces used in changing the objects; for example, what happens when you push on some modelling clay? (The downward force of the push from the hand and the upward force of the table on which the clay sits are both greater than the internal forces holding the clay in its original shape.)

Finally, discuss the recording methods used. Which methods seem to be most effective? Why? Did the children have any problems in recording? What were they? How did they solve them?

Suggestion(s) for extension

Using the knowledge gained from this activity, challenge the children to select other objects which they predict will meet certain criteria, such as *will not bend, will stretch, will twist.* Then ask the children to test their predictions.

Suggestion(s) for support

Help the children to record their results if necessary or appoint a group scribe. Make sure that the children make a prediction before they test the object.

Assessment opportunities

This activity will enable you to assess how well the children can record their results and how well they can relate their predictions to what happens. The discussion after the testing will provide you with an insight into what the children know and have learned about forces and how they can change the shapes of objects.

Display ideas

Ask the children to draw pictures of objects which can bend, stretch, twist or tear, or which cannot bend, cannot stretch, and so on. Mount the pictures on the wall, together with appropriate labels saying what the objects can and cannot do. Display the children's writing about their own investigations with these drawings. Add a collection of objects on a table for the children to sort into two groups: those which can change shape and those which cannot.

Other aspects of the Science PoS covered

Experimental and Investigative Science – 1a, b, c; 2a, b; 3a, c, d, e.

STRENGTH OF SHAPES

The shape of an object can have an effect on the forces needed to change that object.

Individuals or pairs.

60–120 minutes.

Children should take care when using the scissors.

Previous skills/knowledge needed

Pushes and pulls are forces. Forces can change the shapes of objects.

Key background information

A material can be strengthened by altering its shape. For example, a flat sheet of card bends in more directions and

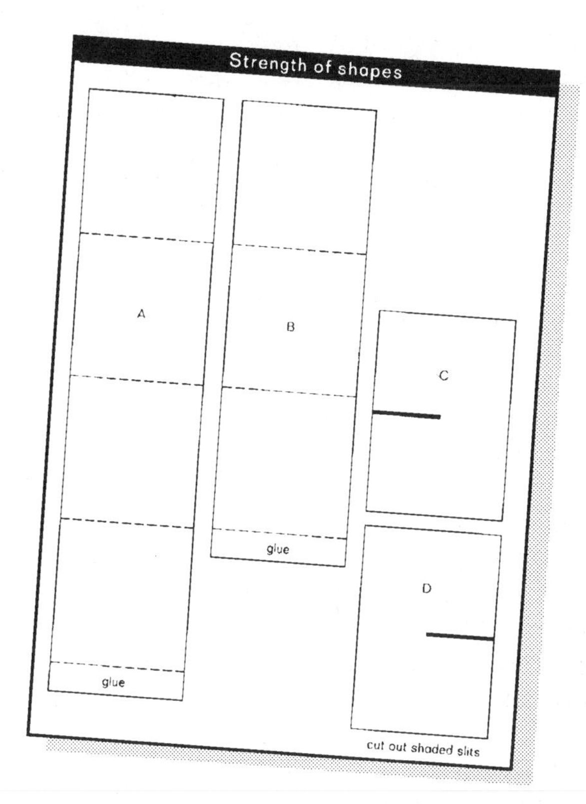

more easily than a corrugated sheet of card. Different shapes joined together in one structure also give strength to the overall structure – for example, arches and triangles are used in bridges because they are 'strong shapes'. In buildings and bridges, the structure is shaped and joined together in a particular way to ensure that this structure is not damaged by any forces acting on it (the forces are thus balanced). But if one external force were stronger than another one, the structure would move or change shape (the forces would be unbalanced).

Preparation

None specifically required for this activity.

Resources needed

One copy per child (or pair) of photocopiable page 123, pencils, scissors, grey board or stiff card, a ruler, adhesive tape, measuring weights, a piece of plywood (approximately 20cm x 14cm) or a thin, hardback book.

What to do

Tell the children that they are going to find out about how strong different shapes can be. Ask the children to name some of the shapes they can see in the classroom. Which of these shapes do they think are strong? Can the children suggest why? Which shapes do they think are not strong? Why? Explain that they are going to look at two shapes in particular: the square and the triangle.

Provide each child or pair with a copy of photocopiable page 123 and ask them to trace the shapes A and B on to the stiff card. Cut out the shapes and score along the dotted lines, using the sharp edge of a pair of scissors and a ruler. Fold shape A into a cube and shape B into a tent shape, using adhesive tape to join the edges. You may need to reinforce the edges with adhesive tape to make the shapes rigid. (See Figure 1.)

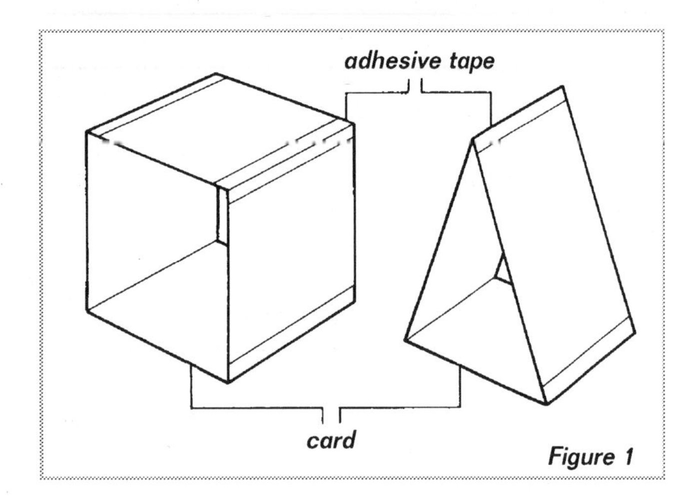

Figure 1

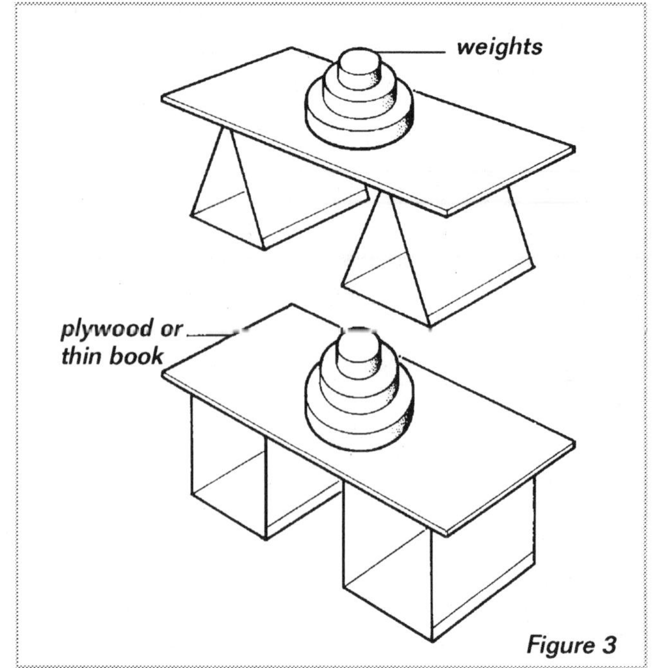

Figure 3

When they have made the shapes, ask the children to test out how strong they are. (See Figure 2.) First, ask them to place the cube on a table or flat surface and hold the base steady by placing a finger on it. Then ask them to push gently on one of the top edges of the square. What happens? Push on the side of the square. What happens to the shape? How does it change? How easily does it change? Try the same things with the tent shape. What happens this time? Which shape is the easier to push? Which shape is the more rigid? Can the children suggest why?

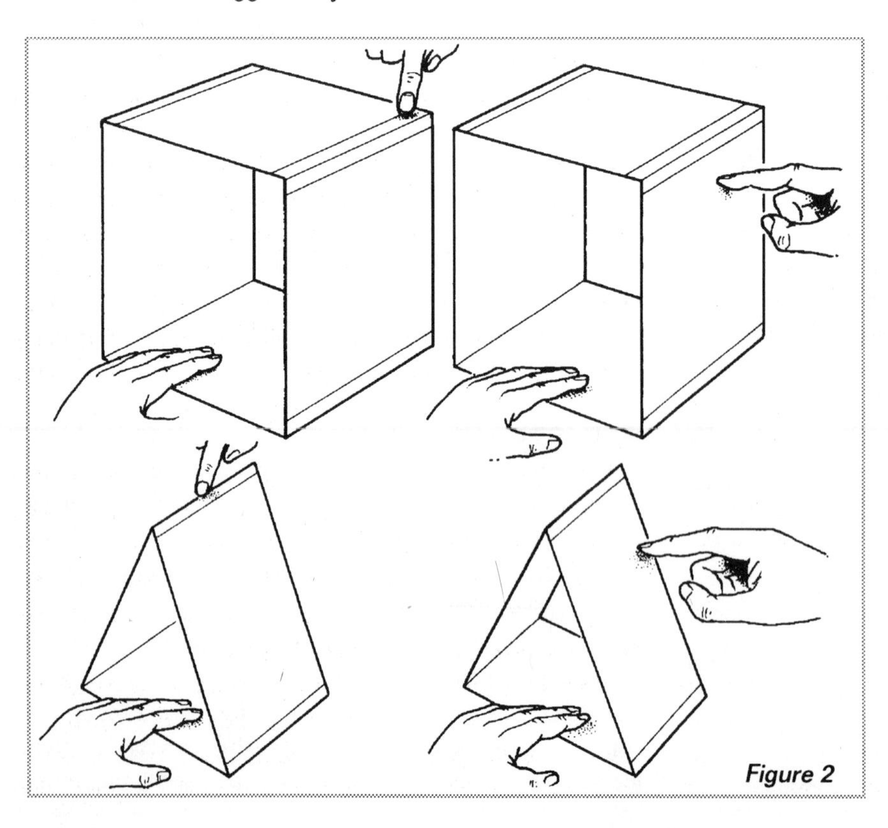
Figure 2

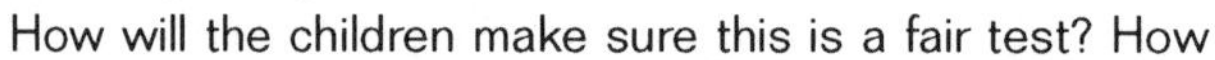

Next, ask the children to make another cube and tent shape, or ask two pairs of children to work together so that they have two of each. Explain that they are going to find out how strong the two shapes are by putting a bridge across the shapes and adding weights until the supports collapse. (See Figure 3.) If you do not have enough measuring weights, use books of the same size to test the bridges. Can the children predict which support (cube or tent) will collapse more easily? Why?

How will the children make sure this is a fair test? How will they record what happens? When the children have completed the task, discuss the results. Which shape was the stronger? How much weight could it hold? How much weight did the weaker shape hold before it collapsed? Would you obtain the same results if the shapes were turned round in a different way? Which way round do the children think they would be strongest? Can they suggest why?

Can the children suggest ways of making the square stronger? Explain that one way would be to use some braces inside the shape. Discuss how frames are used in buildings for this purpose.

Referring them back to photocopiable sheet 123, ask the children to cut out shapes C and D from stiff card. After the two slits have been cut out from the middle, these pieces can be slotted together and placed inside the cube. (See Figure 4.) The bridge test can then be

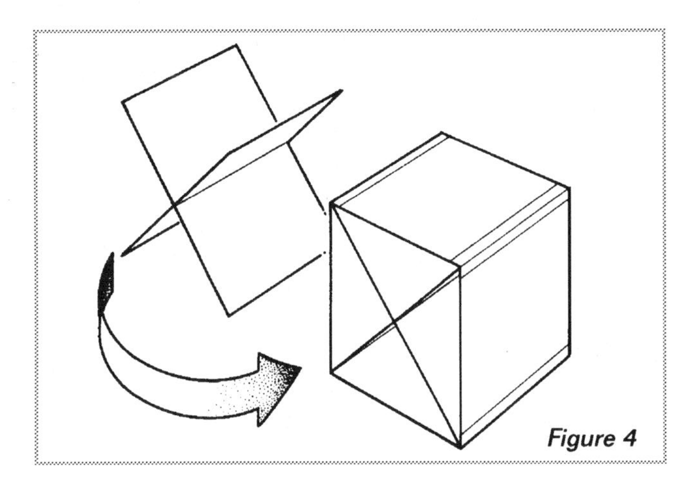
Figure 4

repeated to see if the results are different with the braces inside the cube. How much more weight will the cubic supports now hold?

Discuss these results. What have the children learned from this activity? Consider the materials used – both shapes were made from the same card, yet have different strengths. What does this tell the children? How can some shapes be made stronger? How can these ideas be used in building houses or bridges?

Discuss the actual testing and recording. How did the children make sure it was a fair test? How did they record their results? Do their results support any predictions made? Could the activity be improved in any way? What conclusions can be drawn?

Suggestion(s) for extension

Using the same ideas, the children could make and test two other shapes, perhaps a cylinder and a rectangular box. What happens this time? How do the results compare with those of the first activity?

Suggestion(s) for support

Some children may need help with cutting out the shapes from the card, to ensure that they fit together accurately. Act as scribe if necessary for the recording, or pair up more able children with less able ones.

Assessment opportunities

This activity will enable you to assess how well the children can measure and record their findings. Use the time when the children are making and testing the shapes to talk to individuals about the strength and properties of shapes, and how these affect the way in which forces can be applied to them.

Opportunities for IT

Children could use a simple drawing package to draw the shapes they have made and tested. This would give them opportunities to stretch and bend shape drawings in similar ways to the practical work undertaken. The pictures could be combined with an explanation of the children's work, written using a word processor.

Display ideas

Pictures and drawings of shapes used in buildings and bridges could be mounted on the wall, together with the children's own writing about and drawings of the bridge testing. The model bridges and any other shapes made by the children could be displayed on a table near the wall display.

Other aspects of the Science PoS covered

Experimental and Investigative Science – 1a, b, c, d; 2a, b, c; 3a, b, c, d, e.

Reference to photocopiable sheet

The shapes could be traced directly on to the card using a sharp pencil and a ruler, and pressing hard when outlining the shapes. This will save the time spent using tracing paper.

MAGNETS

There are forces of attraction and repulsion between magnets.

Pairs or small groups.

45–60 minutes.

This activity will need close supervision, because iron filings can damage the eyes.

Previous skills/knowledge needed

None specifically required for this activity.

Key background information

Natural magnets are a kind of iron ore called *magnetite* or *lodestone*. *Permanent magnets* can be made from hard steel (and certain other alloys) by stroking the metal with magnetite in one direction, or by placing it in a magnetic field created by an electric coil. These methods align the atoms in the steel, thereby making it magnetic. The difference between permanent magnets and temporary magnets (whose magnetism soon wears off) is one of degree: the permanence of the magnet depends on how thoroughly the particles have been aligned (that is, how long the metal was treated for and how well it holds magnetism).

All magnets have two specific ends or *poles* (north pole and south pole). When a magnet is suspended, it will align itself approximately in a north-south direction. Like poles repel each other and unlike poles attract. Magnets are surrounded by a *magnetic field*. If a permanent magnet is cut in half, both pieces will become a complete magnet.

If you heat, hammer or frequently drop a magnet, it can lose its magnetism because the atoms become misaligned. If kept properly, permanent magnets retain their magnetism for a long time. Bar magnets should be stored in pairs, side by side, with the north pole next to the south pole and a 'keeper' (a piece of steel or iron which fits across the poles) at both ends. Horseshoe magnets should have a 'keeper' placed across the end.

A temporary magnet can be made by stroking a piece of steel or iron in one direction with a permanent magnet. A steel or iron rod will become magnetised if placed near to, but not touching, a magnet (*magnetic induction*).

Preparation
None specifically required for this activity.

Resources needed
Bar magnets, iron filings in a shaker, stiff paper, four small blocks or empty matchboxes, a needle, string, a compass, paper, pencils, paper-clips.

What to do
Tell the children that they are going to find out about magnets. Provide them with some string, a bar magnet and a compass. Ask them to tie the string around the centre of the magnet so that it balances horizontally when it is suspended. The magnet should turn and align itself along a north-south axis. The children can use the compass to check the direction. Explain that the ends of the magnet are called poles, and that one is a north-seeking or north pole and the other is a south-seeking or south pole.

Challenge the children to find out about the forces of attraction and repulsion between the bar magnets. Ask them to place one magnet on a flat surface and slowly move the other magnet towards it. What happens when like poles are moved together? What happens when unlike poles are moved together? Turn the magnets round and try again. Do you get the same results? Explain that when two magnets stick to each other it is called *attraction*, and when two magnets push each other away it is called *repulsion*. Do the magnets attract or repel each other along their whole length, or just at the ends?

Explain that magnets have a magnetic field surrounding them, and that we can see this by using iron filings to make a pattern. Provide the children with the iron filings, stiff paper, four small blocks and two bar magnets. Place the paper on the four blocks with a bar magnet underneath. Gently sprinkle the iron filings over the paper and gently tap the paper. What happens? Ask the children to record the pattern. (See Figure 1.) Then ask them to place two magnets underneath in various positions – north facing north, north facing south and so on. Record what happens in each case. What differences are there in the patterns?

Finally, explain to the children how magnets can become demagnetised and show them how to store magnets correctly. Explain also how temporary magnets can be made. Provide the children with a bar magnet, a needle and some paper-clips. Ask them to stroke the needle with the magnet in one direction, lifting the magnet clear of the needle before starting another stroke. They will need to repeat this several times. How strong is their new magnet? How many paper-clips will it attract compared to the original bar magnet?

Suggestion(s) for extension
Repeat each activity using different-shaped magnets of different sizes. How do the results compare?

Suggestion(s) for support
Help the children when they are recording the iron filing activity, or choose a more able child to record the results for the group.

Assessment opportunities
Ask the children to write down and/or draw what they have learned about magnets from doing these activities. You could use this as a basis for more in-depth discussions with individual children.

Opportunities for IT
More able children might be able to use a drawing package on a computer to draw the magnetic field patterns they have created. They could draw the patterns using dotted lines, and experiment with curves, arcs and ellipses to gain the desired effects. Different thicknesses or colours could be used to show the strength of the field in different places, thinner lines representing weaker field lines.

Display ideas
Display a collection of magnets of different sizes and shapes on a table, together with a container of paper-clips. Make a sign which challenges the children to find out which magnet is the strongest. The children could then write about and draw what they did, and this work could be displayed on the wall behind the table.

Other aspects of the Science PoS covered
Experimental and Investigative Science – 1a; 2a, b, c; 3c.

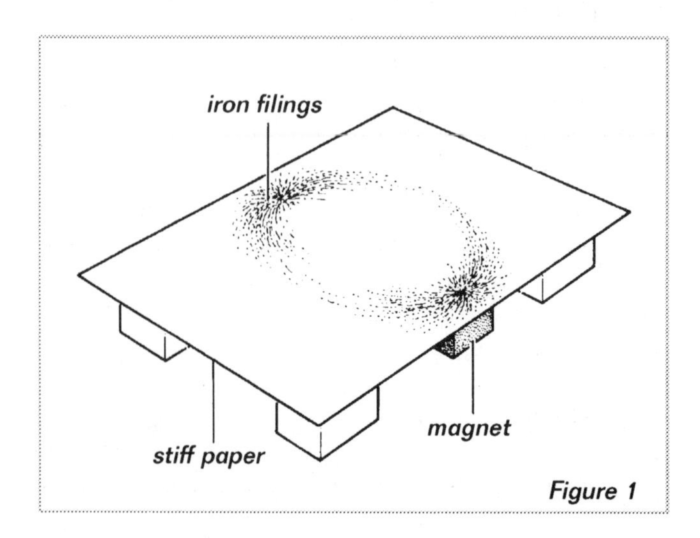

Figure 1

MAGNETIC MATERIALS

Magnets are attracted to some materials.

Pairs or small groups.

45–60 minutes.

Previous skills/knowledge needed

When something sticks to a magnet, this is called attraction.

Key background information

Non-metallic objects are not attracted to magnets, but this does not mean that all metals are. Only iron, nickel and cobalt are attracted. Some alloys are also magnetic, such as steel.

Preparation

None specifically required for this activity.

Resources needed

One copy per child (or pair) of photocopiable page 124, pencils, magnets, a 1p coin, a 10p coin, a £1 coin, an aluminium drink can, a steel can, foil, a spoon, a brass weight, a paper-clip, a copper wire, a tin-plate lid.

What to do

Ask the children to tell you the names of things which they think would be attracted to a magnet. What experiences have they had to help them decide this? Provide each child/pair with a magnet, and ask them to find ten things in the classroom which will stick to it and ten things which will not. They need to record this information in some way.

When the children have completed this task, bring the whole class back together and discuss the results. Discuss the recording methods used. Which methods are the most successful, clear or easy to use? Can the children draw a conclusion yet about the things which are attracted to magnets? What are the things which were attracted made of? What are the things which were not attracted made of?

To find out if all metals are attracted to magnets, provide each child/pair with a copy of photocopiable page 124 and the collection of objects listed. Remind them to make a prediction first before trying out each object.

After the children have completed this activity, draw the whole class together again. What did they find out? Were the results as expected? Were they surprised by any of the results? Why?

What can the children conclude about the types of metals which are attracted to magnets? Explain to the children that only iron, nickel and cobalt are attracted to magnets, and that some alloys (combinations of metals) such as steel are also attracted.

Suggestion(s) for extension

Use the collection of magnetic objects to test the strength of different magnets. How many objects can each magnet pick up? Do round, bar and horseshoe magnets have different strengths? Does the biggest magnet have the greatest strength? Do the magnets have the same strength all along their length, or are the poles stronger?

Suggestion(s) for support

Act as scribe if necessary when the children are recording their results, or pair up a more able child with a less able one.

Assessment opportunities

This activity will enable you to assess how well the children can record a task. It will provide an opportunity to discuss the use of tables, charts and diagrams and to consider the most effective way of using them. The discussion at the beginning of the activity will provide you with an insight into what the children already know about magnetic materials. The discussion at the end of the final task will enable you to assess what the children have learned from the activity, and whether this has changed their ideas about magnetic materials.

Display ideas

A large drawing/painting of a magnet could be mounted on the wall, and the children could draw pictures of things which are attracted and not attracted to a magnet. These pictures could be mounted on each side of the magnet under an appropriate heading. The children's recorded results from the activities could also be put on display. A fishing game, using a magnet attached to a rod by some string, could be placed on a table near the wall display so the children can 'fish' for magnetic things from a collection of objects.

Are all metals magnetic?

Name ______________________ Date ____________

▲ Which of these objects do you think will be magnetic? Predict first, then use a magnet to find out.

▲ Record your results in the chart.

Object	Prediction: Will it be magnetic?	Result: Is it magnetic?
1p coin		
10p coin		
£1 coin		
aluminium can		
foil		
steel can		
spoon		
brass weight		
paper-clip		
copper wire		
tin-plate lid		

▲ What did you find out from this activity? ______________________

Other aspects of the Science PoS covered

Experimental and Investigative Science – 1a, b; 2a, b, c; 3a, b, c, d.
Materials and their Properties – 1a.

Reference to photocopiable sheet

Note that 1p and 2p coins dated after 1992 are made of copper-plated steel and will therefore be magnetic. 1p and 2p coins prior to 1992 are made of bronze (97 per cent copper, 2.5 per cent zinc and 0.5 per cent tin) and are not magnetic. 10p coins are made of cupro-nickel (75 per cent copper and 25 per cent nickel) and £1 coins are made of nickel-brass (70 per cent copper, 5.5 per cent nickel and 24.5 per cent zinc).

Tin plate is thin sheet steel with a coating of tin. Brass is an alloy of copper and zinc. Steel is an alloy of iron and carbon. Stainless steel is a steel which does not rust, due to the addition of chromium.

A magnet can attract a magnetic material even if it is covered in a thin layer of non-magnetic material, so the steel can be attracted even if the label is still attached.

TESTING MAGNETISM

Magnetic force will pass through some materials.

Pairs or small groups.

60–90 minutes.

▲ *Make sure that the lids from the steel and aluminium cans are properly sealed, so they are safe for the children to handle.*

Previous skills/knowledge needed

Some materials are attracted to magnets.

Key background information

Magnetism can pass through most non-magnetic materials, but the ability of the magnet to attract objects depends on several things:

- ▲ how strong the magnet is;
- ▲ how far away the magnet is from the object;
- ▲ how thick the material is.

The magnetic field gets weaker as the distance between the object and the magnet increases.

Preparation

Remove the lids from a steel and an aluminium can and seal the cut edges with tape, so that they are safe for the children to handle. Find eight books of the following thicknesses: 2-3mm, 5mm, 7mm, 10mm, 15mm, 20mm, 25mm, 30mm.

Resources needed

One copy per group/pair of photocopiable sheet 125, pencils, three horseshoe magnets of different sizes, paper, fabric, a wooden ruler, a plastic ruler, a silver spoon, a stainless steel spoon, foil, a tin-plate lid, a plastic lid, a steel can, an aluminium can, a glass jar, cardboard, books of different thicknesses.

What to do

Ask the children to recall any previous work they have completed on magnets. What materials do magnets attract? How can magnets be damaged? How can this be prevented? How should magnets be stored? Explain to the children that they are going to find out more about magnets and how they work. Give them copies of photocopiable page 125 and explain the task to them. Ask the children to predict which objects they think the magnet will work through and ask them to record this on the sheet. Can the children give reasons for their predictions? Does everyone in the class agree? Why/why not?

As the children are carrying out this task, ask questions which will help them decide why the magnet will or will not work through each object: What do you think this object might be made of? What materials do magnets attract? How thick is the object? How far away is the magnet from the paper-clip? These questions will help the children to complete the *What have you found out?* section on the worksheet.

Discuss what the children have found out from this activity as a whole class when everyone has completed the task. Look at the objects which the magnet would work through. What do these objects have in common? (They are made of non-magnetic materials.) Why do the children think a magnet will not work through a magnetic material?

Now refer the children to the second activity on the worksheet. This time, they will use three different-sized magnets to find out whether a magnet will work through different thicknesses of non-magnetic materials such as books. Which magnet do they predict will be the strongest? Will the magnets work through all the books?

When this task has been completed, bring the whole class together again. What did the children find out? Which magnet was the strongest? Were they surprised by any of the results? Did all the groups obtain the same results? What could explain any discrepancies? How many times did they test each thickness? What can they conclude about magnetism from this activity?

Suggestion(s) for extension

Find the average thickness or material that each magnet tested would work through and plot this on a graph. Design and make a magnetic game in which pieces are moved by magnets.

Suggestion(s) for support

Help the children to read and complete photocopiable sheet 125 if necessary, or pair up a more able child with a less able one. Tell the children what the objects are made out of, if they do not know. Help with measuring the thicknesses of the books if necessary.

Assessment opportunities

This activity will enable you to assess how accurately the children can measure. It will also help you to find out how well the children can use their previous knowledge about magnetic and non-magnetic materials to make their predictions.

Opportunities for IT

Children could use graphing software to plot graphs of the thickness of the book and the number of paper-clips the magnet would pick up. This would help them design a fair test to determine the effect of different magnets. Children could draw a line graph for each strength of magnet, print the results and discuss what the graphs show.

If the children use a spreadsheet to record the number of paper-clips picked up for different thicknesses of book, the data in the spreadsheet can be used to plot the graphs, which can be used to focus discussion on the investigation and what has been discovered.

Thickness	Magnet A	Magnet B	Magnet C
3mm	10	6	4
5mm	9	5	3
7mm			
10mm			
15mm			
20mm			
25mm			
30mm			

Testing magnetism

Name ______________________ Date __________

▲ Use your largest magnet to find out if a paper-clip is attracted through these objects

Object	Prediction: Will it work through this?	Result: Did it work through this?	Object	Prediction: Will it work through this?	Result: Did it work through this?
paper			tin plate lid		
fabric			plastic lid		
wooden ruler			steel can		
plastic ruler			aluminium can		
silver spoon			glass jar		
stainless steel spoon			cardboard		
foil			thin book		

▲ What have you found out? ______________________

▲ Now find out how strong your magnets are. Find out whether a paper-clip is attracted through books of different thicknesses. Complete the chart using a tick if the magnet works through the book.

Book	Thickness of book	Magnet size		
		small	medium	large
A	2/3mm			
B	5mm			
C	7mm			
D	10mm			
E	15mm			
F	20mm			
G	25mm			
H	30mm			

Display ideas

Ask the children to draw the objects through which the magnet will work and those through which it will not work. Mount the pictures on the wall on either side of a large drawing or painting of a magnet, together with any writing, drawings or graphs the children have produced during the activity. Provide some magnets and the collection of materials used in the activity on a table near the display.

Other aspects of the Science PoS covered

Experimental and Investigative Science – 1a, b; 2a, b; 3a, b, c, d, e.

Reference to photocopiable sheet

The magnet should not work through the stainless steel spoon, the tin-plate lid and the steel can, as these are made of magnetic materials.

FRICTION

Friction can slow a moving object.

Small groups.

60–120 minutes.

Previous skills/knowledge needed

Many things are able to move. A force is a push or a pull. How to use a measuring tape and a stopwatch.

Key background information

Friction is a force. Whenever one object slides over another object, the friction between them resists the movement. If two surfaces are very smooth, there is little friction and they slide easily over one another. If the surfaces are rough or uneven, the friction is greater and relative movement is more difficult.

Friction can therefore affect the speed of an object moving over a surface. Speed can be calculated as the distance travelled divided by the time taken.

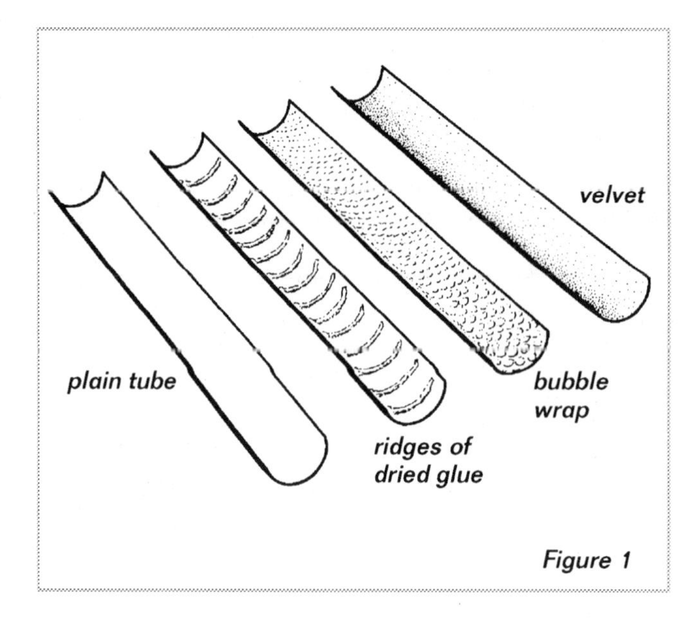

Figure 1

Preparation

Obtain two long cardboard tubes (like those used with wrapping paper). Cut the tubes in half lengthways. Apply some lines of glue across the inside surface of one half-tube, about 2cm apart along its entire length, and allow it to dry (this will make ridges). Glue some bubble wrap to the inner surface of another half-tube. Glue some fabric with a raised texture, such as velvet, to the third half-tube. Leave the last half-tube as it is. (see Figure 1.)

Resources needed

Cardboard tubes (as prepared above), a marble or ping-pong ball, a measuring tape, a metre ruler, a stopwatch, one copy per child of photocopiable page 126, pencils, access to several different floor types such as carpet, wooden floor, vinyl.

What to do

Explain to the children that they are going to find out about the things which can affect how fast an object moves. Show the half-tubes to the children and explain that each one has a different type of surface on it. Tell them that you want them to find out how the type of surface can affect how fast a marble or ping-pong ball moves down the tube when it is positioned like a ramp.

Provide the children with a copy of photocopiable page 126 and explain the worksheet to them. Tell them that they need to position each tube like a ramp, leaning it against some books or a chair. Then they need to place the marble (or ping-pong ball) at the top of the ramp and let it go. They should measure the *distance* the marble travels from the bottom end of the tube to where it stops. They should do this three times for each tube. Discuss why they need to test each tube more than once.

Explain that they can also get a relative indication of the speed at which the marble travels along each tube by measuring the *time* it takes for the marble to move from the top of the tube to a constant distance (such as one metre) marked out on the floor. They can measure this constant distance to calculate the actual speed of the marble.

N.B. Children should not be misled by the worksheet into dividing the distance in the first experiment by the time in the second – this will *not* give a true measure of speed.

Discuss how the children will make sure it is a fair test (slope of the ramp the same, same marble, let the marble go in the same way, and so on). Will there be any safety precautions to consider? (For example, test where no one else will slip on the moving marbles.)

Ask the children to predict on which surface they think the marble will move fastest, and get them to record this on the sheet before they start the activity. As the children are carrying out the task, make sure they are using the measuring tape and stopwatch correctly. Remind them to record the distances and times in the spaces on the worksheet. When they have finished the task, ask the children to complete the last section on the sheet, where they are required to write down their conclusions about the results.

After this, bring the class together to discuss the results. Were the results as expected? On which surface did the marble travel the fastest? Can the children suggest why? Discuss friction. Explain that rough or uneven surfaces cause greater friction than smooth surfaces. Which tubes in the experiment would cause the greatest friction? What effect does this have on the marble? Relate the ideas of friction and ease of movement to everyday experiences such as walking on polished floors and grass. Why do shoes often have rough soles?

Discuss the measuring and timing. What problems did the children experience? How easy or accurate is it to time a marble moving fast? What could be done to make the timing more accurate? Were three tries enough?

Finally, ask the children to consider (and perhaps test) what difference it would make to try the same experiment on different floor surfaces. How might this affect the results?

	a	b	c	d	e
1	Tube	Try 1	Try 2	Try 3	Average
2	Carpet	25	30	29	AV (b2; d2)
3	bubble wrap	15	20	22	AV (b3; d3)
4					
5					
6					
7					

Suggestion(s) for extension
Ask the children to work out the average distances travelled and times taken for all groups in the class on each of the four surfaces. Record the results as a graph.

Suggestion(s) for support
Pair up more able with less able readers and writers to complete the worksheet, or appoint a scribe for the group. Help the children with the measuring and timing if necessary. Act as scribe when individuals are recording their predictions and conclusions.

Assessment opportunities
This activity will enable you to assess how well the children can record their results and how accurately they can use a measuring tape and stop-watch. You can use the time when the children are testing the surfaces to talk to individuals about their predictions and the results they are obtaining. Use the children's written conclusions as a guideline for the class discussion, as they will indicate the extent of the children's knowledge of friction and may also highlight any misunderstandings.

Opportunities for IT
Children could use a spreadsheet to record their results. The spreadsheet can be set up to calculate an average value of the distance travelled by the marble. The children could then use the final average results to plot out a bar chart showing the distances travelled from different tubes. They should then use the graph to decide which surfaces provide the most and the least friction. (See above right.)

Display ideas
Display the tube ramps on a table in front of a wall display showing the children's writing about and drawings of the activity. Make a sign explaining what the task was and what conclusions were drawn from the activity.

Other aspects of the Science PoS covered
Experimental and Investigative Science – 1a, b, d; 2a, b, c; 3a, b, c, d, e.

Reference to photocopiable sheet
The sheet can be given to each child, or a group scribe could be appointed to record the results.

Moving objects

Name ______________________ Date ____________

My prediction:
The marble/ping-pong ball will move fastest along the ____________ surface because ____________

Type of surface	Distance travelled		
	1st try	2nd try	3rd try
plain cardboard			
glue ridges			
bubble wrap			
fabric			

What these results tell me: ____________

Type of surface	Time taken to travel fixed distance		
	1st try	2nd try	3rd try
plain cardboard			
glue ridges			
bubble wrap			
fabric			

What these results tell me: ____________

GRAVITY

Gravity is a force.
Small groups or pairs.
60–90 minutes.

Previous skills/knowledge needed
A force is a push or a pull.

Key background information
Gravity is the force of attraction between two objects as a result purely of their mass. Gravity is the force that pulls an object downwards towards the Earth. The Earth has a large mass, so the force of attraction between it and an object is strong and this force pulls the object to the Earth. The force is called the 'weight' of the object. The force of gravity is always present on the Earth, so there is always a downward pull on objects.

Relatively heavy, solid objects of similar size and shape fall at the same speed, even if they do not weigh the same. Relatively light bjects of the same weight but different sizes or shapes fall at different rates. This is due to *air resistance*, which slows down falling objects. (Strictly speaking, it doesn't slow them down – except in the case of an unfolding parachute – so much as prevent them speeding up under the influence of gravity. Air resistance increases when an object moves faster.) Without air, all objects would fall at the same rate. Because the Moon has less mass than the Earth, objects are pulled downwards with a smaller force. This is why objects are lighter on the Moon, though their mass is the same.

Preparation
None specifically required for this activity.

Resources needed
Modelling clay, a metal tray, kitchen scales, two solid objects of similar size and shape but different weights (such as a large marble and a golf ball), A4 paper, pencils, a stopwatch.

What to do
Ask the children to make four Plasticine balls of different weights, using the scales to measure them. Explain that you want them to find out which one will hit the ground first if dropped from a set height (such as from the hands of someone standing on a chair). Which ball do the children think will reach the ground first? Can they suggest why? Ask the children to tell you how they think they could check which ball travels the fastest (use of stopwatch, dropping them all together to see which one lands first, and so on). Which method do they think they will use in their test? Why? How will the children ensure it will be a fair test? Are there any safety precautions to consider?

Allow the children time to test the balls to find out which one hits the ground first. Ask them to record their results in some way. After they have completed the task, discuss their results with them. What did they find out? What problems did they have? How successful were the timing methods they used? How many times did they test each ball? Could any conclusions be drawn from the activity?

If appropriate, suggest using a metal tray so that the children can hear the first ball landing, and ask them to do the test again to see if they get the same results.

Next, show the children two identical pieces of A4 paper. Do the children agree that the pieces of paper would probably weigh the same? What would happen, then, if they were dropped from the same height? Try it.

Now scrunch one of the pieces of paper into a ball. Would the paper still weigh the same as it did before? If the flat piece of paper and the paper ball were dropped, what would happen? Would they still land together? Try this and observe the results. What explanations can the children give for the flat paper landing last? What slows it down (or rather, stops it speeding up)? Discuss the shape of the paper. Explain that the flatter sheet has a larger surface area, and that the air underneath the sheet as it falls is thus spread out over a larger area. The air underneath pushes up against the sheet (air resistance) and holds it back. The air resistance on the paper ball is less because it has a smaller surface area. It therefore moves more easily (and quickly) through the air.

Discuss the reason for objects falling to the ground. Introduce the term 'gravity'. What can the children tell you about gravity? Mention that gravity is a force which pulls objects to the ground and that when an object falls there is both gravity and air resistance acting upon it.

Now ask the children to try out two solid objects of similar shape and size but different weights. What do they predict will happen? Will they land together, or will one hit the ground first? Ask the children to test this several times and record what happens. Discuss their results. Can they explain why the objects land together?

Ask the children what they think would happen if they repeated the test on the Moon. What can the children tell you about the gravity on the Moon? Explain that there is air resistance on the Moon, so objects of different shapes but the same weight (such as the flat paper and the ball of paper) would fall at the same rate and would hit the ground together.

Suggestion(s) for extension
Ask the children to investigate whether pushing an object off the table (or desk) will make it fall faster than just dropping it.

Suggestion(s) for support
Help the children make and weigh the balls of modelling clay, if necessary. Act as scribe when the children are recording their results, or appoint a group scribe. Explain how the metal tray can be used to detect which object lands first – two sounds will be heard if one object lands before another. Make sure the children try out each object more than once to check their observations.

Assessment opportunities
This activity will enable you to assess how well the children can record their results. It will provide an opportunity for you to discuss how to make sure their test is fair, and will highlight the need for measurements and observations to be repeated in order to obtain more accurate results. You could ask the children to write about and draw the activities after they have completed them. This could be used to discuss the concepts of gravity and air resistance in more detail with individual children.

Opportunities for IT
The more able pupils might like to consider how the investigation could be made more accurate using computer technology. It may be possible to set up two light sensors, so that the first would turn on a computer clock when the clay passes the sensor as it is dropped and the second sensor turns off the clock as it lands. The second sensor could also be a pressure pad which stops the computer clock when the object lands on it. Such a system would ensure that variables to do with when objects were dropped or landed could be eliminated from the results.

Children might like to consider other applications which involve similar systems; electronic timing in sprint races might be one example, with the computer clock starting as the gun is fired and stopping when the light sensor is triggered as the winner crosses the finishing line.

Display ideas
Make three large charts showing illustrations of the three activities carried out. Write the question 'What do you think will happen?' as a large heading underneath all three charts. Mount this on the wall together with the children's own writing about and drawings of the experiments.

Other aspects of the Science PoS covered
Experimental and Investigative Science – 1a, b, c, d, e; 2a, b, c; 3a, b, c, d, e.

WEIGHT

Objects have weight due to the pull of gravity.
Small groups.
45–60 minutes.
Children should take care when handling the scissors.

Previous skills/knowledge needed
A force is a push or a pull. Gravity is a force.

Key background information
The weight of an object is the effect of the pull of gravity on that object. Thus weight is a force, and it can be measured in newtons (N) using a spring balance. 9.81 newtons is the pull of gravity on a mass of 1kg. Many spring balances are calibrated in mass units, such as grams or kilograms.

In everyday language, the term 'weight' is used to describe both mass and weight; but to a scientist, there is a difference between the *weight* of an object and the *mass* of an object. Mass is a measure of the amount of matter in an object. Because weight depends on the pull of gravity, an object would weigh less on the Moon than on Earth, even though its mass would be the same. This is because the Moon is smaller than the Earth and has less mass, so the force of gravity pulling an object downwards on the Moon is smaller than on Earth.

Preparation
None specifically required for this activity.

Resources needed
A newton meter, string, objects to weigh (such as scissors, cup, book, stapler, pencil), an elastic band, a paper-clip, paper. *For extension:* a deep bowl or small aquarium tank, water.

What to do
Ask the children to tell you what they think weight is. Write down their definitions on a large piece of paper, and explain that you will refer back to these statements after the activity to see if any of their ideas have changed.

Show the children a newton meter and explain that it is

used to measure the weight of objects. Allow them to look at the meter, and then ask them to tell you how they think it works. Then show the children how it works. Tie a piece of string around a small object such as some scissors, and hook a paper-clip around the string and an elastic band. (See Figure 1.)

Lift up the elastic band until the scissors are hanging in the air. Ask the children to tell you what has happened to the elastic band. Why do they think this has happened? (You are pulling the elastic band upwards and the force of gravity is pulling the scissors downwards.) Ask the children to predict what will happen if you place your hand underneath the scissors to support them. Why has this happened? Explain that the newton meter works in a similar way to the elastic band. The spring inside stretches when an object is hung on the meter.

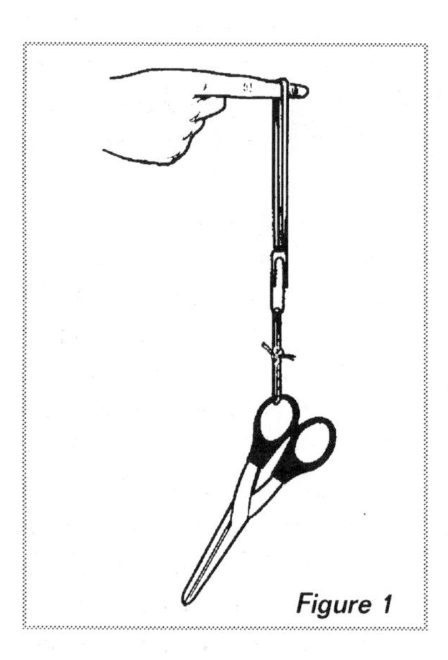

Figure 1

Ask the children to find out the weights of ten classroom objects by tying some string around each one (if necessary) to hook it on to the newton meter. Ask them to record their results.

When the children have completed this, bring them together as a class to discuss what have they found out. How did they record their work? What did they find out? Which objects were the heaviest? Which were the lightest? What did these items measure on the newton meter?

Ask the children to tell you what they think gravity is. Discuss this concept, and tell the children that weight is actually caused by the pull of gravity on an object. Tell them that spring balances, such as newton meters, are used to measure this force.

Ask the children to tell you what they think the items they measured would weigh on the Moon. Would they weigh more or less? Can the children suggest why? Explain that the Moon is a smaller mass than the Earth and therefore there is less gravity on the Moon. Objects would weigh less on the Moon because they are pulled down by a smaller force than on the Earth. (Their actual weight on the Moon can be calculated by dividing the weight on the Earth by six, because the force of gravity on the Moon is one-sixth of the gravity on the Earth.)

Refer the children back to their initial statements about weight, which you wrote down on paper. How accurate were their comments? How have their ideas changed? Can you now write a group definition of weight?

Suggestion(s) for extension
Ask the children to measure the objects again, but this time in water. What happens to the weights of the objects? Can the children suggest why this happens? How does this help us to understand why objects float?

Suggestion(s) for support
The children may need help in securing the string around the objects and in reading the newton meter. Help the children to record their results if necessary, or appoint a group scribe.

Assessment opportunities
You will be able to assess how accurately the children read the meter and how well they record the results. The written statements at the beginning of the lesson will provide you with an insight into what the children already know about the concept of weight, and this will assist you in directing questions as the task progresses.

Display ideas
Draw an Earth and a Moon. Draw the objects the children have weighed using the newton meter, and label them with their weights on the Earth and on the Moon. Mount this on the wall. Make a large heading: 'What do things weigh?' Ask the children to write about the weighing activity and add their information to the display.

Other aspects of the Science PoS covered
Experimental and Investigative Science – 1a; 2a, b, c; 3a, c.

AIR RESISTANCE

Air resistance can slow down a moving object.

Pairs or small groups.

60–120 minutes.

Children should take care when using the scissors.

Previous skills/knowledge needed
A force is a push or a pull. Friction can slow a moving object. Gravity is a force.

Key background information
Objects which are moving through the air experience the force of friction. This is called *air resistance*. Air resistance acts against gravity on falling objects, retarding them (slowing them down) as they fall. The air offers greater resistance to objects which have a larger surface area.

The faster an object moves through the air, the greater is the air resistance acting upon it. Falling objects move faster and faster until the retarding force of the air resistance equals the pull of gravity. Once this happens, the object can go no faster. This is called its *terminal velocity*.

Parachutes are used to slow down the speed of the person

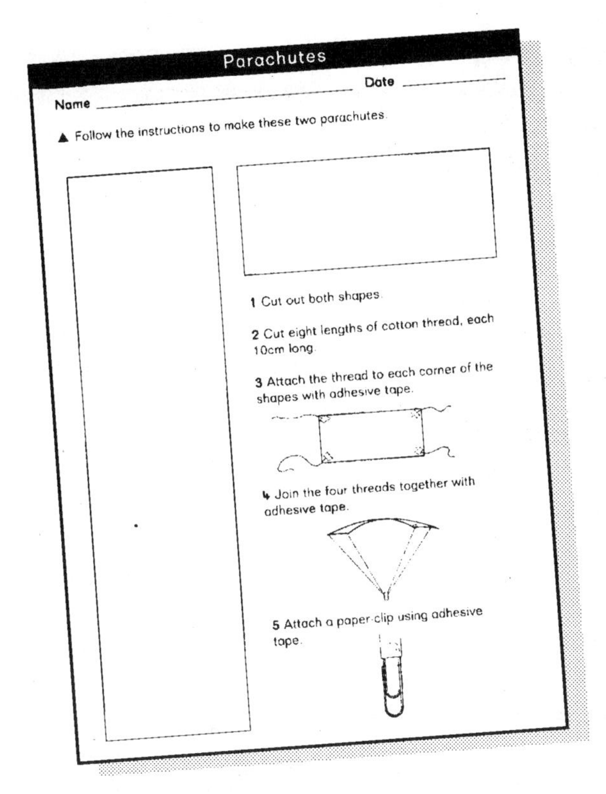
Parachutes

Name ____________________ Date ____________

▲ Follow the instructions to make these two parachutes.

1 Cut out both shapes.

2 Cut eight lengths of cotton thread, each 10cm long.

3 Attach the thread to each corner of the shapes with adhesive tape.

4 Join the four threads together with adhesive tape.

5 Attach a paper-clip using adhesive tape.

or object suspended from the parachute. The parachute is affected by gravity and air resistance. The larger the area of a parachute, the greater the air resistance, so the slower it falls. The part of a parachute which 'catches' the air is called the canopy.

Preparation

None specifically required for this activity.

Resources needed

One copy per pair/group of photocopiable page 127, scissors, cotton thread, adhesive tape, A4 paper, pencils, a ruler, a metre ruler, two paper-clips.

What to do

Ask the children to tell you what they know about gravity. What is it? How does it affect things on Earth? If they have done any other activities to do with gravity, can they recall what they found out?

Show the children two pieces of A4 paper, and ask them to tell you what they think will happen if both pieces are held flat and dropped from the same height at the same time. Why do they think this? Drop the pieces of paper and watch what happens.

Now ask the children to tell you what they think will happen if one of the pieces of paper is held flat and the other one is held edgeways and then dropped. Can the children explain their predictions? Drop the pieces of paper in this way and watch what happens. What causes the flat piece of paper to fall more slowly? Discuss the push of the air upwards underneath the paper, and tell the children that this is called air resistance. The paper which is dropped edgeways is more streamlined and 'cuts' through the air more easily.

Allow the children some time to test these ideas themselves. How do they think a parachute would help to slow down the fall of a person or object attached to the parachute? Explain that they are going to make some parachutes to find out more about air resistance.

Give out copies of photocopiable page 127, and sit with the children while they construct the first parachute, to make sure they know what to do. Then ask them to try out the parachutes by dropping them together from the same height to see which one falls more slowly. Can they predict which one will be slower before they test them? How will they ensure this is a fair test?

Ask them to record their results in some way. How many times do they think they should test each parachute?

After they have completed the task, discuss their results. Which parachute fell more slowly? Can the children suggest why? What is the relationship between surface area and rate of fall? Do they think parachutes of the same surface area but different shapes would fall at the same rate? (Perhaps this could be tried out at a later date.) Were other factors important? For example, did they drop the parachutes with the canopies level or with the paper-clips level? Could this make a difference? Did they consider the amount of adhesive tape used on each parachute? Could this make a difference?

Discuss how they recorded their work, and whether their predictions were correct. What problems did they have? How did they overcome them? What things could they try next with these parachutes?

Suggestion(s) for extension

Challenge the children to test other factors which might affect the rate of fall of parachutes, such as the material used in

	a	b	c	d	e
1	Group	Try 1 sec	Try 2 sec	Try 3 sec	Average
2	Anne/Chris	25	30	29	AV (b2; d2)
3	other names	15	20	22	AV (b3; d3)
4					
5					
6					
7					

the canopy, the length of thread on the canopy, the shape of the canopy, the position of the hanging object, cutting holes in the canopy and so on.

Suggestion(s) for support
Help the children to record their results if necessary, or appoint a group scribe. Some children may need help in measuring and cutting the threads and securing them to the canopy of each parachute. You could prepare the parachutes for those children with very limited manipulative skills.

Assessment opportunities
This activity will enable you to assess how well the children understand the need for a fair test, and how well they can record their results. The activity emphasises the need for checking observations by repeating them. You will thus have an opportunity to discuss why this is important with individuals or the whole class as the activity unfolds.

Opportunities for IT
A class spreadsheet (see page 47) could be set up to record the drop times for each parachute tested. Each line of the spreadsheet could represent a different group. This could be used to help the whole class determine which is the most effective parachute.

Children could also use a word processor to describe their work, how they altered the parachute, and the effect of changing certain variables such as the length of string or the weight of the object.

Display ideas
Make a large parachute and suspend it from the ceiling. Hang the children's writing about and drawings of the activity from the parachute. All the children's parachutes could also be hung from the ceiling for an eye-catching display.

Other aspects of the Science PoS covered
Experimental and Investigative Science – 1a, b, c, d; 2a, b, c; 3a, b, c, d, e.

Reference to photocopiable sheet
Some children may need help with following the instructions and making the parachutes.

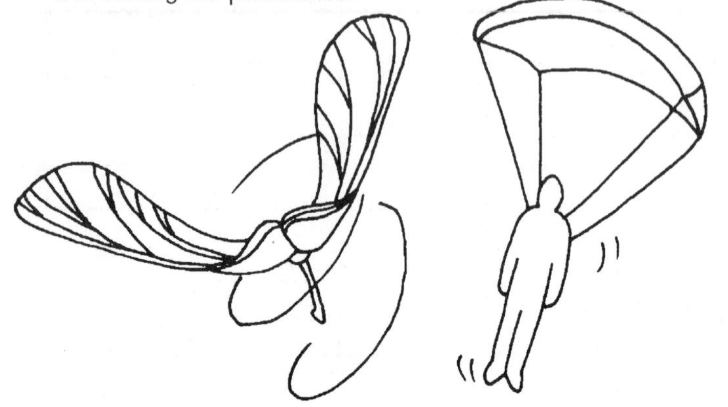

ELASTIC POWER

When elastic bands are stretched, they exert a force on whatever is stretching them.

Pairs or small groups.

60–120 minutes.

Children should take care when using the saw and hammer to make the buggy.

Previous skills/knowledge needed
A force is a push or a pull. Forces can change the shape of an object.

Key background information
When a push or a pull is applied to an object, the object does not always move – sometimes it changes shape. Elastic objects, such as elastic bands, will stretch and then bounce back to their original shape after they have been released. The stretched elastic exerts a force on the object stretching it. When released, a stretched elastic band could be used to catapult an object or turn a propeller. If the elastic is stretched beyond a certain limit (the elastic limit), however, it will break or stay out of shape permanently.

Preparation
A large open space with a smooth floor may be necessary, such as the school hall or corridor. It may take some time for the children to make the buggies, so several lessons may be needed for this activity. You may wish to build a buggy of your own to use for demonstration purposes (see 'Suggestion(s) for support' below)

Resources needed
A collection of materials such as different-sized elastic bands, old tights, cotton fabric, woollen fabric, plastic and paper. For the buggy: wood pieces, a long length of wood (about 0.5m), a long and strong elastic band, nails, hammer, saw, one copy per pair/group of photocopiable page 128, measuring tape.

What to do
Provide the children with the collection of materials listed above, and ask them to handle them and then to predict which ones they think will stretch the most. What do they base their predictions on? Allow the children time to try and stretch each material to find out which ones stretch the most. What do the stretchy materials have in common? Why are stretchy materials useful to us? What happens when the stretchy materials are stretched and then released? Can the children suggest why this happens? Do the children know of any toys or machines which use elastic bands? How does the elastic band work in these objects?

Explain to the children that they are going to find out some more about what happens when elastic bands are stretched

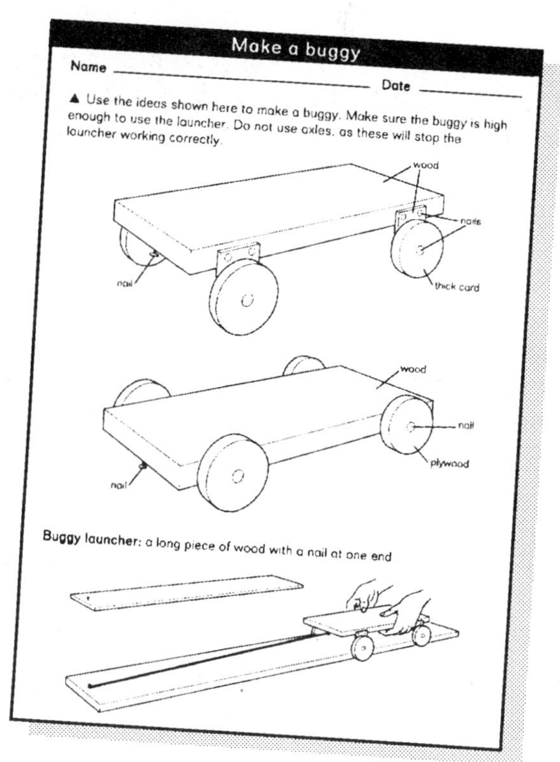

Make a buggy

Name ______________________ Date ______________

▲ Use the ideas shown here to make a buggy. Make sure the buggy is high enough to use the launcher. Do not use axles, as these will stop the launcher working correctly.

wood
nails
nail
thick card
wood
nail
plywood
nail

Buggy launcher: a long piece of wood with a nail at one end

by making and testing a model buggy. Give out copies of photocopiable page 128 and go through the sheet with them, making sure that they know what materials they will need, how they will make the model and what they are testing.

The children will need to make the buggy and launcher, and then test the buggy by stretching the elastic band to different lengths and letting the buggy go to see how far it will travel. They will need to measure how far back they pull the elastic band, and how far the buggy goes before it stops.

Can the children predict what the outcome of the testing might be? Why do they think this? Encourage them to record the results in some way. How will they make sure it is a fair test? How many times will they test each amount of stretch? Are there any safety considerations?

After they have completed the task, bring the whole class together to compare results. What did they find out about stretching the elastic bands? Can they explain how the elastic band catapults the buggy? Why does the buggy go further the more the band is stretched? Is there a limit to the amount the band will stretch? Was this the same for all the groups?

How were the results recorded? How many times were the buggies tested for each amount of stretch? What problems did the children experience? How did they overcome these problems? Did they carry out a fair test? What have they learned about the forces involved in stretching elastic bands? What could they try next?

Suggestion(s) for extension

Ask the children to draw a graph of the amount of stretch and the distance travelled by the buggy. Find the average distance travelled for each amount of stretch in all the groups. Do the test again using other elastic materials such as tights, and compare the results.

Suggestion(s) for support

Use a prepared buggy if time is short or you think the children will have difficulty making one. Help the children decide how to make the test fair, and encourage them to test out the buggy more than once for each amount of stretch. Help the children with measuring and recording if necessary, or make sure that each group includes a more able child who can assist the others.

Assessment opportunities

This activity will enable you to assess how accurately the children can measure and how well they can record a task. It will also provide an opportunity to discuss fair testing and the importance of repeating observations and measurements. While the children are testing the buggy, you could talk to individuals about their ideas concerning the forces involved in the test and how elastic materials behave when stretched and released.

Opportunities for IT

A class spreadsheet could be set up to record all the buggy tries. Each line of the spreadsheet could represent a different group.(The figure below shows an example.) This could be used to help the whole class determine which group's buggy went the furthest. They might consider the reasons for this: was it the elastic band or the design of the buggy which made the difference?

Display ideas

Display the children's buggies on a table. Ask the children to write about and draw the activity, and mount this work on the wall behind the table. Add other toys which use elastic power to make them move. Make a sign challenging the children to work out how the elastic band makes these toys move.

	a	b	c	d	e
1	Group	Try 1cm	Try 2cm	Try 3cm	Average
2	Anne/Chris	53	32	44	AV (b2; d2)
3	other names	28	26	45	AV (b3; d3)

Other aspects of the Science PoS covered

Experimental and Investigative Science – 1a, b, c, d, e; 2a, b, c; 3a, b, c, d, e.

Reference to photocopiable sheet

The buggies shown on the sheet are only offered as a guide. The children may want to use the ideas to design their own buggies.

SPRINGS

When a spring is compressed, it exerts a force on whatever is compressing it.

Pairs or small groups.

60–120 minutes.

Children should take care when making the spring tester. When the tester is made, make sure that the children put a cork on the end of the wire or dowelling so that they do not injure their eyes when they are using it.

Previous skills/knowledge needed

A force is a push or a pull. Forces can change the shape of an object.

Key background information

Metal springs are specially made so that they behave in an elastic way: they will return to their original shape after stretching or compressing. Springs can become overstretched, however, and will become permanently deformed if their *elastic limit* is exceeded.

Many springs are made to react to being squashed or compressed. These springs will push back at the object compressing them. The amount of push needed to make a spring contract by a certain amount is often equal to the amount of pull needed to make it stretch by the same amount.

Preparation

You may wish to construct your own spring tester for demonstration purposes (see 'Suggestion(s) for support').

Resources needed

Several different types of springs of different sizes, stiff metal wire or thin dowelling (about 50cm in length), Blu-Tack, a drill or hammer and a large nail (same diameter as the wire/dowelling), two screw-in eyelets, two blocks of wood (about 15cm x 5cm x 2.5cm), a cork, a small piece of very stiff cardboard, scissors, rulers, paper, pencils, one copy per pair/group of diagram based on Figure 1.

What to do

Provide the children with the collection of springs and ask them to find out what they can about them. What is different about the different springs? What is the same? What could the springs be used for? Where are springs used? How do springs behave?

Ask the children to push down on the springs. What happens? What happens when they let go? Are some springs harder to push down than others? Why could this be? Ask the children to try and stretch the springs. What happens? What happens when they let go? Why?

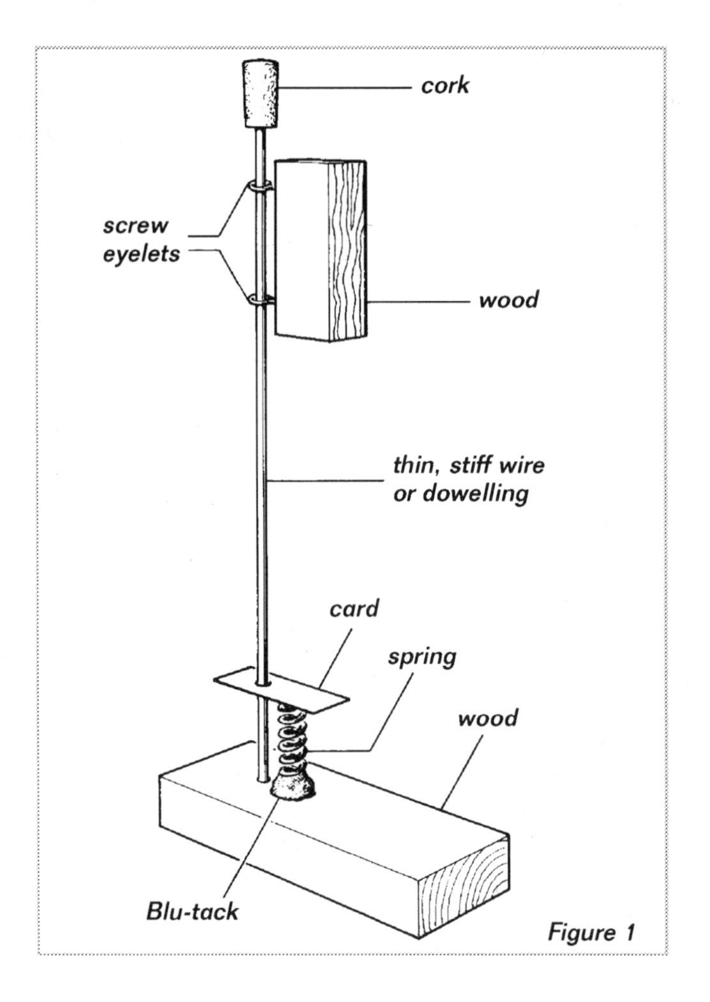

Figure 1

Provide the children with copies of the diagram and explain that they are going to make a testing machine to test how well the springs work. Tell the children that you want them to find out more about the way the springs 'push back' after they have been pushed in. Explain that the spring tester is designed to drop a piece of wood on to a spring and to measure how far the wood will bounce back. Which springs from the collection do the children think will be the 'springiest'? Can they explain why? Ask them to record their predictions individually or as a group.

Go through the diagram with the children to make sure they know how to make the tester; then allow them time to make it. You may need one session to make the tester and another session to test the springs.

The aim then is to attach a spring by pressing it on to the Blu-Tack, and see how far the piece of wood bounces back when it has been released from the top of the wire. How will they measure this? How will they record what happens? How many times should they test each spring? How will they make sure this is a fair test? Are there any other safety precautions to think of apart from protecting their eyes from the wire?

	a	b	c	d	e
1	Group	Try 1cm	Try 2cm	Try 3cm	Average
2	Spring 1	12	12	14	AV (b2; d2)
3	Spring 2	28	26	25	AV (b3; d3)
4	Spring 2				

After the children have completed the investigation, discuss their results as a class. What problems did they experience? How did they overcome these? How closely did the results match their predictions? Were they surprised by any of the results? Is there a pattern in the results? What forces are involved in the spring tester? What conclusions can be drawn from the results? What recording methods did the children use? How accurate were these? How could the investigation be improved? What could they try next?

Suggestion(s) for extension
Ask the children to find the average height the wood bounced for each spring and then draw a graph of the results.

Suggestion(s) for support
Some children may not have the skills necessary to make the spring tester. If this is the case, you could prepare it; or alternatively one group could make a tester for everyone to use. Some children may need help with measuring and recording. You could assist these children or appoint a group scribe and measurer.

Assessment opportunities
This activity will enable you to assess how well the children can measure, record and draw conclusions. The children's recordings will be an invaluable starting-point for discussing ideas in more depth with the whole class or individuals.

Opportunities for IT
Children could set up their own spreadsheet to record their group's investigation with the spring tester (see above).
The results could be used to draw a graph, which would show which spring was the most effective. The group could also use a word processor to write about their results, including the table from the spreadsheet and explaining what they have found out about the different springs.

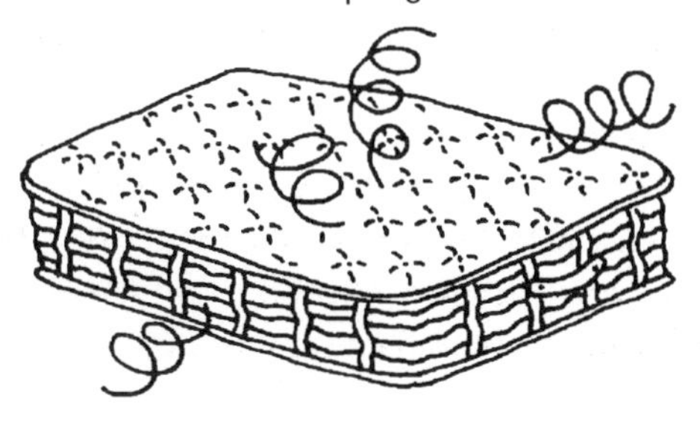

Display ideas
Display the spring testers and collection of springs on a table. Mount the children's writing and drawings about the investigation on the wall behind the table. Make a large heading: 'Investigating springs'. Add pictures of things which use springs.

Other aspects of the Science PoS covered
Experimental and Investigative Science – 1a, b, c, d; 2a, b, c; 3a, b, c, d, e.

DIRECTION OF FORCES

Forces act in particular directions.
Small group or whole class.
45–60 minutes.

Previous skills/knowledge needed
A force is a push or a pull. Forces can change the shape of objects. Gravity is a force. Friction and air resistance can slow down moving objects. Stretching and compression can exert forces.

Key background information
Forces act in particular directions. Forces always act in pairs. For example, when an object is stationary on the ground, there are two forces acting upon it: the downward force of gravity and the upward force from the ground (*reaction force*). The reaction force results from the force of an object pushing down – that is, when one object pushes against a second object, the second object pushes against the first. This is Newton's third law: *every action has an equal and opposite reaction.*

Arrows can be used on drawings to represent forces. The direction of the arrow indicates the direction of the force and the length of the arrow indicates the strength of the force.

Preparation
None specifically required for this activity.

Resources needed
One copy per child of photocopiable page 129, pencils, a tennis ball.

What to do
Ask the children to tell you what they think forces are. Compare the children's answers – do others agree? Tell the children that you are going to roll a tennis ball gently along a table top (or floor), and ask them to watch what happens. Can they decide what forces are acting on the ball? What provided the initial force? (The push from your hand.) Are there forces acting on the ball as it rolls along? Discuss the answers the children offer.

Explain that a moving object will continue to move unless another force acts upon it. (Newton's first law of motion: *an object continues in a state of rest or uniform motion in a straight line unless it is acted on by some external force.)* What things do the children think will cause the ball to slow down? (Friction slows the ball down: when the ball rolls along the table top, friction creates a force in the opposite direction, slowing the ball down.)

Now place the ball on the table so that it does not move. Ask the children to tell you if they think there are any forces acting on the ball now. If there are, what are they? Discuss the children's answers. Explain that even when something is not moving, there are forces acting upon it. There are two forces acting on the stationary ball: the downward force of gravity and an upward force from the desk. The size of the forces are the same, and so the ball does not move. When one force is larger than another, (as when the ball is pushed), the object moves.

The children may find it difficult to believe that the desk is also exerting a force. Reaction forces can be demonstrated by using two kitchen spring scales as shown in Figure 1. Press on the scales against the wall. The readings on both scales should be the same.

Tell the children that scientists use arrows to show forces on diagrams. Tell them that the length of the arrow indicates the strength of the force and the direction of the arrow shows the direction of the force. Use a chalkboard or piece of paper to draw some examples, like the ones shown in Figure 2.

Hand out a copy of photocopiable page 129 to each child

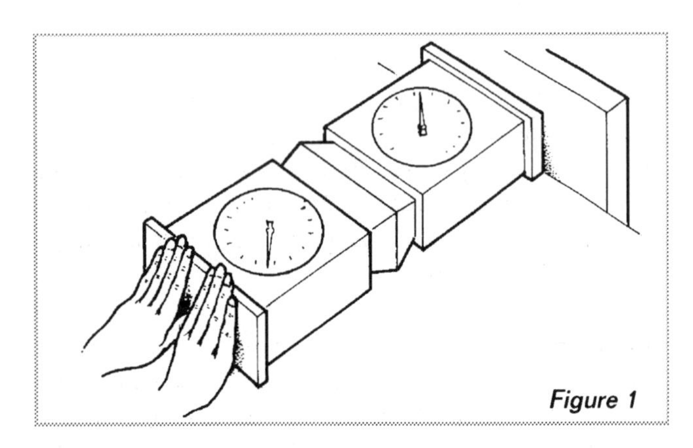

Figure 1

and explain that you would like them to consider the forces involved in the pictures shown on the sheet. Ask the children to work individually or in pairs to draw arrows on the pictures showing the direction and strength of each force involved, as well as writing down what they think the forces are doing in each case.

When the children have completed the task, bring the whole class back together to discuss their drawings. Go through the pictures one at a time and discuss the forces the children think are acting in each case. Do they all agree? Have they remembered to show the strength of the force by the length of the arrow? Tell the children the correct answer in each example and discuss any discrepancies.

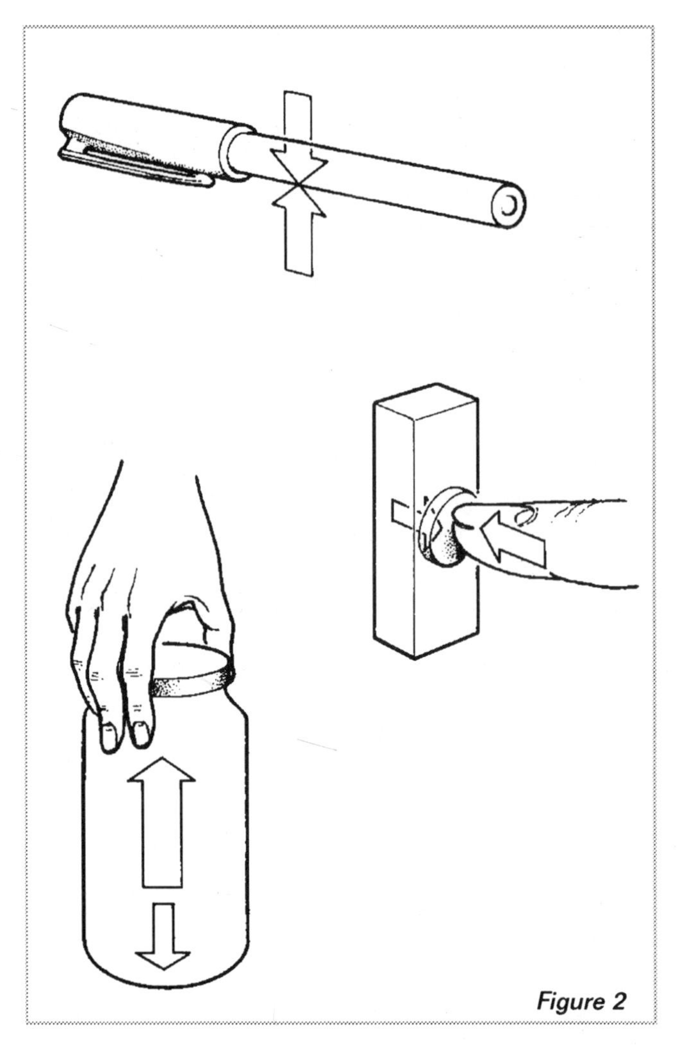

Figure 2

Suggestion(s) for extension

Ask the children to draw pictures of five objects in situations where forces are acting on them. Get them to swap drawings and mark the forces involved in each case. Do they agree with their partners?

Suggestion(s) for support

Discuss several of the pictures with the children as they are completing the sheet. Remind them about the forces which act on objects which are at rest. Help them to decide the direction and strength of the forces involved.

Assessment opportunities

The children's answers on photocopiable page 129 will provide you with an insight into the children's knowledge about the size and direction of forces. The worksheet could be used again at a later date to assess how well the children have retained the information from the lesson.

Display ideas

Draw large pictures and arrows of the examples used on photocopiable page 129 to mount on a wall. Ask the children to write about the forces acting in each picture. Add their writing to the picture display.

1. The kick pushes the ball into the air. Gravity pulls the ball down. The kicking force is bigger than the pull of gravity. The ball moves.

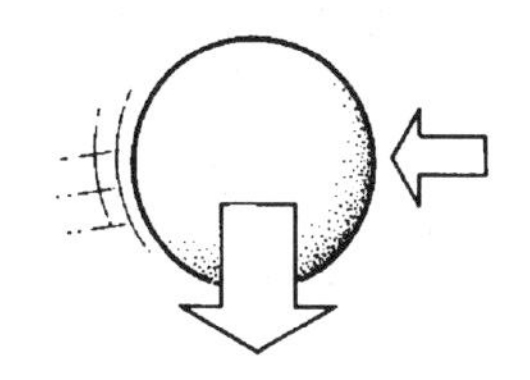

2. Gravity pulls the ball down. Air resistance slows the ball.

3. The person's hand provides a push which slows the ball down and stops it.

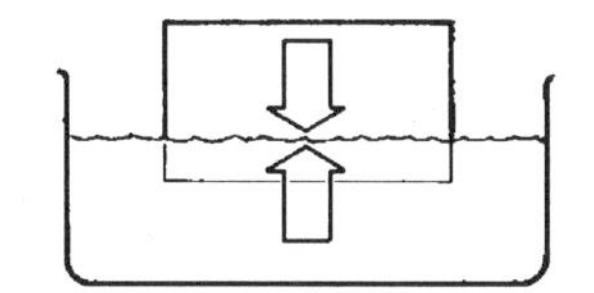

4. Gravity pulls down the wood. Upthrust from the water pushes the wood up. The forces are equal.

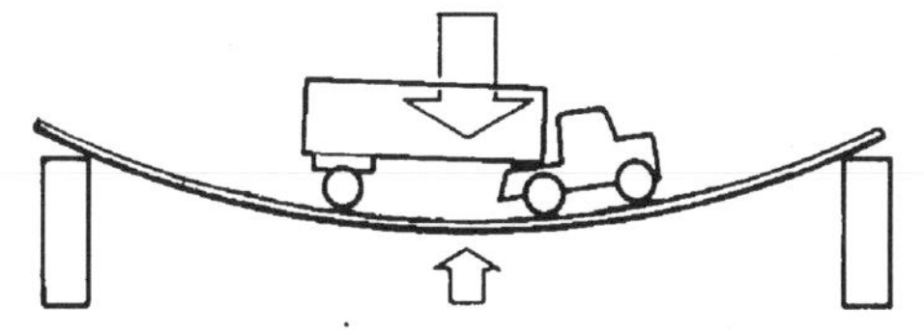

5. The force down (gravity) is greater than the upward force of the bridge. The bridge moves and could eventually break or collapse.

Figure 3

Reference to photocopiable sheet

Figure 3 shows some 'model answers' to the questions on photocopiable sheet 129.

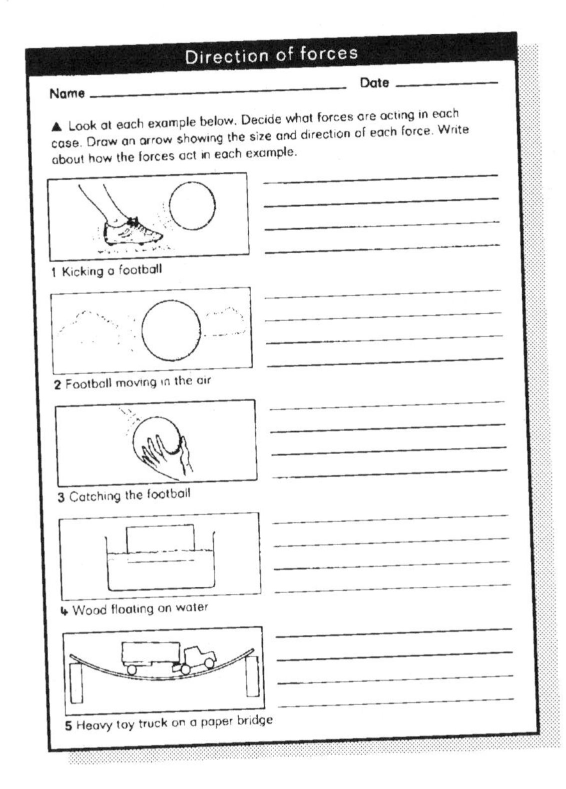

Direction of forces

Name ______________ Date ______________

▲ Look at each example below. Decide what forces are acting in each case. Draw an arrow showing the size and direction of each force. Write about how the forces act in each example.

1 Kicking a football

2 Football moving in the air

3 Catching the football

4 Wood floating on water

5 Heavy toy truck on a paper bridge

FLOAT OR SINK?

Forces can be balanced or unbalanced.

Pairs or small groups.

60–120 minutes.

Previous skills/knowledge needed

A force is a push or a pull.

Key background information

Whether or not an object will float in water depends on:

▲ its density in relation to water;

▲ its shape;

▲ the material from which it is made.

Things which float are lighter or less dense than water. When an object is put into water, it pushes down on the water; but the water also pushes upwards on the object (*upthrust*). Things which are more dense than water push down more strongly than the upthrust and so they sink. When an object is in water it 'takes up space', that is it *displaces* water. If the weight of the object is greater than the weight of the water it displaces, the object will sink. If the object's weight is *equal* to the weight of the displaced water, the object will float. If an object that floats is pushed below the surface of the water, it is now displacing a weight of water *greater* than its own weight – thus the upthrust will push it to the surface until it is partly out of the water, and the forces are balanced.

Preparation

None specifically required for this activity.

Resources needed

Kitchen scales, a small plastic lid with high sides, paper-clips or other small weights such as 1p coins, salt, a teaspoon, water, a washing-up bowl, a jug, a small container large enough to float the plastic lid.

What to do

Explain to the children that you want them to find out about floating and sinking. Can they tell you why they think things float? What causes things to sink? Provide the children with a washing-up bowl nearly full of water and challenge them to select five things in the room which they think will float and five things which they think will sink.

Before they test each object, ask the children to tell you why they think the objects will float/sink. Do the others in the class agree? Where have they learned about floating and sinking? What has helped them to decide on their selection of objects?

Ask the children to test each object to see if their predictions were correct. Were they surprised by any of the results? How could some of the 'sinkers' be made to float? How could some of the 'floaters' be made to sink? Try out some of the ideas.

Next, provide the children with a plastic lid and a small container of water and ask them to float the lid on the water like a boat. Ask them to put paper-clips into the 'boat' one at a time until it sinks. What do they notice about the boat as each paper-clip is put in? Does the boat sit lower in the water? Why? Record the number of paper-clips the boat held before it sank. Try this several times to check the result. If the sides of the boat were higher or lower, what effect would this have on the number of paper-clips it could hold before it sank?

Now ask the children to remove the boat and stir one teaspoon of salt into the water. Try the same experiment. How many paper-clips does the boat hold before it sinks this time? Record the result. Try this several times to check the result. Can the children suggest why the boat holds more paper-clips? What do they think will happen if they put in two, three and then four teaspoons of salt? Allow them time to try this out and record their results.

What conclusions can be drawn? Is there a pattern in the results? Discuss the factors which may affect the results, such as how the paper-clips are placed in the boat (not all on one side, for instance). Compare the results with everyday experiences, such as how much easier it is to float in sea water than in fresh water. Explain that this is due to the *density* of salty water. Salt water is denser than fresh water, and therefore it has more *upthrust* or push on objects floating in the water. The salt in the experiment made the water more dense, so the boat was able to hold more weight than when it was in fresh water.

Finally, explain to the children that they can understand more fully why things float by finding out how much water an object pushes out of the way, or *displaces*, when it is in water. Place the kitchen scales, with the pan removed, in the washing-up bowl. Put the container used to hold the boat on to the scales and fill it with water until it is almost overflowing. Record the weight. Now place the number of paper-clips needed to sink the boat in fresh water into the boat, and gently place the boat into the water. Some water will spill into the washing-up bowl. Remove the scales and container from the bowl and replace the pan on the scales. Readjust the scale needle to zero. Pour the water from the bowl into the pan and record the weight. Then weigh the boat with the paper-clips inside it. The weight of the displaced water should be less than the weight of the boat.

Explain that if the amount of water pushed away or displaced is the same as the weight of the object, then the object will float (the force pushing down on the water equals the force of the water pushing up – they are balanced). But if the weight of the water displaced is less than the weight of the object, then the object will sink (the force pushing down on the water is greater than the force pushing up – the forces are unbalanced). Relate this to how large, heavy boats are able to float. (They displace the same amount of water as they weigh, and therefore they float.)

Suggestion(s) for extension

Ask the children to plot their results on a line graph. Is there a correlation between the amount of salt and the number of paper-clips held before the boat sinks?

Suggestion(s) for support

Act as scribe if necessary when the children are recording their results, or appoint a group scribe. Ensure that the children use the same size of paper-clips when testing the boats, to make it a fair test. The water displacement activity can be done as a demonstration.

Assessment opportunities

This activity will enable you to find out what the children already know about floating and sinking. It will also provide an opportunity to assess recording skills.

Opportunities for IT

Children could set up a spreadsheet to record their measurements with the paper-clips and different-strength salt solutions. The results could be used to plot a line graph showing the number of paper-clips carried for the different saline strengths. The children should discuss what the graph shows and write about their conclusions.

The children could use a word processor to write about why some of the tested objects sank and others floated. These writings could be printed out and used for a floating and sinking display.

Display ideas

Draw a large picture of an aquarium tank with water in it. Ask each of the children to draw a picture of an object which floats or sinks, and to write an explanation of why it floats or sinks. Attach the drawings and writings to the picture of the tank and mount them on the wall. Place a real aquarium with water and the objects that were drawn on a table in front of the display, so the children can retest the objects.

Other aspects of the Science PoS covered

Experimental and Investigative Science – 1a; 2a, b, c; 3a, b, c, e.

Light

The activities in this section of the book encourage children to explore the properties and everyday effects of light. In the course of carrying out the activities, the children will gain experience in questioning, observing, predicting, recording, measuring and making conclusions. They will also have opportunities to work co-operatively and to share their ideas with others.

Light is a form of energy that we can see. Objects which produce their own light are called *luminous*. Natural light reaches the Earth from our nearest star, the Sun. Other sources of light include:

▲ flames;
▲ electric lights;
▲ television sets;
▲ some animals such as glow-worms.

We see objects because they reflect the light from the Sun and other luminous objects.

Light travels in waves which move in straight lines. It can pass through air, water, glass and many other materials. Materials which allow light to pass through them are called *transparent*. Some materials allow light to pass through, but the light is spread out and a blurred image is seen. These materials are called *translucent*. Some materials do not let light through at all. These materials are called *opaque*. A shadow is formed by opaque objects which block out the light. The closer an object is to a light source, the larger and less distinct is the shadow.

LIGHT SOURCES

Light travels from a variety of sources.
Whole class, then small groups.
45–60 minutes.
▲ *Do not allow children to handle the matches. Warn children of the dangers of looking directly into a light source.*

Previous knowledge/skills needed

None specifically required for this activity.

Key background information

Light travels from a variety of sources. The Earth's natural source of light is the Sun. Other sources of light include:

▲ flames such as candles and fires;
▲ electric light;
▲ television sets;
▲ some animals which produce light through chemical reactions, such as glow-worms.

Objects which produce light are referred to as *luminous*.

Preparation

Prepare a room so that it is dark before starting the activity. Clear away any obstacles!

Resources needed

One copy per child of photocopiable page 130, pencils, dark room, five or six torches of different strengths, a candle, matches.

What to do

Provide each child with a copy of photocopiable page 130, and explain that the picture shows a room with several different sources of light in it. Ask the children to complete the worksheet by writing down the names of the things in the picture which produce light, as well as making a list of other things they can think of which produce light.

When this is done, discuss the answers together as a whole class. Does everyone agree? What other things have the children listed which are not in the picture? Make a class list of these things. Which of these things are natural? Which things have been made by humans? Discuss the fact that some animals, such as glow-worms and some deep-sea creatures, have chemical reactions occurring inside their bodies which produce light. How might this help them? How does light help us?

Discuss which of the light sources the children think is the strongest. Why does the Sun produce light? What is happening in the Sun to make the light? How do torches and electric lights produce light?

Show the children the candle and the collection of torches. Can they predict which one will provide the brightest light? Why? Darken the room or visit a darkened room to find out. What can the children see in the room without a light being on? Light the candle. What can be seen now? Ask the children to describe the light. How far does it spread out? In which directions? Blow out the candle and turn on one of the torches. How is this light different from that of the candle? Try the other torches. Which light appears to be the strongest? Can the children suggest why? What advantages and disadvantages are there in having candles as a light source, and in having torches as a light source?

Divide the class into five or six groups, each with a torch. Ask them to find out as much as they can about the torch itself and the light it produces. These questions may help to guide the children in their investigation: Does the width of the torch beam vary? Can you measure the length of the torch beam? Are you able to alter the shape of the beam? What happens to the light when the torch is held downwards/upwards/to the side? Can the brightness of the light be altered? How? How do you think the torch works?

When the children have finished their observations, bring the whole class together again to discuss and compare the results. What apparatus did they use, if any? How did they record what they found out? What have they learned from doing the activity? What would they like to find out now?

Suggestion(s) for extension

Ask the children to draw the different sources of light listed at the start of the activity, using reference books to find living things which produce light. Then ask them to sort the light sources into groups – very bright, bright, not very bright – and glue the pictures on to paper arranged in these groups.

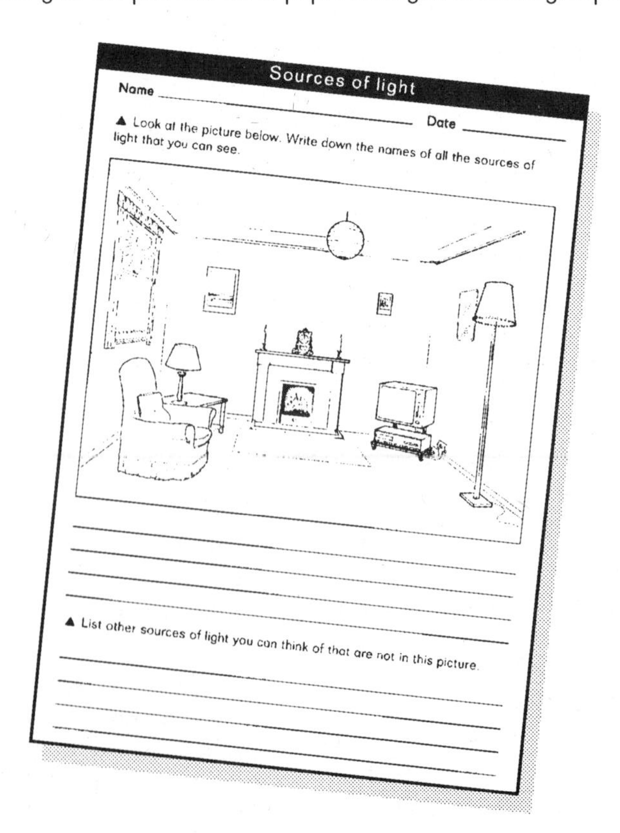

Sources of light

Name ______________________ Date ____________

▲ Look at the picture below. Write down the names of all the sources of light that you can see.

▲ List other sources of light you can think of that are not in this picture.

Light

Suggestion(s) for support
Act as scribe if necessary when the children are writing down the names of the sources of light on the photocopiable sheet, or ask the children to circle the objects in the picture rather than write them down.

Assessment opportunities
The children's answers on the photocopiable sheet will enable you to assess how much the children already know about light sources. This will help in the planning of future learning activities.

Display ideas
Ask the children to paint large pictures of things which are sources of light. The pictures could be made into a large wall display. On a table in front of the display, make a collection of things which can produce light.

Other aspects of the Science PoS covered
Experimental and Investigative Science – 2a; 3b.

Reference to photocopiable sheet
Less able children could circle the sources of light in the picture rather than write down the names. They could also draw other things which produce light rather than write a list.

HOW LIGHT TRAVELS

Light travels in a straight line from a source.

Pairs or small groups.

45–60 minutes.

Children should take care when handling the scissors. Warn children of the dangers of looking directly into a light source.

Previous skills/knowledge needed
Light comes from a variety of sources.

Key background information
Light travels in straight lines.

Preparation
Prepare a darkened room before starting this activity.

Resources needed
Torch, two pieces of cardboard about the size of an exercise book, scissors, a shoe box, pencils, white paper, rulers, two chalkboard dusters.

What to do
Ask the children to explain to you why we cannot see round corners. Tell them that they are going to do some activities which will help them to answer this question.

First, they need to make a small hole in the middle of each piece of card. Arrange the cards so that they are about 5cm apart, one in front of the other, the one behind being about 3cm in front of a torch light. The holes in the cards need to be in line with each other. Ask someone else to look through the holes at the light. Then move one of the cards to the left or right slightly. What happens? Why can the light no longer be seen? (See Figure 1.)

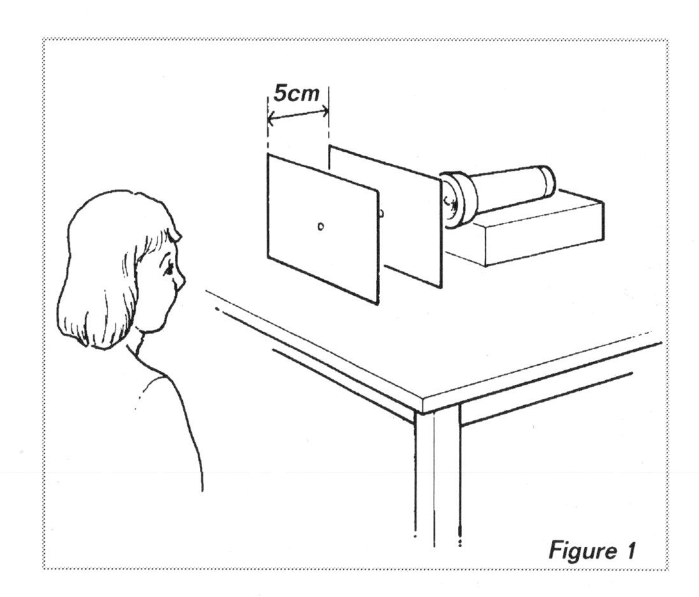

Figure 1

Next, provide the children with a shoe box and ask them to make a small slit in one end, about 3mm wide and 30mm long. Place the torch inside the box and turn it on. Replace the lid of the box. Put a piece of white paper underneath the box at the end where the slit is. What do the children notice about the beam of light which shows up on the paper? They could use a ruler to trace the edge of the beam. What do they notice? (See Figure 2.)

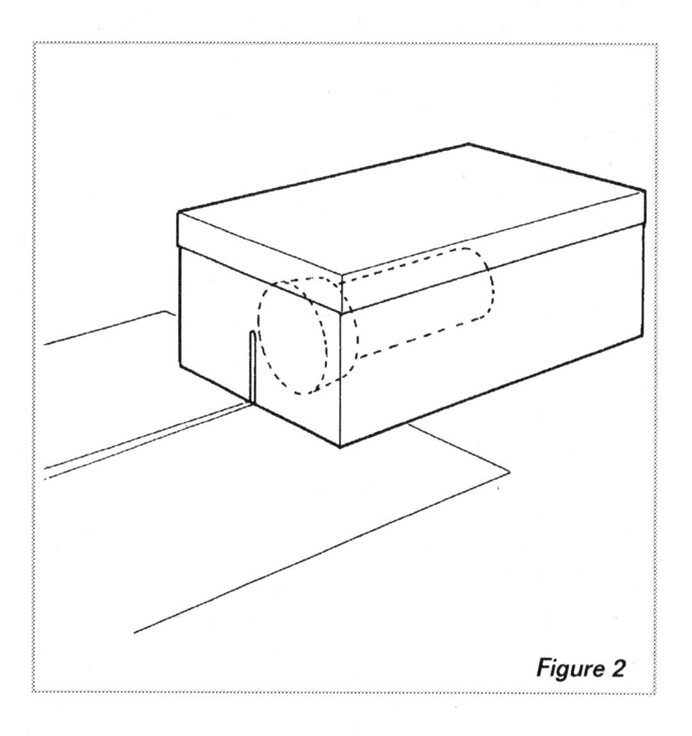

Figure 2

What happens if the children place an object on the paper in front of the box? Explain that the light travels in straight lines and that when it hits the object, it cannot bend around it to light up the area behind the object. What do they notice is happening to the beam of light when it hits the object? What happens behind the object?

Finally, shine a torch on to a wall in a darkened room. Bang two chalkboard dusters together in the torch light. What do the children notice? What are the edges of the beam like? (This is called the Tyndall effect.)

Suggestion(s) for extension
Ask the children to write down what they did and what they found out. Ask them to use this information to answer the original question: Why can't we see round corners?

Suggestion(s) for support
Help the children to make the holes in the card and the slit in the shoe box, if necessary.

Opportunities for IT
Children could write a short description of 'why we can't see round corners' using a word processor for display in the classroom. They could experiment with different fonts and sizes to present their writing for the display.

Display ideas
Display the children's writing about and drawings of the activities under a heading: 'Light travels in straight lines'.

Other aspects of the Science PoS covered
Experimental and Investigative Science – 1a; 2a, b; 3c.

TRANSPARENCY

Light can travel through some materials.

Small groups.

45–60 minutes.

Children should take care when using the scissors. Warn the children to avoid staring directly into light sources.

Previous skills/knowledge needed
Light travels from a variety of sources.

Key background information
Some materials allow light to travel through them. You can see through them clearly, and they are called *transparent*. Some materials allow light to pass through, but the light is spread out or diffused. Things look blurred when you look through these materials and they are called *translucent*. Some materials will not let light through at all. It is not possible to see through these materials, and they are called *opaque*.

Preparation
None specifically required for this activity.

Resources needed
A torch, a shoe box, scissors, a collection of different materials such as card, Cellophane, clear plastic, paper, tissue-paper, glass, tin lid, plastic lid, wood, different fabrics, foil.

What to do
Explain to the children that you want them to test whether light will pass through different materials. Provide them with the collection of materials, torch, shoe box and scissors. Explain that they can test other materials as well if they want to.

First, the children will need to cut out one end of the shoe box. They can then place each material between the torch and the box, so that any light which goes through can be seen clearly inside the box. (See Figure 1.)

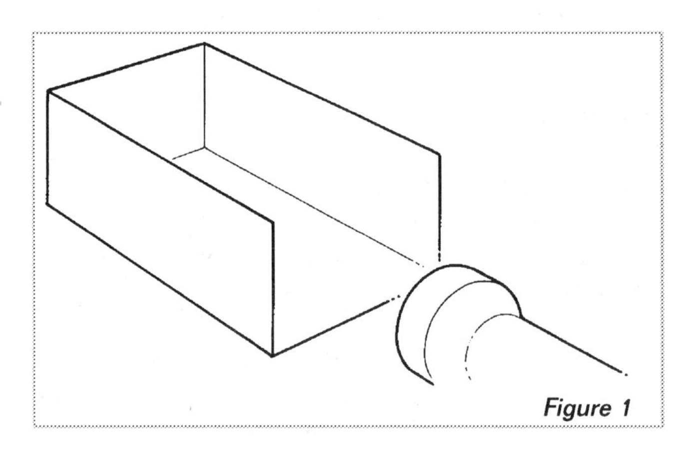

Figure 1

Ask the children to predict which materials they think the light will shine through. Then ask them to test each material and to record their results. When they have completed this task, ask the children to sort the materials according to how much light is let through. Introduce the terms 'transparent', 'translucent' and 'opaque'. Do the children know what these words mean? Discuss the meanings and then ask the children to sort the materials into these three groups. Do the other groups of children agree? What do the transparent and opaque materials have in common with each other? What do objects look like through translucent or transparent materials? Can anything be seen through opaque materials?

What objects in the classroom could be described as transparent, translucent or opaque? Make a class list of these items.

Suggestion(s) for extension
Ask the children to draw some of the objects from the class list which are transparent, translucent and opaque. Then ask them to write down a definition for each of these words, and to comment on what the objects in each group have in common with each other.

SHADOWS

Shadows are formed when light cannot pass through materials.

Pairs or small groups.

30–45 minutes.

▲ *Warn the children of the dangers of looking directly into a light source.*

Previous skills/knowledge needed
Light cannot pass through some materials.

Key background information
Opaque objects are objects which do not allow light to shine through them. You cannot see through an opaque object. Shadows appear behind opaque objects when light shines on them. This is because light travels in straight lines which cannot bend around corners.

Preparation
Place some small objects, such as a 50p coin, a paper-clip, a ring, a safety pin, a small battery, a pencil and a feather, in separate envelopes. Do not let the children see the objects or feel the envelopes. A darkened room may need to be prepared for part of this activity.

Resources needed
Envelopes as described above, a torch, a cup, a spring, a toy car, a cube, a cassette case with insert removed, one copy per child of photocopiable page 131, pencils.

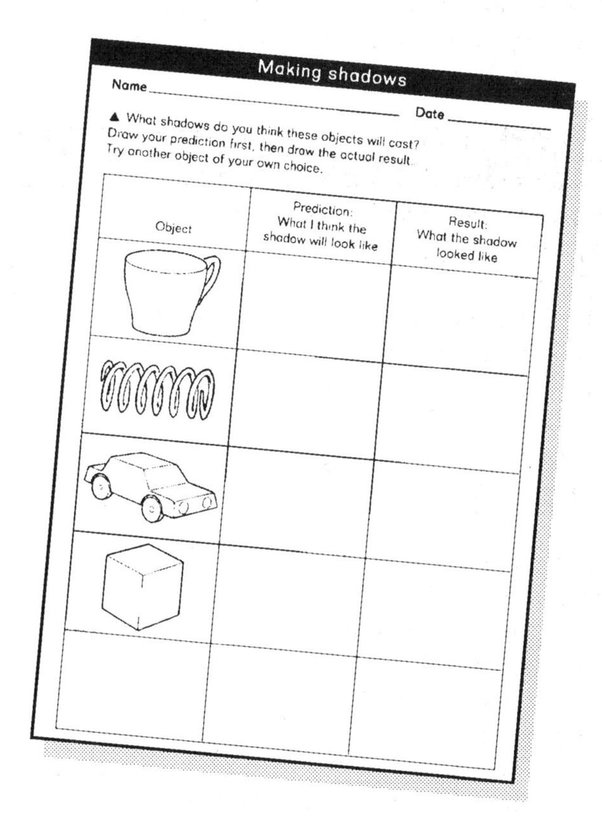

Making shadows

Name ______________________ Date ______________

▲ What shadows do you think these objects will cast? Draw your prediction first, then draw the actual result. Try another object of your own choice.

Object	Prediction: What I think the shadow will look like	Result: What the shadow looked like
(cup)		
(spring)		
(car)		
(cube)		

Suggestion(s) for support
Assist the children when they are recording their results, or appoint a group scribe to do the recording.

Assessment opportunities
This activity will enable you to assess recording skills. The ability of the children to sort the materials into opaque, transparent and translucent will be evident from their recording, and you will be able to use this to discuss the meanings of the terms.

Opportunities for IT
Children could use a word processor to present their list under the three headings of opaque, transparent and translucent materials. This activity could be used to introduce the idea of tabs to the children, so that three columns can be lined up without using the space bar.

opaque	transparent	translucent
(tab)wood	(tab)glass	(tab)tissue-paper

Once the children have been taught how to set the tabs, they can experiment with this facility to get the best layout in relation to the size of the words. They could also explore the use of different fonts, text sizes and effects (for example, bold for titles) to present their chart for a classroom display.

If the children have access to a light sensor and measuring software, they could use the computer to measure the amount of light coming through any of the objects. Alternatively, they could use a photographic light meter to achieve the same results.

Display ideas
Display a collection of objects which are opaque, transparent or translucent on a table, perhaps using hoops to distinguish the groups. Write the words 'opaque', 'transparent' and 'translucent' on large labels and attach these to the wall behind the table. Make another sign providing information about the activity the children have carried out. Display the children's findings from this activity.

Other aspects of the Science PoS covered
Experimental and Investigative Science – 1a, b; 2a, b, c; 3a, c, d.

What to do

Explain to the children that you have some envelopes with mystery objects inside them. Tell them that you want them to guess what these are by looking at their shapes only. Hold each envelope up in front of a window or a torch, so that the light shines through. Can the children see the outline of the object? Can they guess what the object is? Show the children each object after they have guessed correctly.

Ask the children to explain why they could see a black outline of the object in each envelope. Why didn't the light shine through it? Refer them back to any previous work done on testing the transparency of objects. What would happen if a transparent object were placed inside the envelope? Place a clear plastic cassette case inside an envelope and hold it against the light source. What can be seen? Remove the case and look at its edges. Can they see through these? Can they see through the sides? Try out some other transparent and translucent objects. Does the light pass through them?

Remind the children that when light cannot pass through an object, it is called opaque. The black outline seen is a shadow. When else do the children see shadows? How else can they be formed? How well can we match up the shape of a shadow with the real object? Tell the children that they are going to find out. Give them copies of photocopiable page 131, plus the objects listed on that page. Ask them to look at the objects and predict what the shadow would look like if the objects were placed on a table and a torch shone on them from behind. (A darkened room may be necessary.) What shape would the shadow make on the wall? Allow the children time to draw their predictions on the sheet and then allow them to test each one. They can test other objects as well if they wish. (Figure 1.)

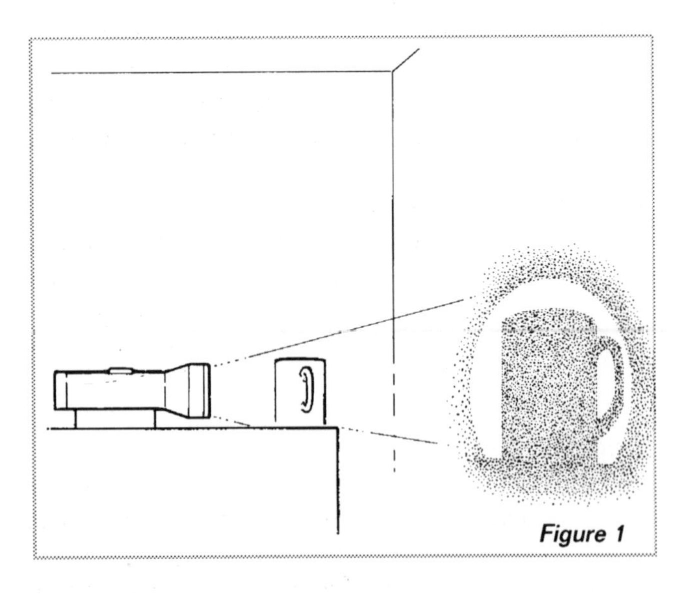

Figure 1

When the children have completed this, discuss their results. How close were their predictions? Were they surprised by any of the results? Did the windows in the toy car have shadows? Why not? Compare the other objects the children tested. Can other children tell what an object is by looking at a drawing of its shadow?

Suggestion(s) for extension

Using the same objects, try out different light sources such as different types of torches, table lamps, candles, overhead projectors. What differences are there between the shadows they produce? Which light source provides the most distinct shadow?

Suggestion(s) for support

Some children may find it very difficult to draw the shadows. This can be overcome by shining the torch on a large piece of paper fixed to the wall. The shadows can then be traced. This paper would replace the need for photocopiable page 131.

Display ideas

Trace shadows of different objects on to black paper using chalk. Cut out the shapes. Mount these on the wall. Place the objects used on a table in front of the wall display. Make a sign challenging the children to match the objects to the shadows.

Other aspects of the Science PoS covered

Experimental and Investigative Science – 1a, b; 2a, b; 3a, c, d.

Reference to photocopiable sheet

This sheet need not be used by those children who may find it difficult to draw the shapes of the shadows. They could trace the shadows made on to a sheet of paper fixed to the wall instead.

SHAPES OF SHADOWS

The shape of a shadow is affected by the object and the position of the light source.

Pairs or small groups.

45–60 minutes.

Warn the children of the dangers of looking directly into a light source.

Previous skills/knowledge needed

Light cannot pass through some materials, and shadows are formed.

Key background information

When a light is shone on an object, some of the light rays will be blocked by the object, forming a shadow. The kind of shadow formed depends on the size (or position) of the light source. If light is coming from a small (or distant) light source, the shadow behind the object will be black and distinct. This is called the *umbra*. If the light source is large (or close), the shadow may have a grey area, called the *penumbra*.

Preparation

Prepare a darkened area of the room for part of this activity.

Resources needed

Three torches of different sizes/strengths, a collection of everyday objects such as a cup, a toy, a plant and so on, paper, pencils, a darkened area of a room.

What to do

Provide the children with the torches and the collection of objects and set them a challenge: What can have an effect on the shape of a shadow? Tell the children to record what they find out in some way, and encourage them to make predictions about what they think will happen for each object they test. Then allow them time to do the investigation.

After they have completed the task, discuss what they have found out. Was the shape of the shadow what they expected for each item tested? How did the position of the torch affect the shadow formed? Did they try the torch from above at different heights and angles, and from the sides at different heights and angles? What happened to the shadows? Was there a difference in the sizes of the shadows? Were some shadows more distinct than others? When? Can they suggest why?

Did they test the different torches? Did the size/brightness of the torch have an effect on the shadow produced? Is it possible to have more than one shadow of one object? Did they try using two or three torches at once? What happened? Can they explain the results? Did the smaller torch produce a different type of shadow from that cast by the larger torch?

Discuss the children's predictions and the methods they used to record what happened. How useful were drawings/illustrations? Would other people be able to understand what they have done from looking at their records? If the children did not try out all the things discussed, allow some more time for exploration or try them out together as a class.

Suggestion(s) for extension

Measure the height and angle of the torch from the object and look at the effect these have on the shape of the shadow. Make a shadow stick and relate the position of the Sun at different times of day to the torch angles. Look at the effect the Sun's position has on the shadows produced.

Suggestion(s) for support

Assist the children in recording their results, or appoint a group scribe to do the recording. Suggest things to try out if the children are struggling for ideas of their own – try the torch from different heights, different angles, and so on.

Assessment opportunities

This activity will enable you to assess how well the children can record what they have done and found out. The group discussion at the end of the task will help to highlight what the children have learned from the activity, and will help you to plan the next activity.

Opportunities for IT

Children could record their shadow stick measurements of the changes in shadow size during the day. These measurements could be entered into a graph-plotting software to create a line graph of the changes during the day. Alternatively, the measurements could be added into a spreadsheet set up by the teacher or children and then used to plot a graph of the results.

This work could be extended to look at shadow lengths at different times of the year and to compare the results. If the children have access to electronic mail through CAMPUS or the internet, they could ask for measurements from different parts of the world and compare the results at different latitudes.

Display ideas
Ask each child to select one object and to draw the shadow produced with the torch at different heights and angles. Wall-mount these pictures, together with the children's writing about the activity. Make a large heading: 'What can have an effect on the shape of a shadow?'

Other aspects of the Science PoS covered
Experimental and Investigative Science – 1a, b, c; 2a, b; 3b, c, d, e.

SIZES OF SHADOWS

The size of a shadow is affected by the positions of the object and the light source.

Pairs or small groups.

30–45 minutes.

Warn the children of the dangers of looking directly into a light source.

Previous skills/knowledge needed
Light cannot pass through some materials, and thus shadows are formed.

Key background information
If an opaque object is positioned close to a source of light, it blocks out a lot of the light and the shadow is large. If the object is positioned further away from the light source, then the shadow is smaller.

Preparation
A darkened room will need to be prepared for part of this activity.

Resources needed
Torches, empty matchboxes, paper, pencils, metre rulers, small rulers, a dark room.

What to do
Ask the children to tell you what they think may affect the size of a shadow. Explain that they are going to do an activity to help them find out. Provide them with the resources needed and ask them to place the matchbox in an upright position near the edge of a table by a blank wall. Next, they need to place the metre ruler on the table so that they can measure the distance between the torch and the matchbox. The aim of the task is to compare the distance between the torch and the matchbox with the height of the shadow projected on the wall. The small ruler can be used to measure the height of the shadow. (See Figure 1.)

Encourage the children to decide on a set number of values for the distance between the torch and the matchbox, such as 70cm, 60cm, 50cm, 40cm, 30cm, 20cm and 10cm. Ask the children to record what happens. Can they predict what might happen? Why do they think this?

After the children have completed the task, discuss their results. What happened to the shadow as the light source got closer to the object? Can the children explain why? Did the shadow change in any other way? When were the edges more distinct? How did the children record their results? Does this method of recording make the results clear to other people who may read them? How many times did the children repeat each measurement? Why is it important to repeat measurements? Is there a pattern in their results? Were their predictions correct? What conclusions can be drawn from this activity? What could they try next?

Suggestion(s) for extension
Make a graph showing the relationship between the distance of the object from the light source and the length of shadow produced.

Suggestion(s) for support
Act as scribe if necessary when the children are recording their results, or appoint a group scribe. Help with measuring, if necessary.

Assessment opportunities
This activity will enable you to assess how well the children can record their results and how accurately they can measure. It will also provide an opportunity to make comparisons and to discuss how patterns can sometimes occur in results.

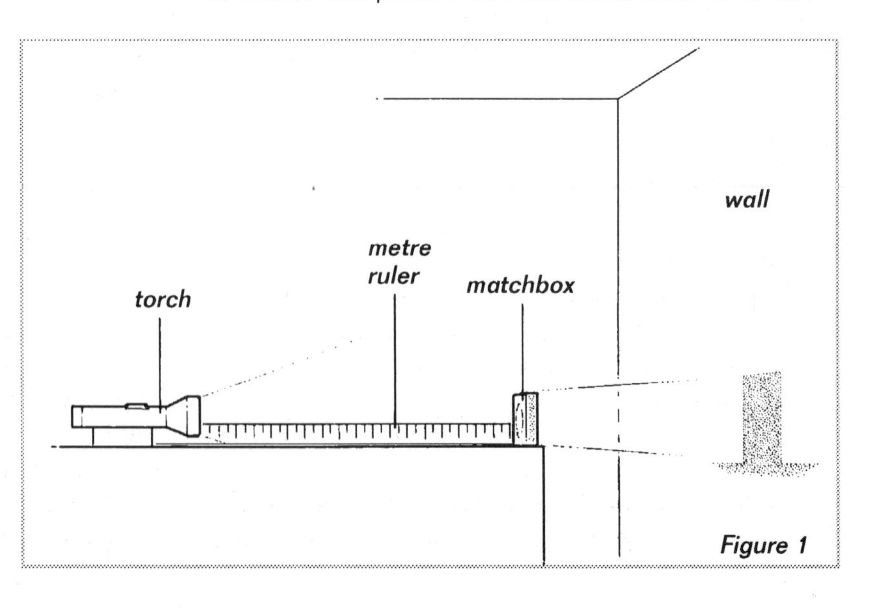

Figure 1

Opportunities for IT

Children could use graph-plotting software to draw a graph showing the relationship of shadow size to distance from the light source. This could be shown as a block graph and then converted to a line graph, so that the children could estimate the size of the shadow at other distances from the light source.

The measurements could also be collected and entered directly into a spreadsheet, from which the graphs can be plotted directly.

Display ideas

Draw a torch with an object close to it and a torch with an object far away from it. Mount these on the wall with the heading: 'What can affect the size of a shadow?' Add the children's writing about and drawings of the investigation.

Other aspects of the Science PoS covered

Experimental and Investigative Science – 1a, b; 2a, b, c; 3a, b, c, d, e.

REFLECTIONS

Light can be reflected.
Pairs or small groups.
60–120 minutes.
Warn the children about the dangers of looking directly into a light source (or a reflection of one).

Previous skills/knowledge needed

Light travels from a variety of sources.

Key background information

When light rays hit an object, they bounce back off it. This is called *reflection*. Different surfaces reflect light to different extents. Some surfaces reflect a lot of light, and these are described as shiny. Flat, shiny surfaces produce the best reflections. Most mirrors are made of flat sheets of highly polished glass with a shiny silver backing. Curved surfaces on shiny objects produce distorted images.

Preparation

None specifically required for this activity.

Resources needed

A collection of shiny objects such as Christmas tree baubles, spoons, shiny wrapping paper, metal lids, plastic lids, foil, flexi safety mirror, bottles, shiny fabrics and so on; a torch, paper, pencils.

What to do

Provide the children with the collection of objects and ask them to handle each one carefully, then decide what they

have in common. Discuss the term 'shiny' – what do the children think this word means? Ask the children to look at themselves in the surface of each of the items. What do they notice? What does 'reflection' mean? Does their image look the same in the surface of every object? What differences are there? Which objects give the clearest reflection? What is the difference between the shiny things in which the children can see themselves clearly and those in which they cannot?

Ask the children to look at themselves in the front of a spoon and the back of a spoon. Ask them to draw what they see. What difference is there in the reflection? Can the children explain why? (They may observe that two different reflections are possible in the front of a spoon: very close up, there is a magnified reflection which is the right way up; from a distance, there is a small reflection which is upside-down.) Ask the children to sort the objects according to how well they reflect.

Ask the children to shine a torch on each of the objects. What do they notice? Shine the torch on some objects which are not shiny, to see the difference. What do they notice? Does the torch make things look shinier? Can the children explain why? How is a mirror different from the other shiny objects? Can the children explain why?

Finally, challenge the children to investigate which material would make the best reflective strips on clothing or a bicycle. A darkened room may be needed to test the materials. How will they go about the investigation? What things will they need? How will they ensure this is a fair test? What safety considerations will be necessary? How will they decide which material is 'best'? What do they predict will happen? How will they record and present their results? (Record sheets like those shown on pages 94 and 95 could be used to record this investigation.)

When the children have completed their investigation, discuss their results. Were their predictions correct? What problems did they encounter in doing the investigation? How did they solve these? How did they ensure it was a fair test? How did they record their results? What conclusions can be drawn? What could they try next?

Suggestion(s) for extension

Ask the children to use the objects explored in the activity to make a 'hall of mirrors' display, revealing a different type of image at each stop along the display. They could also group reflecting surfaces into categories such as flat or curved, convex or concave, and so on.

Suggestion(s) for support

When the children are sorting the objects according to how well they reflect, help them to decide how clear their image is in each object. Assist with recording if necessary, or appoint a group scribe. Help the children decide how they will make the investigation a fair test, and how they could record the results. Remind them of any relevant safety issues, if necessary.

Assessment opportunities

This activity will enable you to assess how well the children can sort objects, and how observant they are when making comparisons. It will also enable you to assess how well the children can set up their own investigation and carry it out. You will have an opportunity to assess how well the children understand the need for a fair test, and how clearly they can record their results.

Display ideas

Place the collection of shiny objects on a table in front of a wall display showing the children's writing about and illustrations of their investigation.

Other aspects of the Science PoS covered

Experimental and Investigative Science – 1a, b, c, d, e; 2a, b, c; 3a, b, c, d, e.

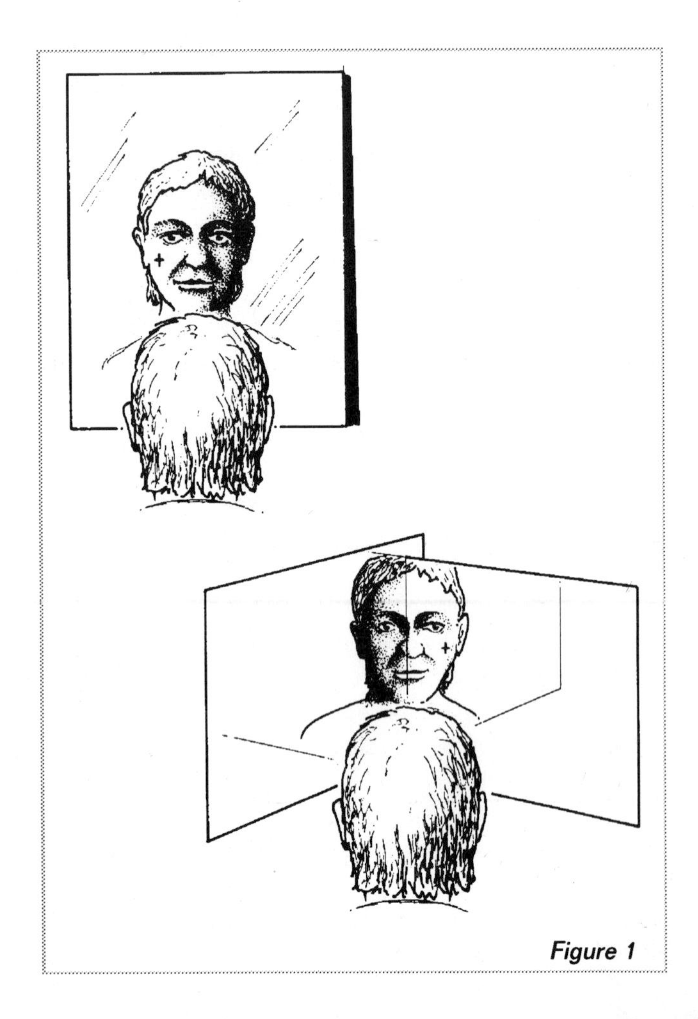

Figure 1

MIRRORS

The image seen in a mirror is reversed.

Whole class working together in pairs.

45–60 minutes.

Previous skills/knowledge needed

Light travels in a straight line from a source. Light can be reflected.

Key background information

Mirrors are made of a highly polished glass with a special reflective silver film on the back. Light rays travel in straight lines; as they hit the surface of the mirror, they are reflected back to our eyes and we see a reversed image. When two mirrors are used at right angles to each other, it is possible to see a 'true' image because each mirror reflects half of the image on to the adjoining mirror. Each half of the image is thus reversed and then reversed again before the light hits our eyes. (See Figure 1.)

Preparation

None specifically required for this activity.

Resources needed

Safety mirrors, Blu-Tack, one copy per pair of photocopiable sheet 132, paper, pencils, small toys.

What to do

Provide the children with a mirror each (or one between two). Tell the children they are going to find out more about mirrors. Ask them to use the mirror to look at their own reflection. If they touch their chin with their hand, what happens to the image? How is the movement they make different from the movement the image makes?

Now ask the children to look into the mirror and try to write their name on a piece of paper. How easy is this? What is the difference between writing your name while looking in

Using mirrors

Name ______________________ Date ______

1 2 3 4 5 6 7 8 9 10 11 12

lob

a mirror and writing it normally? Can the children find any words which look the same in the mirror? Why are these not changed?

Discuss when we use mirrors. What would life be like without them? How are they used for safety purposes? Discuss driving mirrors and mirrors used on 'blind' road intersections, for example.

Ask the children to find out how to use a mirror to do the following:

▲ look behind them;
▲ look at the ceiling;
▲ look at the side of their face;
▲ look at the sides of their legs when they are sitting down;
▲ look underneath a table;
▲ look around a corner.

Where do they need to hold the mirror each time? How is it possible to see things which are behind us?

Challenge the children to use two mirrors to create a 'real' image of themselves, not a reversed image. (The mirrors can be kept in place on a table using Blu-Tack.) If they cannot find a way, show them how to position the two mirrors at right angles to each other. Why do the children think they can now see their 'real' selves? Can they use the mirrors to see all sides of a small toy in the same way? Ask the children to move the mirrors closer together, then further apart. What do they notice about the number of images? How many reflections can be seen? If another mirror is added to make a triangle and the toy is placed in the middle, what effect does this produce? Talk about kaleidoscopes and how these work.

Finally, provide the children with copies of photocopiable page 132 and challenge them to use the mirrors to make different patterns with and changes to each picture on the sheet, or alternatively write down some or all of the following challenges for them to explore:

Picture 1 Make: a square, a rectangle, a pyramid, an L-shaped figure, a shape with six squares inside it and a 'hinge' in the middle, an arrowhead, a rectangle with four squares inside it, a small square inside an L-shaped figure, a kite.
Picture 2 Make: a diamond, an arrowhead, four triangles, a quadrilateral, a bow-tie shape, a very small triangle, a six-sided figure.
Picture 3 Make: a circle, an oval, a segment, a piece of cake with one slice missing, two semicircles.
Picture 4 Make: a whole car, a circle underneath an arch, a lamp with a shade, two kites, a set of steps, one kite, one circle.
Picture 5 Make: a happy face, two sad faces, a sad face with no nose, an empty oval, a face with four eyes and no nose or mouth, a face with two eyes and no nose or mouth.
Picture 6 How many different ways can you make: 2 dots, 3 dots, 4 dots, 5 dots, 6 dots, 7 dots and 8 dots?
Picture 7 How many different lines and shapes can you make?
Picture 8 Make: a single straight line, two crosses, two arrowheads, one arrowhead.
Picture 9 Make: 1, 2, 3, 4, 5, 6 flowers.
Picture 10 Make: a circle and a triangle, a square, a circle, an archway.
Picture 11 Make: two straight lines and no dots, two arrowheads and no dots, one arrowhead, four lines and four dots, two dots, two arrowheads and one dot.
Picture 12 Make these words: doob, dob, lol, lool.

Encourage the children to find other shapes and patterns with these pictures.

Suggestion(s) for extension

Ask the children to design and make a kaleidoscope. Ask them to design their own 'mirror pictures', like those on the photocopiable sheet, for others to try out.

Suggestion(s) for support

Help the children to position the mirror if they cannot find out how to see behind them or to their side, or how to position two mirrors to see their 'real' selves. Pair up the children when using the photocopiable sheet if you think some children may need the support of a partner; or cut out just one or two of the mirror pictures from the sheet if you think some children would prefer fewer pictures to work with.

Assessment opportunities

The discussion with the children as they are trying out the mirror to see how it works can give you some insight into how the children think the mirror reflects images.

Display ideas

Make a display of different mirrors on a table. Include concave and convex shapes. Mount the photocopiable sheet and/or the mirror pictures the children have designed on to card and cover them with clear adhesive plastic. Make a sign inviting the children to use a mirror with the cards to make shapes and patterns. On the wall behind the table, mount drawings the children have made to show where they need to hold a mirror to see behind them, the ceiling, their feet when sitting down, around a corner, their 'real' selves, and so on.

Other aspects of the Science PoS covered

Experimental and Investigative Science – 1a; 2a, b; 3e.

Reference to photocopiable sheet

The children could use the whole sheet, or the page could be cut into separate pictures so that some children can use just a few of them.

ANGLES OF REFLECTION

Light reflects off mirrors at the same angle as the angle at which it arrives.

Pairs or small groups.

45–60 minutes.

Warn the children of the dangers of looking directly into a light source (or a reflection of one).

Previous skills/knowledge needed

Light travels in a straight line from a source. Light can be reflected.

Key background information

Light can be made to change direction. When light strikes a mirror at an angle, it is reflected back at the same angle in a different direction. (In other words, the *angle of incidence* equals the *angle of reflection*.) This is why if you can see someone's eyes in a mirror, they can see you too.

Preparation

You will need to prepare a darkened room for part of this activity.

Resources needed

A torch, black paper or thin card, adhesive tape, a safety mirror, paper, a tennis ball, a darkened room.

What to do

Tell the children that you would like them to find out more about how light travels. Provide them with a torch, a mirror and a piece of white paper. Ask them to use these things to make the beam from the torch bounce off the mirror on to the paper. What happens to the light when it hits the mirror? Where do you need to place the paper so that the light shines on it?

Demonstrate the idea of the light bouncing off the mirror and changing direction by rolling a ball at an angle against a wall and watching what happens. Explain that the light behaves in a similar way. Allow the children to roll the ball against the wall at different angles. What happens on the rebound? Is there a pattern in the way the ball bounces back? Would the children be able to predict in which direction the ball will bounce back if they rolled the ball at a particular angle?

Tell the children they can relate what happens to the ball to the way light reflects off a mirror. Ask the children to cover the end of the torch with two pieces of black paper or thin card so that only a very thin slit is made in the centre. Use adhesive tape to hold the pieces of paper on the torch. (See Figure 1.)

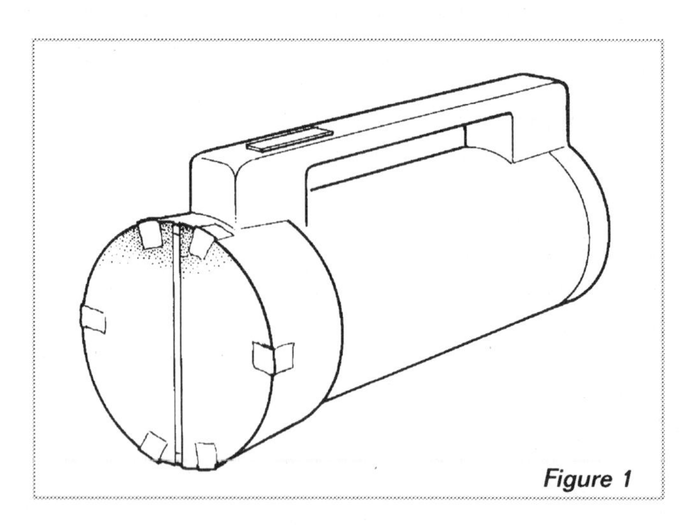

Figure 1

In a darkened room, place a piece of white paper on a table and ask one of the children in each pair to hold the mirror vertically on the paper. The other child should then shine the torch so that the thin beam of light hits the mirror. How is the beam reflected back? Change the angle of the torch. What happens to the angle of the reflected beam? (See Figure 2.)

Discuss what the children have found out. Tell the children

that the angle at which the beam hits the mirror is always the same as the angle of the beam being reflected from the mirror. Discuss how this helps to show us that light travels in straight lines.

Suggestion(s) for extension

Challenge the children to use what they have learned from this activity to make a periscope to see round corners. What angles do the mirrors need to be at for the periscope to work? (See Figure 3.)

Suggestion(s) for support

Help the children to understand what is happening when the ball is bounced off a wall by encouraging them to try rolling the ball at an angle from each side and then centrally to see what happens. Do they always get the same result? What factors could influence the result? (The ball may hit a bump on the wall or floor, for instance.) Help the children to attach the paper to the torch securely, if necessary. Make sure the slit is as straight as possible.

Assessment opportunities

You will be able to assess how observant the children are when doing these tasks by listening to and responding to the children's comments about what happens. You can use this time to talk to the children about their ideas on how light travels and is reflected.

Display ideas

Ask the children to write down their ideas about how light travels and about reflection. Wall-mount this work, together with a collection of materials/objects which reflect light.

Other aspects of the Science PoS covered

Experimental and Investigative Science – 1a, b; 2a, b; 3b, c, d, e.

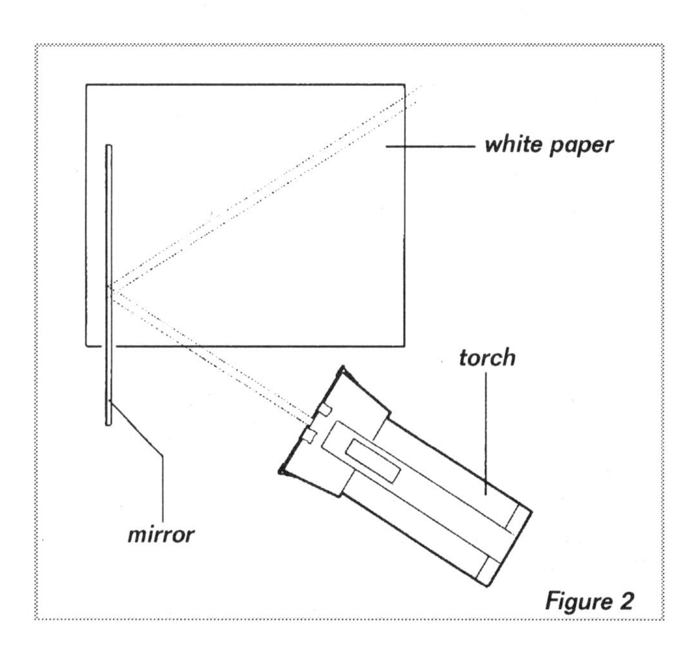

Figure 2

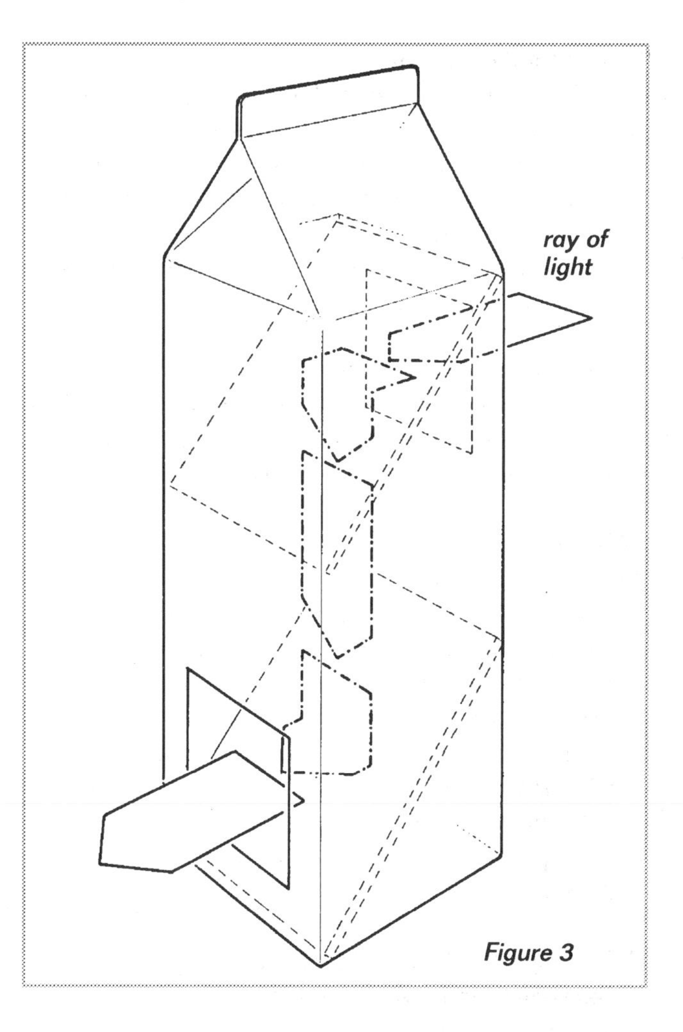

Figure 3

HOW WE SEE

Objects can be seen when light reflects off them into our eyes.

Whole class.

30–45 minutes.

Previous skills/knowledge needed

Light travels from a variety of sources. Light travels in a straight line from a source. Light can be reflected.

Key background information

We see things when light is reflected from objects into our eyes. The light enters the eye through the *pupil*. The *pupil* is able to contract or expand (like a shutter of a camera) in order to control the amount of light which enters the eye. A *lens* behind the pupil focuses the light on to the *retina* at the back of the eye. The retina is covered with tiny 'receptors'. These send messages to the brain, which interprets the image. (See Figure 1.)

Preparation

Make a large drawing of the parts of the eye with labels naming each part. Sensitive handling will be necessary for any child who has impaired vision.

Resources needed
A drawing of the eye, paper, pencils, safety mirrors.

What to do
Provide the children with a safety mirror and ask them to look closely at their eyes. What things do they notice? What parts of the eye can they name? What different eye colours do the children in the class have? What purpose do the eyelashes and eyelids serve? Can blood vessels be seen? Why would the eye need these? Ask the children to move their eyes gently from side to side. How far can they see without turning their heads? What body part would help us to move the eyes?

Show the children the drawing of the eye without, and then with, the parts labelled. How many of these parts did the children already know? Can the children tell you how the eye works? Do they know how we see things? Ask the children to draw a stick-person sitting down outside in the sunshine. Tell them to put arrows on the drawing showing how they think the person sees the grass near them. Ask the children to compare their drawing with that of a partner. Do they agree? Compare the drawings of the whole class – do they all agree?

Explain that we see things because light is reflected off objects into our eyes. Explain briefly how the eye works, referring to the drawing of the eye.

Some children find it very difficult to understand that we see things because light reflects off objects. Many children believe that rays come from the eyes themselves, and so they add arrows going from the eyes to the grass in their drawings. You can help them overcome this misconception by explaining that if rays came from our eyes, we would be able to see in the dark.

Some children may draw rays going from the light source to the eyes and then rays going from the eyes to the grass. You can help these children to challenge their ideas by asking them to shroud their eyes from the light source while looking at an object. They will discover that the object is just as clear and bright as it was before. Discuss how the arrows should be drawn in the picture, to make sure that the children are aware of the correct interpretation.

Suggestion(s) for extension
Ask the children to draw other examples of how they think we see things, for example how a person sees a television screen at night with a lamp on in the room. Ask them to draw arrows showing how the person sees the object.

Suggestion(s) for support
Some children may need reassurance when they find out that their answers to the drawing activity are incorrect. Emphasise that all their ideas are valuable, and that often scientists begin with a 'wrong' idea and then set out to disprove it.

Assessment opportunities
The children's drawings will enable you to assess what they understand about how we see things. They can be a very useful starting-point for discussions with individuals or groups of children during the activity. The children could be asked to repeat the task at a later date to assess how much of the information they have retained.

Opportunities for IT
Children could use an encyclopaedic CD-ROM to find out more about how their eyes work. You could prepare specific questions for the children to research and show them how to phrase questions or move around the CD-ROM to find the answers they need.

Children could use graph-plotting software to make a bar chart of the numbers of children with different eye colours. There may need to be some discussion at the start about putting eye colours into categories, to make sure that the results are consistent across the sample.

Display ideas
Ask the children to draw a picture of their eyes. Prepare a graph showing the colours of children's eyes in the class. Mount the pictures and the graph on the wall, together with the large drawing of the eye with labelled parts. Add some of the children's drawings of how we see things.

Other aspects of the Science PoS covered
Experimental and Investigative Science – 2b.

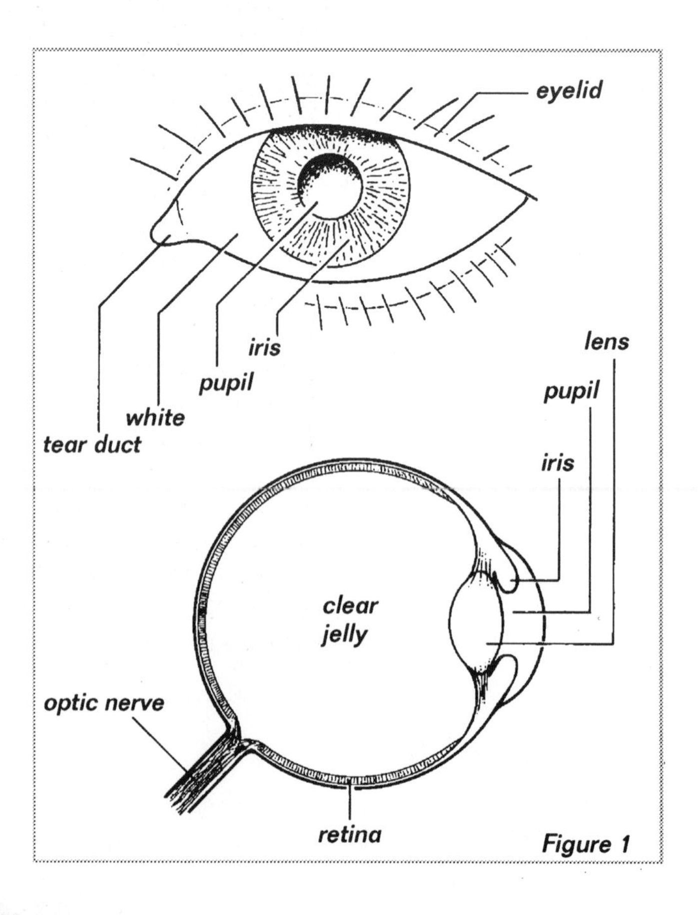

Figure 1

Sound

The activities in this section of the book encourage children to explore the properties of sound. In the course of carrying out the activities, the children will gain experience in questioning, observing, predicting, measuring and drawing conclusions. They will also have opportunities to work co-operatively and to share their ideas with others.

Sounds are made when objects vibrate. The vibration of the object causes air molecules to move. When the object vibrates outwards, it packs the air molecules into a smaller space (*compression*); and when the object vibrates inwards, there is more space (*decompression* or *rarefaction*). This pattern of compressions and rarefactions forms a *wave motion*. When these waves reach the ear, we hear them as sound.

SOUNDS IN SCHOOL

Sounds are all around us. Sounds travel away from sources and get fainter as they do so.

Pairs.

60–80 minutes.

▲ *Discuss with the children the importance of not leaving the school grounds during this activity.*

Previous skills/knowledge needed

How to use a trundle wheel.

Key background information

Sounds are made when objects vibrate. The sound travels away from the source in a wave. The further away from the source, the fainter the sound becomes.

Preparation

Choose suitable sites in the school grounds to carry out this activity. Sensitive handling will be necessary for children with hearing impairments.

Resources needed

One copy per child of photocopiable page 133, pencils, clipboards, trundle wheels.

What to do

This activity is best carried out by pairs of children at different times during the day, enabling them to compare the different sounds made. Discuss the purpose of the activity with the whole class before dividing the children into pairs.

First make sure the children know how to use the trundle wheel correctly. Provide each child with a copy of photocopiable page 133 and explain to them how to complete the sheet. Explain that they need to decide on the loudest sound in each place and then measure how far away from the source of the sound they need to be standing before they can no longer hear the sound. The best way for the children to do this might be for one child to stand at the chosen place, while the other child moves slowly away until she can no longer hear the sound. The child standing still can help by letting the other child know if the sound stops. The child standing still can then walk to the second child, using the trundle wheel to measure the distance.

It may also be appropriate to discuss with the whole class what sounds they predict they will hear at each site. Which sounds do they think might be loudest? Softest? Will there be any constant sounds? What sounds may only be occasional?

Once everyone has completed the survey, bring the whole class back together as a group. Compare their findings. What were the loudest sounds at each place? Does this alter according to the time of day? Which was the noisiest place? The quietest place? Were their predictions correct? Were they surprised by some of the sounds which they heard?

What did they notice about each sound as they walked further away from it? Which sounds could be heard from a long way? Were the loudest sounds different in some way from the other sounds? Why do the children think these sounds could be heard above the rest? Which sounds were more constant than others? Which sounds did the children like/dislike? What does the survey tell us about sounds in the school? Are some sounds too loud? How could their volume be reduced?

Discuss the children's recordings. Did they check their results by measuring the distances several times? What problems, if any, did they have? How did they overcome them? How could they improve the survey if it were done again?

Suggestion(s) for extension

Using the information gathered in the survey, make a chart of the loudest sounds at each place, collating the times into two main sessions – morning and afternoon. Use this information to discuss ways of reducing noise levels.

Suggestion(s) for support

Pair up more able children with less able ones to help with recording the sounds heard. Make sure the children know exactly what to do by working through the section of the photocopiable sheet for the classroom, including the measuring, so that the children will know what to do at the other sites. You may consider restricting some children to two or three places to reduce the amount of recording and measuring.

Sounds in our school

Name ______________ Date ______________

▲ At each place, stop and listen to the sounds you can hear. Write down the sounds. Decide on the loudest sound and underline its name. Measure the distance you need to walk away before you can no longer hear the loudest sound.

Place	Sounds heard	Distance away when loudest sound no longer heard
classroom time		
corridor time:		
school office time:		
playground time:		
in front of school time:		

Assessment opportunities
This activity will enable you to assess how well the children can conduct a survey and complete a table. It will also provide opportunities to discuss the accuracy of the measurements and the need to check these measurements by repeating them.

Display ideas
Draw or take photographs of each place used in the survey. Draw pictures of the sources of the loudest noises at each place. Outline these pictures in red zigzag lines to make them stand out, and mount them on the wall with a heading saying 'Loudest sounds in our school'. The children could make posters of ways to quieten these sounds to add to the display.

Other aspects of the Science PoS covered
Experimental and Investigative Science – 1a, b; 2a, b, c; 3a, b, c, d, e.

Reference to photocopiable sheet
Pair up more able children with less able ones if writing skills are limited. If your school does not have an office, substitute another place before photocopying the page. Some children may visit only two or three places, to reduce the amount of recording and measuring.

MAKING SOUNDS

Sounds can be made in many ways.

Individuals, pairs or small groups.

60–120 minutes.

▲ *Children should take care when handling the scissors.*

Previous skills/knowledge needed
None specifically required for this activity.

Key background information
Sounds are made when things vibrate. We can make sounds by plucking, shaking, blowing, scraping and banging.

Preparation
None specifically required for this activity.

Resources needed
A round, plastic ice-cream container with a lid, elastic bands, rice, scissors, paper, pencils, a ruler.

What to do
Provide the children with the ice-cream container, rice, elastic bands, ruler and scissors and challenge them to make as many different sounds as they can using these things. They can change the container in any way they like, but make them aware that they should try out all the sounds they can with a complete container first, then make alterations to it.

Discuss with the children how they are going to record what they do. They will need to keep a running record using drawings and/or writing about what they do and the sounds which result, in order to share this information with the others later. Encourage them to try and make as wide a variety of different sounds as possible.

Different sounds could be made in the following ways:

- ▲ banging the container with the ruler;
- ▲ banging the container on a table;
- ▲ hitting the lid against the top and bottom of the container;
- ▲ banging the ruler inside the container;
- ▲ putting rice inside and shaking it;
- ▲ putting rice inside and slowly swirling it;
- ▲ altering the amount of rice inside;
- ▲ placing elastic bands around the container (with the lid on or off) and plucking the bands;
- ▲ placing the ruler under the elastic bands to make a bridge;
- ▲ running the ruler across the elastic bands;
- ▲ cutting a hole in the lid and plucking bands over the hole;
- ▲ cutting a hole in the side of the container and shaking the ruler through the hole.

When the children have completed their investigation, bring the whole class together to discuss their findings. Compare the things the children have tried out. How many different ways could be found to use the equipment? How many different types of sounds could be made? Encourage the children to describe the sounds made. What words can be used to describe them? Are some sounds louder than others? Do some sounds last longer than others? Which sound is 'best'? Why? Which musical instruments are used in similar ways to the ways tried out? Is there a method not tried out (perhaps blowing)?

Discuss their recording. Was this difficult to do? What problems did they have? Were diagrams useful? Could other people use their recordings to make the sounds in the same way? (This could be tried out by asking the children to swap instructions for other children to try and follow.) What have the children found out about sounds by doing this activity?

Suggestion(s) for extension
Using the knowledge gathered from this activity, the children could make a collection of musical instruments from other materials that produce a range of sounds.

Suggestion(s) for support

Pair up children who are good at recording with those who are not, or act as scribe if necessary. Help the children decide how the sounds they make are different by talking about them: Is this a loud or soft sound? Is it a high or low sound? Does this sound last a long time? Can the materials be used in another way? Introduce the ideas of banging, plucking, shaking and scraping if the children appear to be short of ideas.

Assessment opportunities

This activity will provide the children with experience in making close observations and comparisons. Discussions with the children as they are making the sounds will enable you to assess how well they are discriminating between the sounds and how well they are using the materials provided. The recording methods will be a valuable discussion point in considering how best they can record what happens in an investigation and how effective and useful diagrams can be.

Opportunities for IT

Children could work in pairs using a word processor to write about how they used the instrument to make a sound. They could experiment with different fonts and font sizes to present their writing for a class display.

Display ideas

Each pair or group of children could display one way of making a sound with the container by preparing the 'instrument' and adding their own diagrams of it and writing about how to use it, how it was made and a description of the sound. The containers could be displayed on a table with the children's information mounted on the wall above it, or made into a small book and placed near the container.

Other aspects of the Science PoS covered

Experimental and Investigative Science – 1a; 2a, b; 3a, b, c.

VIBRATIONS

Sounds are made when things vibrate.

Small groups.

60–80 minutes.

Previous skills/knowledge needed

Sounds can be made in a variety of ways.

Key background information

Sounds are made when objects vibrate. The vibration of the object causes air molecules to move. When the object vibrates outwards the air molecules are pushed together (*compression*), and when the object vibrates inwards the molecules are pulled further apart (*decompression* or *rarefaction*). This pattern of compressions and rarefactions forms a *wave motion*. When these waves reach our ears we hear them as sound. The air molecules themselves do not move across the room: they just vibrate to and fro.

Preparation

None specifically required for this activity.

Resources needed

A ruler, a comb, tissue-paper, a balloon, a jam jar, an elastic band, rice.

What to do

Tell the children that they are going to find out how sounds are made. Place a ruler over the edge of a table and flip the end of it. What happens? Does it make any sound when it stops vibrating? Move the ruler so that greater and lesser amounts are extending over the edge of the table. What happens to the sound? (See Figure 1.)

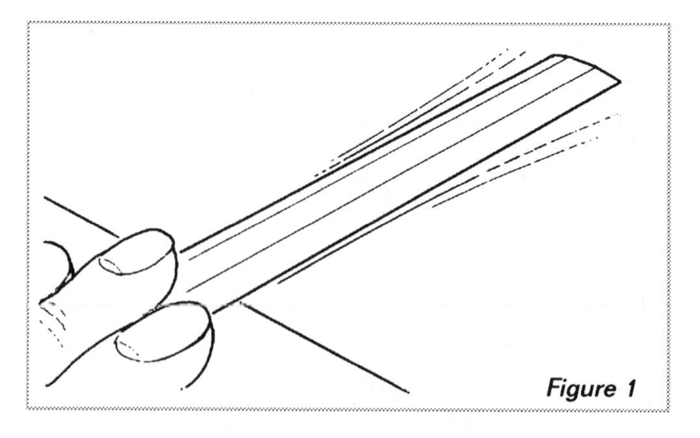

Figure 1

Ask the children to stretch an elastic band taut and then pluck it. What happens to the band? What sound can be heard? Blow up a balloon and hold the neck with two hands, stretching and releasing it as the air escapes. What happens? (See Figure 2.)

Explain to the children that when an object vibrates, it makes a sound. Tell them that when something vibrates, it moves the air around it, causing molecules in the air to vibrate back and forth. This creates a wave of movement in the air. When the wave reaches our ear, we hear a sound.

Explain that we can feel vibrations in two ways. Place some tissue paper over a comb and blow. What can be heard? What can be felt on the lips? Ask the children to place their fingertips at the front of their throats and make long 'ah' and 'oh' sounds. What can they feel? Explain that when we speak our vocal cords vibrate, and this causes the air in our mouths to vibrate. The vibrations travel out and a sound is heard. (See Figure 3.)

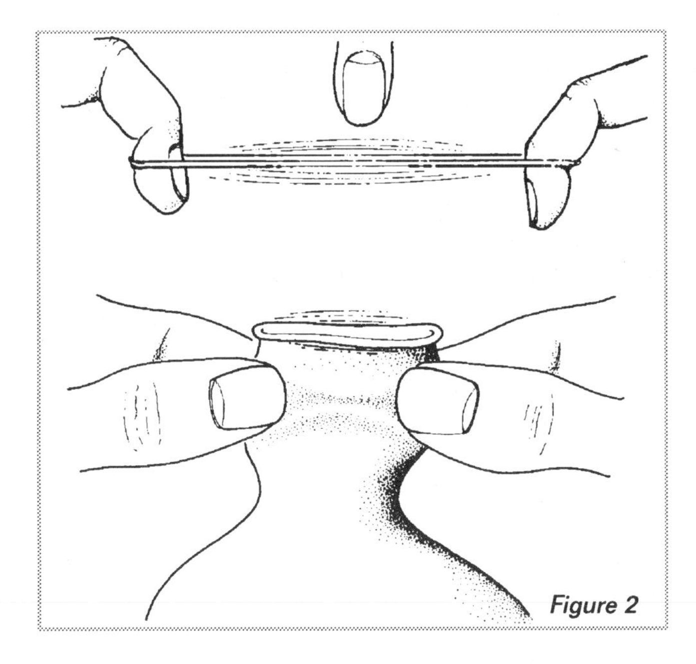

Figure 2

Finally, explain to the children that they are going to make a musical instrument which uses vibrations to make different sounds. Place a handful of rice grains inside a jam jar. Cut the neck off a balloon and stretch the remaining balloon rubber tightly over the neck of the jar. Secure it with an elastic band, if necessary. Tell the children to hold the jar upside-down and flick the balloon rubber with their fingertips. What happens to the rice inside? What sounds can be heard?

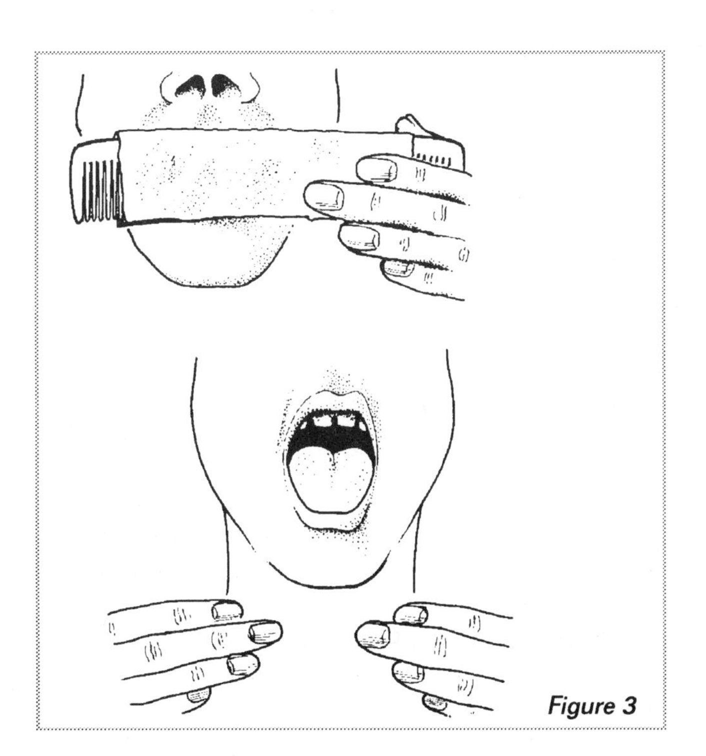

Figure 3

Ask the children to experiment further with this 'instrument'. Wrap an elastic band lengthways around the jar from top to bottom. Pluck the band on the balloon rubber. Watch the rice. Listen to the sounds made. (See Figure 4.)

Slowly swirl the rice around on the balloon rubber. What sounds can be heard? How different are they from the other sounds? Allow the children time to experiment with the instrument, to make as many different sounds as they can.

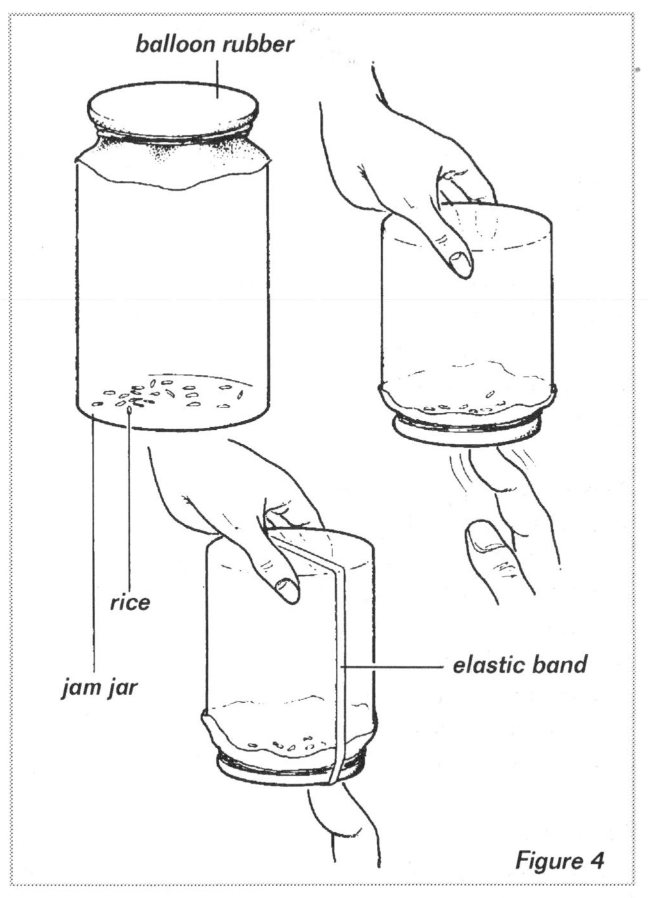

Figure 4

Discuss the children's findings. Which sounds did they like best? Why? Does a longer vibration make a longer-lasting sound? Can sounds be heard if nothing is moving? Explain that although it is vibrations that cause sounds, the vibrations are not always directly visible, such as those we make with our vocal cords or the vibrations that cause thunder.

Discuss real musical instruments. Ask the children to tell you what causes the vibrations in a recorder, guitar, drum and shaker. Compare these with the things the children have just tried out (recorder – letting the air out of the balloon, guitar – plucking an elastic band, drum – tapping the balloon rubber on the jar, shaker – rice in the jar).

Suggestion(s) for extension

Ask the children to make their own recorder, drum, shaker and guitar, using the ideas gained from the activity. They could select their own materials and make more permanent instruments. These could then be used as part of a class band.

Suggestion(s) for support

Children should not need a great deal of support in this activity, but the teacher could assist with the making of the jam jar instrument if necessary. The most important thing is to make sure that the balloon rubber is very tightly fitted to make the best sounds.

Assessment opportunities

When the children are carrying out the activities, you can discuss various aspects with individual children, such as what causes the sound and how it moves to our ears.

Opportunities for IT

Children could use a word processor to write and present their work on making musical instruments for a class display. They may also be able to include pictures in their work by using a drawing or art package to draw the picture, by using pictures taken from CD-ROMs or other commercial clipart collections or by scanning hand-drawn pictures and including them in their writing.

Older or more able children could create a simple multimedia presentation about musical instruments and how they work. Children would need to be taught how to use authoring software to create a linked presentation, and will probably need support during this activity. You could prepare a structure in advance, so that by clicking on a menu of different instruments children would be taken to a separate page for each one.

A picture of each instrument, either taken from clipart (or CD-ROM) or drawn and scanned by the children, could be accompanied by a sample of the sound taken from recorded music or recorded by appropriate software (using a microphone attached to the computer). Text could also be added to show which part of the instrument makes the sound and how. Arrows on each page will enable the children to move around the presentation, perhaps back to the main menu or on to another instrument.

Display ideas

Ask the children to draw or paint musical instruments. Mount these on the wall. Add labels showing which part of the instrument vibrates to make the sound. The children can write about the activity and add their writing to the wall display. If the children have made their own musical instruments, place these on a table in front of the wall display. Group them according to how the vibrations are made: plucked, banged, shaken, and so on.

Other aspects of the Science PoS covered

Experimental and Investigative Science – 1a; 2b, c; 3c.

LOUDNESS

Sounds vary in loudness (or volume).

Small groups.

60–120 minutes.

Children should take care when handling the scissors.

Previous skills/knowledge needed

Sounds are caused when an object vibrates.

Key background information

Sounds can be loud or soft. The volume depends on the amount of energy in the sound wave. This is decided by how strongly the source of the sound compresses the air and how much air is made to vibrate. If an object is vibrated in a cavity, as in a guitar or a bell, the sound is *amplified* (made louder) and can last longer. This happens because the sound waves inside the cavity hit the walls, bounce back and reinforce each other. This effect is called *resonance*.

Preparation

Sensitive handling will be necessary for any child who has impaired hearing.

Resources needed

Tubes from rolls of paper towel, elastic bands, a jam jar, rice, plastic bags, a tambourine, pictures of a guitar, bell, violin and drum (or real instruments), scissors, a collection of junk materials.

What to do

Tell the children that they are going to find out more about sounds and how they can be different from each other. Clap your hands softly, then loudly. Ask the children to tell you how the sounds differed. Discuss loud and soft sounds further. Ask the children to name some soft sounds and then some loud sounds. What do they think affects whether a sound is loud or soft? Ask them to make a soft, long 'oh' sound with their voices and then make a loud, long 'oh' sound. What did they have to do to make the sound louder? Ask the children to make a soft sound with the tambourine and then a loud sound. Can the children suggest why the sounds differ? What did they have to do to change the sounds?

Explain that some musical instruments have a box or cavity to make their sounds louder. Show the children some pictures of, or real, musical instruments which have cavities, such as a guitar, violin, bell and drum. Can the children suggest why the cavity makes the sound louder? Tell them that they are going to make some instruments of their own to explore their ideas.

Begin by asking the children to make a sound with their voices and then make the same sound with a cardboard tube in front of their mouths. What happens to the sound? Can the children suggest why? (See Figure 1.)

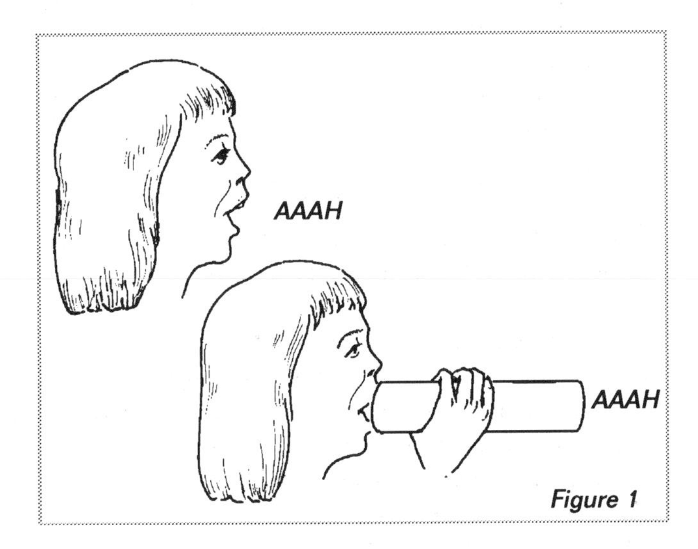

Figure 1

Next, flick a taut elastic band with your thumbs. What sound can be heard? Then place the band lengthways over a jam jar and flick it again. How has the sound changed? Why? (See Figure 2.)

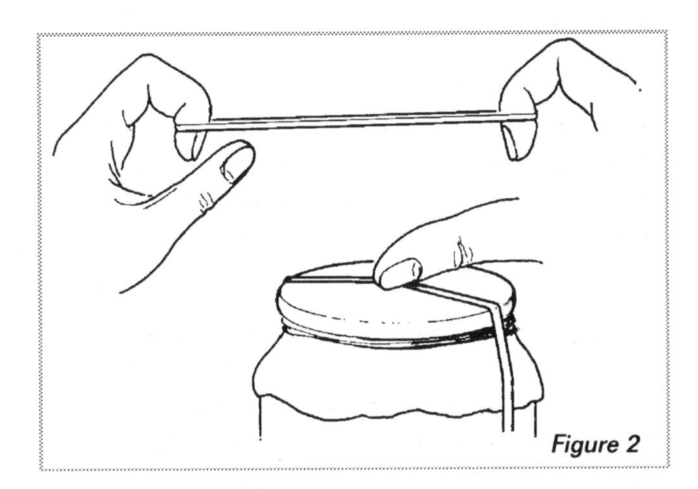
Figure 2

Finally, the children can cut one cardboard tube into three different lengths. Cut some plastic from a plastic bag to fit over one end of each tube, and secure it with an elastic band so that the plastic is tight. Place the same number of rice grains inside each tube (about 20) and shake the tubes. What are the differences between the sounds made? Can the children suggest why? Explain that the loudness depends on how much the air around the object is made to vibrate. (See Figure 3.)

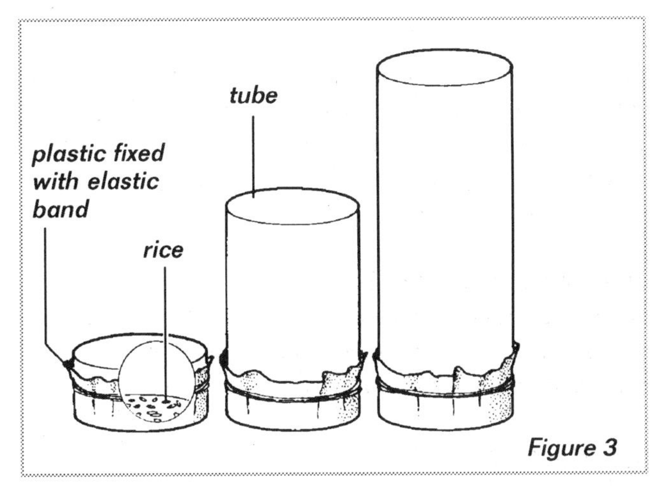

Figure 3

The children can then go on to explore these ideas further by making their own instruments from junk materials. Discuss their efforts when they have completed them. How did they make the sounds softer and louder in each case? How do the results compare with real musical instruments?

Suggestion(s) for extension

The children could use the instruments they have made to make up a short piece of music which uses soft and loud sounds.

Suggestion(s) for support

Some children may need help in securing the plastic around the tubes. Adhesive tape may prove more effective if the bands squash the tubes too much. You may need to suggest to some children ideas for making their own instruments. These could include:

▲ putting elastic bands around an ice-cream container;
▲ putting pasta inside containers with lids;
▲ stretching balloon rubber over a large jar;
▲ stretching elastic bands between nails banged into wood.

Assessment opportunities

You will be able to use the instruments the children have made to discuss with individuals how they have made the sounds louder or softer. This will also provide an opportunity to discuss the problems the children may have had in making the instruments and how they found ways of overcoming them.

Opportunities for IT

Children could use a microphone attached to a computer to look at the loudness of different sounds produced. The accompanying software will usually display the sound as a wave form: the louder the sound, the higher the peaks. The children could use this to gain an idea of the volume that they create either from different sound sources or by playing the instrument in different ways. They could record and save samples of different sounds and then compare them for loudness.

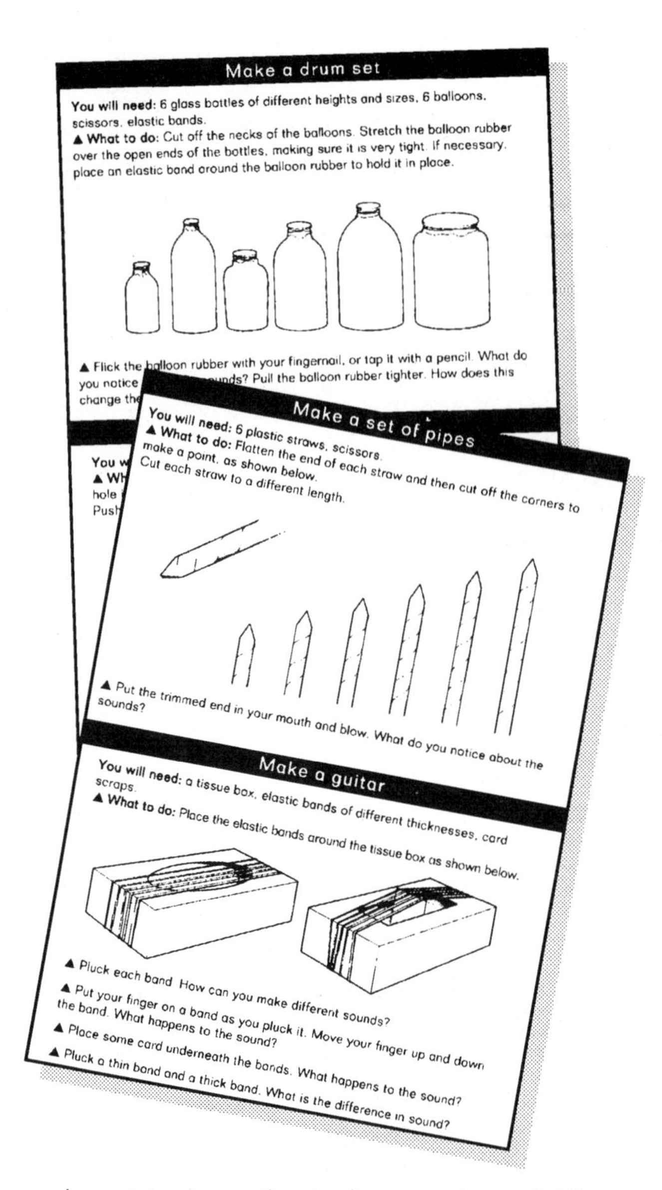

Display ideas

The children's instruments could be displayed on a table with a sign challenging people to make a soft sound and a loud sound with the instruments. On the wall behind the table, mount pictures, drawings and/or names of things which make soft or loud sounds in the classroom or school, labelling the groups 'Loud' and 'Soft'.

Other aspects of the Science PoS covered

Experimental and Investigative Science – 1a, e; 2a, b, c; 3b, c, e.

PITCH

Sounds vary in pitch.

Small groups.

60–120 minutes.

▲ *Children should take care when handling the scissors.*

Previous skills/knowledge needed

Sounds are made when objects vibrate. Sounds can vary in loudness.

Key background information

Sounds can vary in *pitch*. Some are high and some are low. The faster something vibrates, the higher the pitch. The word *frequency* is used to describe the rate at which something vibrates. It measures the number of vibrations per second, in a unit called the *hertz* (Hz).

The size of the resonating chamber (that is, the size of the sound box or length of tube) affects the pitch. If the chamber is small, the vibrations are fast and the pitch is high. Large resonating chambers make low sounds.

Preparation

Make one copy per child of photocopiable sheets 134 and 135. Cut the pages into the four different activities and glue them on to stiff card. Cover these with clear, sticky-backed plastic to make four different activity cards.

Resources needed

One copy per child of photocopiable pages 134 and 135, scissors, six plastic drinking straws, a large tubular cardboard container with a plastic lid and a tin end (such as a gravy granule container), pencils, six glass containers of different heights, six balloons, elastic bands of different thicknesses and lengths, a tissue box, scraps of cardboard.

What to do

Give an activity card to each group of children without any prior discussion, so that they are left to discover things about sound for themselves. Alternatively, begin by discussing pitch, and use the activity cards as a follow-up to the discussion. Either way, the following points will need to be discussed with the children.

▲ The shorter the pipe in a musical instrument, the higher the pitch. The shorter straws will therefore have a higher pitch than the longer straws. The sound produced by the trimmed end of the straw is acting like a reed in a musical instrument such as a saxophone.

▲ The larger the resonating chamber, the lower the sound. Also, the tighter the skin on a drum, the higher the pitch. A tall bottle drum will usually make a lower sound than a short drum, but it will also depend on the size of the neck and how tightly the skin is stretched. In the sliding instrument, the

Sound

further the lid is pushed in, the higher the pitch, because the resonating chamber becomes smaller.

▲ On a stringed instrument, the shorter the length of string, the tighter it is pulled and the lighter it is, the higher the pitch will become. Hence thick and/or long elastic bands will make lower sounds than thin and/or short bands.

Once the children have had a chance to make the instruments, bring the whole class together to discuss the results. What things change the pitch of a stringed instrument? What affects the pitch of an instrument with a tube and a reed? How can the pitch of a drum be changed? What other things did the children find out? What difficulties did they have? How did they overcome them?

Suggestion(s) for extension

Using the ideas and examples presented in the activity cards, the children could go on to design and make their own pitched instruments.

Suggestion(s) for support

Make sure the groups contain more able children who can help with reading the instructions on the activity cards, or can read out the information to less able children. Make the materials readily available, so the children do not need to gather them themselves. Assist the children in making the instruments, if necessary.

Assessment opportunities

You can assess how well the children understand pitch by talking to them when they are making and using the instruments. Ask questions such as: How can you make the sound higher on the 'guitar'? Why do you think this happens? Show me how to make a low sound on the 'drums'. Why do you think this happens? Which pipe makes the highest sound? Why do you think the short pipe makes a higher sound than the long pipe?

Opportunities for IT

Children could use a microphone attached to the computer to look at the pitch of different sounds produced. The accompanying software will usually display the sound as a wave form; the higher the pitch, the closer together the peaks in the wave form will be (*frequency*).

The children could use a word processor to write about the instrument and include a printout of the wave pattern. The different pieces of work could be used as a class display.

Display ideas

Ask the children to write down and/or draw how they made the sounds higher and lower on the various instruments made in the activity. Mount this work on the wall above a display of the instruments which the children have made.

Other aspects of the Science PoS covered

Experimental and Investigative Science – 1a; 2a, b, c; 3b, c, e.

Reference to photocopiable sheets

This activity could be carried out with the whole class working in four different groups, either at the same time or at various times throughout the week. Alternatively, duplicate the activity cards so that eight smaller groups are created.

HEARING SOUNDS

Vibrations from sound sources can travel through some materials to the ear.

Small groups.

60–80 minutes.

Previous skills/knowledge needed

Sounds can be made in many ways. Sounds are made when objects vibrate. Sounds can vary in pitch and loudness.

Key background information

Sound will not travel through a vacuum. It needs a medium such as air, water or the ground. The vibrations from the object making the sound are transmitted through a substance in waves. If the temperature remains constant, these waves travel at a constant speed. Sound travels faster through warm air than through cool air. It travels even faster through solids

and liquids. High-pitched sounds and low-pitched sounds travel at the same speed.

Preparation

This activity needs to be carried out where there are two adjoining rooms connected by a solid wooden door. If possible, one of the rooms should be soundproofed.

Sensitive handling will be necessary for any child with a hearing impairment.

You may need to organise extra supervision so that another adult is present in the second room.

Resources needed

A portable cassette player with a numbered volume control, a music cassette, paper, pencils, a pitched instrument such as a xylophone, measuring tape, a trundle wheel, two adjoining rooms connected by a solid wooden door, a ground-floor window, a solid brick or wooden wall with no windows.

What to do

Explain to the children that you would like them to find out how well sound can travel through things. Begin by discussing the sounds the children can hear at the moment, from outside. How far away do they think some of the sounds are? Which sounds can they hear easily from outside? (For example, aircraft, police sirens.) Why do the children think we can hear these sounds more easily? Discuss loudness and pitch.

Explain to the children that they are going to test loudness and pitch to see if they have an effect on how easily we can hear sounds. They are also going to find out which materials we can hear sound through.

Provide the children with the cassette player and cassette and the pitched instrument. Discuss how to use the cassette player correctly. Try out the instrument. How do you make a note louder? How do you change the pitch? Use the cassette first. Ask some of the children to take the cassette player and go into the next room, closing the door. Ask them to play the music with the volume on '1' first. Can the other children hear the music while standing behind the closed door? If they can, ask them to walk slowly away from the door until they can no longer hear it. Measure the distance between them and the door. Continue in the same way, changing the volume control until the music is playing at its loudest level. Ask the children to record the distances each time.

After this activity has been completed, bring the children together again as a class. What did they find out? At what distance away could the loudest music still be heard? Did this vary between different people? How many times did they check their results? How did they record the activity? Compare the methods used.

Explain that you would like them to try out the pitched instrument in the same way by playing a soft low note, a loud low note, a soft high note and a loud high note. Can the children predict what will happen? Why?

When this activity has been completed, bring the children together again to discuss their findings. Were the results as expected? Can high-pitched notes be heard more clearly than low notes? Can you think of an everyday use for this? (For example, high-pitched emergency sirens.)

The children could then go on to test how well sounds travel through a glass window and a solid wall. Ask them to predict first which material they think sounds will travel through best. Were the results as expected? What differences were there in the results for all three materials tested (door, window and wall)? Which material does the sound travel through most easily? Can the children explain why? Which material does not let sound through very well?

Discuss the children's recording methods. Did they use tables? How clear are these? How could they improve their recording methods? How could they improve the investigation if it were repeated?

Suggestion(s) for extension

The variation in distance travelled (before the sound can no longer be heard) with change in volume could be presented in a graph for each material tested (door, window, wall). More accurate comparisons could then be made between the different materials.

Suggestion(s) for support

Act as scribe if necessary when the children are recording, or appoint a more able child as a group scribe. Check that the children are measuring accurately, and help with measuring if necessary. Remind the children to check their measurements several times to ensure accuracy.

Assessment opportunities

This activity will enable you to assess how well the children can record a task and how accurately they can use measuring equipment. It will also enable you to find out if the children understand the differences between a low- and a high-pitched sound. The activity requires a lot of co-operation, as the children need to split into two groups and to work out ways of helping and communicating with each other. Hence you will be able to assess how well the children work together as a group.

Opportunities for IT

Children could make more quantitative measurements of the amount of sound passing through different materials, using a microphone attached to the computer. The waveform patterns created by the software could be used as a guide to the volume of sound and when the sound is no longer audible. It will be interesting to compare the point at which children can no longer detect the sound but the microphone can, or vice versa. This might be used to focus attention on the sensitivity of the ear.

Display ideas

Paint large pictures of a door, a window and a wall and attach them to the wall to make large lift-up flaps. Make a large heading saying: 'How well can sound be heard through these things?' Mount the children's science work underneath each picture, so people have to lift the flaps to find out the answer to the question.

Other aspects of the Science PoS covered

Experimental and Investigative Science – 1a, b, c; 2a, b, c; 3a, b, c, d, e.

HOW WE HEAR

Our ears are used to detect sounds.

Pairs.

45–60 minutes.

Previous skills/knowledge needed

Sounds are made when things vibrate.

Key background information

The outer part of the human ear helps to channel sound waves into the ear. The vibrations meet a thin, tightly stretched membrane called the *ear drum*. The ear drum then vibrates, and the vibrations are amplified by three tiny bones in the middle ear (the *hammer*, the *anvil* and the *stirrup*). The vibrations then reach the inner ear, which has a long coiled tube called the *cochlea*. The cochlea is filled with fluid and has a membrane which has tiny receptor cells on it. These cells translate the vibrations into nerve impulses which are sent to the brain, where they are interpreted as sounds. (See Figure 1.)

Having two ears helps us to locate the direction of a sound, because the sound will be heard more loudly (and very slightly earlier) in one ear than in the other. When a sound is directly in front or behind, the sound reaches both ears at the same time, making it difficult to locate.

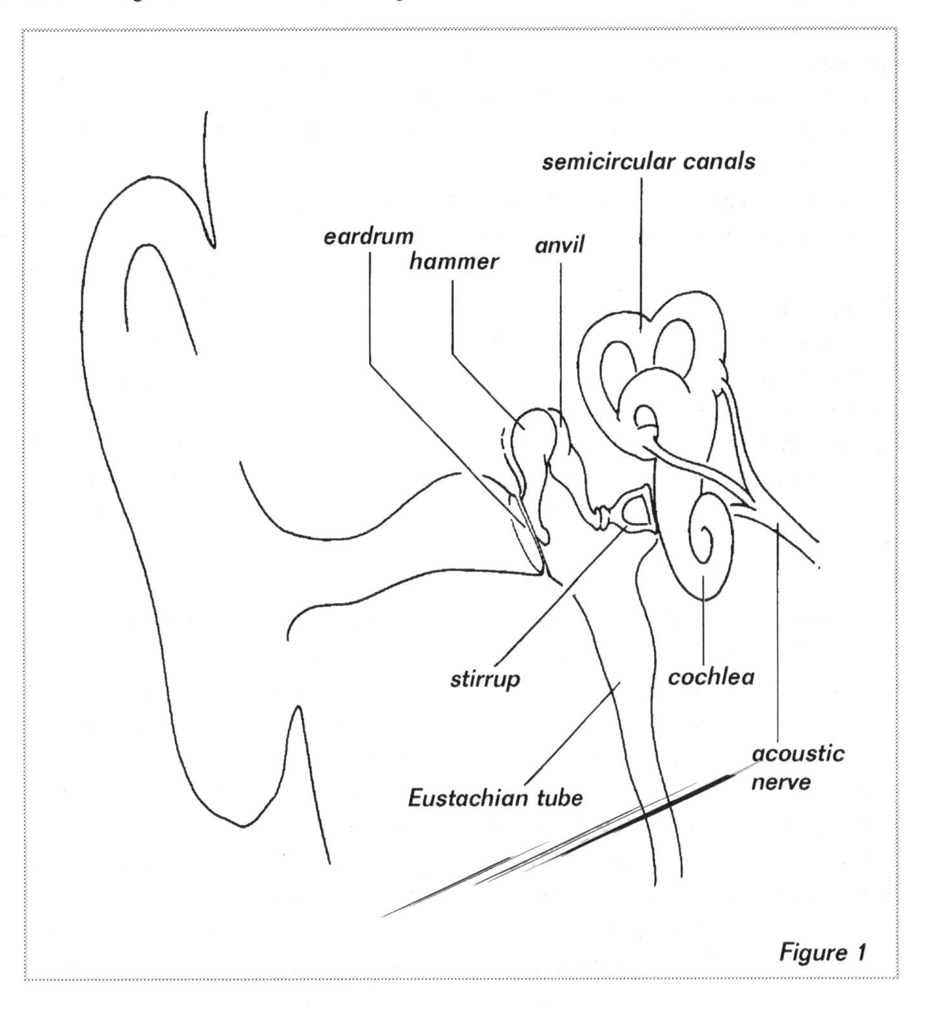

Figure 1

Preparation

The children will need a quiet area to work in and it may be best to organise the activity so that each pair of children takes it in turns to go to this quiet area to work. An extra helper may be required to supervise the children in the quiet area. Sensitive handling will be necessary for children with impaired hearing.

Resources needed

A jar with a screw-top lid, rice, paper, a pencil, a quiet area for the children to work in.

What to do

Explain to the children that they are going to find out more about how we hear. Ask them to tell you why they think we have two ears and not just one. How would our hearing be affected if we were deaf in one ear? How do colds affect our hearing?

Tell the children that they are going to find out how good they are at detecting the direction of sounds. This part of the activity will need to be carried out in the quiet area. Give one member of each pair the container filled with rice, and a pencil and some paper to record what happens. Tell the other child to sit on a chair with his eyes closed. Ask this child to detect the direction of the sound made by the shaker by pointing in the direction he thinks it is coming from. The first child should stand a distance away and, moving very quietly, shake the container first to the left of the seated child, then centrally, then to the right. She should then record whether her partner guessed the direction of the sound correctly in each case.

The children could then change places and record the results again. They could also try covering up each ear in turn with their hand and repeating the experiment, to see what effect this has on the results.

When all the children have completed the task, bring the whole class together to discuss the results. How accurately could they detect the sounds? When was it most difficult to detect the direction? Can the children explain why? Compare the results using both ears with those using only one ear. How do they differ? How important is it to have both ears working well? What dangers might there be if one or both of our ears are not functioning well?

Discuss the recording methods used. How did the children record the results? Did they repeat any of the observations to check them? Which recording method worked best? What can they conclude from the activity?

Suggestion(s) for extension

Repeat the activity, taking distance into account. Try the shaker at one-metre intervals away from the child listening, until he can no longer hear the sound. Does the accuracy with which the direction of sounds can be detected vary with distance?

Suggestion(s) for support

Pair up a more able child with a less able child if recording problems are likely. Ensure the children are carrying out the activity correctly by supervising the first recordings.

Assessment opportunities

This activity will enable you to assess the children's recording methods, as well as how well the children co-operate in what may be an unsupervised activity.

Opportunities for IT

Children could use an encyclopaedic CD-ROM to find out more information about how the ear works. If this is a new activity, they may need to be shown how to set up a search and move around the CD-ROM, and how to print out their results or save them to a disk for later use in a word processor.

Display ideas

Make three large drawings of ears. Place two ears together on one side of a wall display and the other ear on the other side. Mount the children's results from testing two ears and those from testing one ear on the appropriate side of the wall. Make a large heading: 'How good are your ears?'

Other aspects of the Science PoS covered

Experimental and Investigative Science – 1a, c; 2a, b, c; 3a, b, c, e.

The Earth and beyond

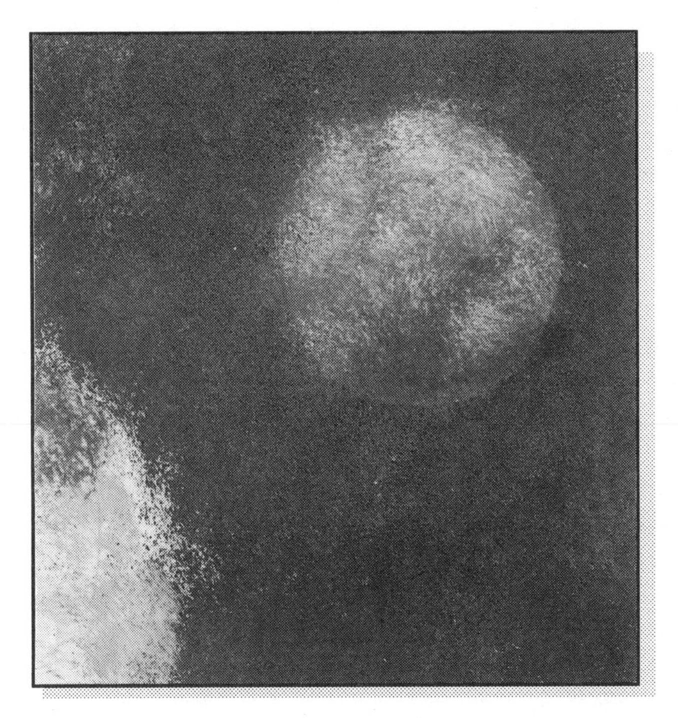

The activities in this section of the book encourage the children to explore everyday phenomena such as day and night and the formation of shadows related to the Sun's apparent movements across the sky. They also introduce the broader concepts of understanding the Earth's relationship with the Moon and the Sun.

In the course of carrying out the activities, the children will gain experience in questioning, observing, predicting, recording, measuring and drawing conclusions. They will also have opportunities to work co-operatively and to share their ideas with others.

The Earth, Moon and Sun are approximately spherical bodies. The Sun has a diameter of 1,392,530km and completely dwarfs both the Moon (diameter 3,476km) and the Earth (diameter 12,756km). The Earth is approximately 152,000,000km from the Sun. The Sun is essential for life on Earth. It provides us with heat and light and is the ultimate source of energy for our planet.

The Earth spins round on its own axis once every 24 hours, giving rise to day and night. The Earth also moves in an orbit around the Sun. One orbit takes a year to complete and gives rise to the different seasons. The Moon's orbit of the Earth takes approximately 28 days and gives us the familiar phases of the Moon.

EARTH, MOON AND SUN

The Earth, Moon and Sun are separate, spherical bodies.

Whole class.

45–60 minutes.

▲ *Explain to the children the importance of not leaving the school grounds (during this activity).*

Previous skills/knowledge needed

None specifically required for this activity.

Key background information

The Earth, Moon and Sun are approximately spherical in shape. The Earth has a slight 'bulge' at the equator and is about 12,756km (7,913 miles) in diameter. It is surrounded by an atmosphere about 400km deep.

People have not always thought that the Earth was a sphere – many ancient peoples thought it was flat. The Ancient Greeks were probably the first to believe that the Earth was round, because they noticed that the shadow of the Earth during eclipses of the Moon was round and that when ships sailed away from the land, the hull would be seen to disappear first and then the masts. Today, the most obvious evidence we have for believing the Earth is a sphere are photographs taken of it from space.

The Sun has a diameter of 1,392,530km (865,134 miles) and the Moon has a diameter of 3,476km (2,171 miles). The Earth is approximately 152,000,000km (93,000,000 miles) from the Sun and the Moon is approximately 384,622km (240,388 miles) from the Earth. The Moon reflects light from the Sun – it does not produce light.

Preparation

Make three card models of the Sun, Earth and Moon, using the following rough scale: 1mm = 4,880km.

▲ Sun – circle with a diameter of 286mm

▲ Earth – circle with a diameter of 2.6mm

▲ Moon – circle with a diameter of 1mm

Choose a suitable site in the school grounds to carry out part of this activity.

Resources needed

Books containing colour pictures of the Earth seen from space, spherical objects, a globe, card models as described above, a trundle wheel, a large open space (such as a field or playground).

What to do

Ask the children to tell you what they think the shape of the Earth is. How do they know this? Explain to them that many years ago, people thought the Earth was flat. Tell them that today, we have photographs taken of the Earth from space which show us that the Earth is a sphere.

What other objects do the children know which are spheres? Show the children some spherical objects and talk about their shape. Show the children a colour photograph of the Earth in a book. What are the blue, brown and white areas in the photograph?

How do we know that the Moon is round? How do we know what the surface of the Moon is like? Discuss how humans have landed on the Moon and taken samples.

Show the children the globe and relate the blue and brown areas seen in the photograph to the equivalent areas on the globe. Find where the children live on the globe and move the globe around, imagining they are on a journey starting from this place and going round the world. What places would they pass by?

Do the children know how large the Earth is? Which is the biggest – the Earth, the Moon or the Sun? Tell the children the diameter of each one and show them the card models to compare their sizes. Make sure you remind the children that these models are flat and that the real bodies are spheres. How far away is the Earth from the Sun? Tell the children they can get an idea of this by taking the models outside and measuring the approximate distance, using a scale of 1 metre = 1 million kilometres. Ask one child to hold the Sun model, then ask two other children to take the Earth model and measure out 150m from the Sun model using the trundle wheel. (The field or playground may not be large enough, but this will give the children a good idea of the scale of the distances involved.)

Suggestion(s) for extension

Ask the children to make papier mâché models of the Sun, Earth and Moon, using a suitable scale to compare their sizes.

Suggestion(s) for support

Make sure the children understand what a sphere is by using tennis balls and other items as examples. Compare these with flat, round shapes. Assist with measuring the distance outside if necessary.

Assessment opportunities

The discussion at the beginning of the lesson about the shapes of the Earth, Moon and Sun will enable you to assess how well the children understand this concept.

Opportunities for IT

Children could use an encyclopaedic CD-ROM (or one on the theme of space) to find out more information about the Earth, Moon or Sun. If this is a new activity, they may need to be shown how to set up a search and move around the CD-ROM, and how to print out their results or save them to a disk for later use in a word processor.

Different groups of children could be asked to research different aspects from the CD-ROM. If the children download text from the CD-ROM, it is important that they are shown how to put this text into a word processor and then to edit it to present the information they want in a form which is appropriate for them and their audience.

This activity might be used to introduce children to some of the editing and organising commands on the word processor, such as *cut and paste* or *drag and drop*, to move parts of the text around the screen. Children could then present their work for a classroom display or booklet, selecting appropriate fonts, styles and formats.

Display ideas

Make three-dimensional papier mâché models of the Earth, Moon and Sun. The models could be painted using appropriate colours. Hang these from the ceiling in front of a wall display showing photographs of the Earth from space and information about the Sun, Earth and Moon.

Other aspects of the Science PoS covered

Experimental and Investigative Science – 2a, b; 3b.

TRACKING THE SUN

The position of the Sun appears to change throughout the day.

Small groups or whole class.

20 minutes discussion. 5-minute observations three or four times during the day.

Warn the children of the dangers of looking directly at the Sun, as permanent damage to the eyes can occur. Ask the children to shade their eyes and look to one side of the Sun instead. Explain the importance of not leaving the school grounds (during this activity).

Previous skills/knowledge needed

The Sun is a separate spherical body.

Key background information

The position of the Sun appears to change throughout the day because the Earth is rotating on its axis. One complete rotation takes 24 hours. The Earth rotates from west to east, making the Sun appear (in the northern hemisphere) to rise in the east and set in the west. The height of the Sun varies because the Earth's axis is tilted. It looks low in the morning, high in the middle of the day and low again in the evening.

Preparation

This activity needs to be carried out on a sunny day. Select a place on the south side of the school where the Sun can be seen without obstruction during the day. Place a marker cone or flag in a fixed position and do not move this during the day.

Resources needed

Pencils, paper, clipboards, a marker cone or flag, a globe.

What to do

Take the children out to the marked place early in the morning and ask them to draw an outline of some of the things they can see from this spot. Then ask the children to mark on the drawing the approximate position of the Sun in relation to the objects drawn. Ask them to write down the time underneath the position of the Sun on their drawing. Then ask them to predict where the Sun might be in an hour's time. What do they base their prediction on?

Make three or four more observations throughout the day, marking the position of the Sun each time. Make sure the children stand in the same spot each time when viewing. Were their earlier predictions correct? Has the Sun changed position as expected?

After the children have completed their observations, discuss what they have found out. How did the position of the Sun change throughout the day? When was the Sun lowest/highest in the sky? Is it likely that the Sun will be in the same positions at the same times tomorrow? Will the

Sun's position change throughout the year? Can the children explain why?

Ask the children to tell you why they think the position of the Sun changes throughout the day. What causes this to happen? Tell the children that the Sun only *appears* to move across the sky, but it is actually the Earth that is moving. Show the children the globe and slowly turn it from west to east, explaining that the Earth spins on its axis from west to east each day. Do the children know how long it takes for the Earth to spin round once? Ask the children to stand up and turn slowly from west to east. They should notice that their surroundings appear to turn in the opposite direction. Tell the children that this is why, as the Earth turns from west to east, the Sun *appears* to move from east to west.

Finally, ask the children to write down an explanation of why the Sun's position in the sky appears to change throughout the day. Ask them to add this writing to their drawings.

Suggestion(s) for extension

If possible, the children could repeat the activity throughout the year. They could then compare the position of the Sun at the same time of day during different seasons. What would be the reason for any variation in the Sun's position?

Suggestion(s) for support

Provide the children with a drawing of the area seen from the marked position if they have limited drawing skills. Help the children decide where to mark in the Sun on their drawings, if necessary. Write down the children's explanations if their writing skills are limited.

Assessment opportunities

The children's predictions about the height and position of the Sun will provide you with an insight into what they already know about this topic. The children's written work will help you assess how much they have understood from the discussion, and can be a useful starting-point for further discussions with individuals.

Opportunities for IT

Children could record their results using a simple graphics package, creating a pictorial representation of the position of the sun during the day. This would provide an opportunity to introduce some basic drawing commands such as creating circles, filling them with colour, duplicating the shape and moving it into different positions. Text could be added, and a timeline placed at the top or bottom of the picture.

Display ideas

Mount the children's observational drawings and pieces of writing about the 'movement' of the Sun on the wall. Make a large picture of a Sun to add to the display, together with the heading: 'Does the Sun move?'

Other aspects of the Science PoS covered

Experimental and Investigative Science – 1b; 2b; 3b, c, d.

SHADOW CHANGES

Shadows change as the position of the Sun appears to change throughout the day.

Small groups or whole class.

20 minutes discussion. 5-minute observations at hourly intervals throughout the day.

Warn the children of the dangers of looking directly into a light source, particularly the Sun. Explain to them the importance of not leaving the school grounds (during this activity).

Previous skills/knowledge needed

The position of the Sun appears to change throughout the day.

Key background information

Opaque objects are objects which do not allow light to shine through them. Shadows appear behind opaque objects when light shines on them. This is because light travels in straight lines and cannot bend around the sides of objects.

Shadows are formed outside when light from the Sun strikes an opaque object. The lengths of shadows change throughout the day. This is due to the tilt of the Earth's axis. Long shadows are formed when the Sun is low in the sky. The shadows are longer because the Sun's rays hit the Earth more obliquely. Shorter shadows are formed in the middle of the day, when the Sun is higher in the sky.

Shadow sticks can be used to track the position of the Sun every hour and can thus be used to tell the time.

Preparation

Bang a large nail into a piece of wood with a sheet of white paper on it. (See Figure 1.)

The activity needs to be carried out on a sunny day. Select a suitable place in the school grounds where the wood with the nail in it will be in sunshine all day.

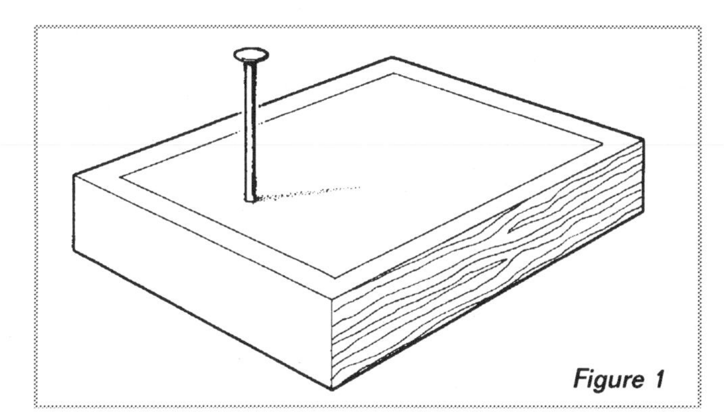

Figure 1

Resources needed

A piece of wood with a large nail, paper, pencils, a ruler, a torch.

What to do

Place the wood with the nail in it in the pre-selected place in the school grounds. Do not move the wood once it is in position. Ask the children to look at the shadow cast by the nail. Can they tell you why there is a shadow? What causes it?

Ask a child to trace the shadow on the piece of paper which is attached to the wood. Measure the length of the shadow and record this. Ask the children to check each other's measurements to see how accurate they are.

Can the children predict where the shadow will be in one hour's time? Do they think the shadow will be the same length, longer or shorter? Can they explain why?

Ask the children to look at the shadow stick once every hour during the day, and to trace the shadow and measure its length each time. Ask them to label each shadow with the time of the observation. At each visit, ask the children to predict what will happen to the shadow next time.

At the end of the day, remove the paper from the piece of wood and look at the drawings and measurements. What do the children notice? Why did the shadows move round? Why did the shadows change length? Could the shadow stick be used to tell the time? How accurate would it be? Would the shadows be different at different times of the year?

Discuss why the Sun appears to move across the sky each day. Use a torch to shine a beam of light on to a small object from above and from both sides. Compare the torch beam and the object to the Sun and the nail on the shadow stick. Demonstrate how the shadow is short when the torch light is overhead, and how the shadow becomes longer as the torch light is lowered. Ask the children to look out for shadows over the next few days to see when they are longest and shortest. Discuss what they find out.

Suggestion(s) for extension

Ask the children to draw a graph of the time and the length of the shadow cast by the shadow stick. At what times were the shadows shortest/longest?

Suggestion(s) for support

Help the children to measure the lengths of the shadows and to tell the time, if necessary.

Assessment opportunities

This activity will enable you to assess how accurately the children can measure. It will also enable you to assess how well they understand why shadows are formed.

Opportunities for IT

Children could measure the length of the shadow at different times of the day and plot their results using graph-plotting software to show how the shadow length changes during the day. They could use a word processor to record, explain and present their findings for a class display about the Sun and shadows.

This work could be extended to looking at shadow lengths at different times of the year and comparing the results. If the children have access to electronic mail through CAMPUS or the internet, they could ask for measurements from different parts of the world and compare the results at different latitudes.

Display ideas

Make a large heading, 'Changing shadows', to put on the wall above the piece of paper with the shadow stick markings. Ask the children to write about and draw how the nail forms a shadow and how the shadow changes throughout the day. Add this work to the wall display. Place some real sundials or pictures of sundials in books on a table in front of the display, together with the shadow stick the children used.

Other aspects of the Science PoS covered

Experimental and Investigative Science - 1a, b; 2b, c; 3b, c, d, e.
Physical Processes - 3a, b.

DAY AND NIGHT

Day and night are caused by the Earth spinning on its axis.

Whole class.

45–60 minutes.

Warn the children of the dangers of looking directly into a light source.

Previous skills/knowledge needed

The position of the Sun appears to change throughout the day.

Key background information

The Earth rotates on its axis, which is tilted at an angle of 23.5 degrees relative to the plane of its orbit, around the Sun. (The plane of this orbit is aligned with the North Star.) One complete rotation takes 24 hours. The Earth rotates from west to east, making the sky appear to move from east to west. The rotation gives rise to day and night; each place on the Earth is facing the Sun for part of the time (day) and facing away from the Sun for the remainder (night). The amount of time spent in day and night depends on the distance the place is from the equator, and on the season. At the equator, day and night are always exactly 12 hours long.

Preparation

A slightly darkened room is required for this activity. For the card figure, draw a person on card, about 3cm tall, then cut out the figure.

Resources needed

A globe, a projector or torch, Blu-Tack, a small card picture of a person, one copy per child of photocopiable page 136, pencils.

What to do

Ask the children to write down how they think day and night occur. What happens to the Sun at night-time? Discuss the children's ideas as a whole class. Do they all agree? Show the children the globe and explain that the Earth is actually tilted on what is called its *axis*. Show them how the Earth turns around slowly each day. Do the children know how long it takes for the Earth to turn around once? What effect does this turning have on the appearance of the Sun during the day? Discuss any previous work the children may have done on tracking the Sun and measuring the lengths of shadows using a shadow stick. Remind the children that the Earth spins from west to east, which makes the Sun and the stars appear to move from east to west.

In a slightly darkened room, shine the torch or projector on the globe. What do the children notice about where the light falls? Which side has light? Which side is in darkness? Why does this happen?

Next, mark the position of a place on the Earth by attaching the card person with some Blu-Tack. Turn the globe very slowly anticlockwise. What happens to the amount of light the person receives? When is the person in light/darkness? Tell the children that this is how day and night arise. When it is daytime in one part of the world, it is night-time in other parts. (See Figure 1.)

Turn the globe slowly again. When do the children think the Sun would be directly overhead in relation to the card person? When would the Sun be getting low in the sky? Relate this to the lengths of the shadows seen during the day.

Now provide the children with photocopiable sheet 136, and ask them to work on the activities individually or in pairs.

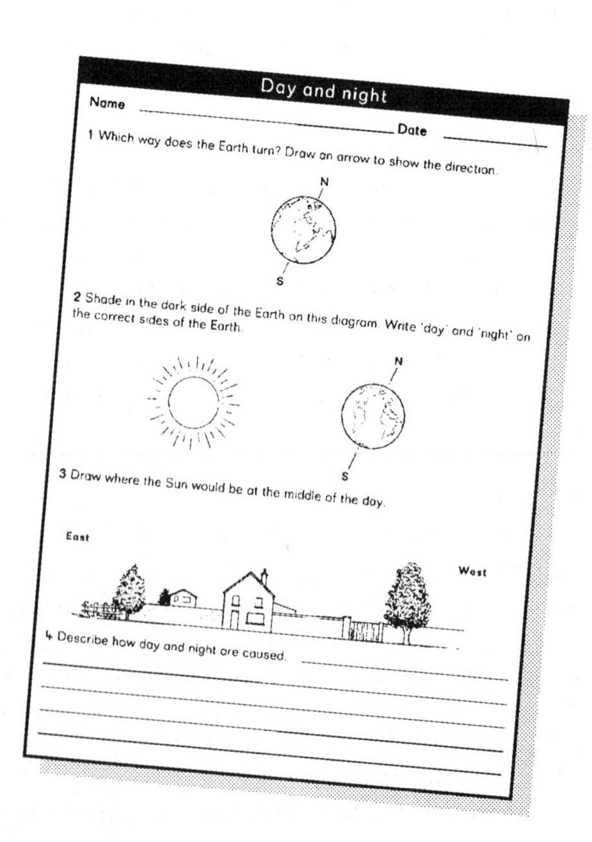

Day and night

Name ______ Date ______

1 Which way does the Earth turn? Draw an arrow to show the direction.

N
S

2 Shade in the dark side of the Earth on this diagram. Write 'day' and 'night' on the correct sides of the Earth.

N
S

3 Draw where the Sun would be at the middle of the day.

East
West

4 Describe how day and night are caused. ______

Figure 1

When they have completed the sheet, discuss the children's answers. Use the globe and torch or projector again, if necessary, to demonstrate the answers.

Suggestion(s) for extension

Ask the children to place two or three card people at different points on the globe. Turn the globe and ask questions such as: Who would have night first? Who would have the shortest day? Who would have the most sunshine?

Suggestion(s) for support

Act as scribe if necessary when the children are writing their initial ideas about day and night. Pair up a more able writer with a less able one when they are completing the activity sheet; or if the children are working individually, tell them you will help them read the questions and write the answers if necessary. Provide extra time for a small group to work with the globe and projector if they are having trouble grasping the basic ideas.

Assessment opportunities

The piece of writing completed at the beginning of the lesson will provide you with a valuable insight into what the children already know about the causes of day and night. The writing can be used for more detailed discussions with individual children, either during the lesson or at a later date. By comparing the children's writing with the answers given on the photocopiable sheet, you will be able to assess whether or not the lesson has corrected any misconceptions the children had. The photocopiable sheet should not only provide you with an insight into how much the children have understood from the lesson, but could also be used again at a later date to assess retention of knowledge.

Display ideas

Make two large murals of a scene in the daytime and in the night-time. Mount these on the wall. Make a large heading: 'What causes day and night?' Draw or paint a picture showing the Earth and the Sun, with half the world in light and the other half dark. Place this drawing in the middle of the two murals, such that the half of the world in light is next to the daytime picture and the dark half is next to the night-time picture. Add the children's writing about how day and night are caused.

Other aspects of the Science PoS covered

Experimental and Investigative Science – 2b; 3b, c.

Reference to photocopiable sheet

For answers to questions 1, 2 and 3, see Figure 2. Answer to question 4: Day and night are caused by the Earth spinning on its axis. When a place is in the light of the Sun, it is daytime; when it is away from the Sun, it is night-time.

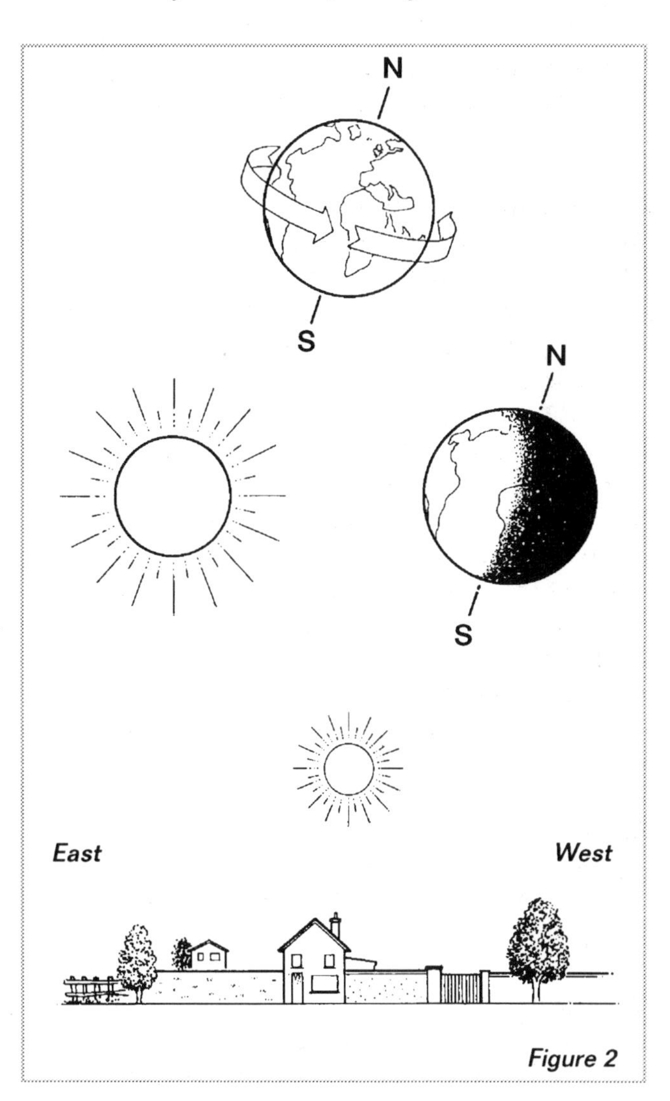

Figure 2

WORLD TIME

The Earth's rotation causes time differences between different parts of the world.

Small groups.

30–45 minutes.

Warn the children of the dangers of looking directly into a light source. Care should be taken when handling the pins.

Previous skills/knowledge needed

The position of the Sun appears to change throughout the day. Shadows change as the position of the Sun appears to change. Day and night are caused by the Earth spinning on its axis.

Key background information

The Earth spins on its axis, rotating 360 degrees during 24 hours. This means the Earth spins through 15 degrees every hour. At any place on Earth, there is a time of day when the Sun is directly overhead, called midday or noon. As you move from east to west, the occurrence of (physical) noon changes such that at any particular point in time, the time of day it is varies continuously. In order to simplify this, we divide the Earth into *time zones* – every place in one time zone has the same time of day. There are 24 time zones, so each zone differs from the next by one hour. The time zones are calculated from the prime meridian at Greenwich, England. When you travel east from the prime meridian, you add an hour; when you travel west, you subtract an hour.

Preparation

This activity should be carried out on a sunny day. Alternatively, a torch could be used to model the Sun, and the activity be carried out indoors.

Resources needed

A torch, pins, a tennis ball, one copy per child of photocopiable page 137, pencils, a globe.

What to do

Use the globe to remind children about the tilt of the Earth's axis and how the Earth rotates around its axis. Do the children know what this rotation gives rise to on the Earth? Shine the torch on to the globe to demonstrate how one half of the Earth is in light and the other half is in darkness.

Now ask the children to stick a pin into a tennis ball and either go outside in the sunshine, or use a torch to shine a light on the ball. Can they see the shadow cast by the pin? What happens to this shadow if the ball is slowly turned around, keeping the light in the same position? Now ask the children to stick in another pin, in the same 'hemisphere' but in a different place. What difference do they notice between the shadows of the two pins? Ask them to try the pin in different places to see how the lengths of the shadows produced vary.

Angle the ball so that one of the pins has the light directly overhead ('midday'). Now turn the ball slowly so that the other pin is at midday. Use this demonstration as the basis for a discussion on how the time difference between two places in the world depends on the difference in *latitude* (that is, the proportion of the Earth's rotation measured as an angle) between them.

Tell the children to try and imagine themselves at a spot on the Earth at noon. If they walked east and the Earth were slowly rotating, tell them, the next place they walked to would have its noon about one or two minutes later, and so on as they continued to walk. What problems could this cause in a country? Discuss how much confusion would be caused if noon on clocks were allowed to differ minute by minute as you passed through a country from east to west.

Provide the children with photocopiable sheet 137, and explain how the world is divided into time zones such that each place in a zone is at the same time of day. Ask the children how long it takes for the Earth to revolve once. Explain that there are 24 time zones, so each one differs from the next by one hour. If the Earth turns through 360

World time zones

Name Date

1 Why do you think some of the time zone lines are not straight?

2 How many degrees does the Earth turn in one hour?

3 How long does it take for the Earth to turn one degree?

4 If it is noon in Greenwich, what time is it in these places?

Paris Rome

Tokyo Sydney

degrees in 24 hours, how many degrees would it turn through in one hour? Ask the children to use this information to work out the answers to the questions on the photocopiable sheet. Discuss the answers with the children once they have completed the task.

Suggestion(s) for extension
Ask the children to write a leaflet for some visiting extraterrestrials explaining why the world is divided into time zones.

Suggestion(s) for support
Point out the differences in the lengths of the shadows made by the pins on the tennis ball, if the children cannot see these for themselves. Discuss why the lengths are different. Keep trying the pins in different places to look at the effects on the shadows, until the children grasp the idea. Provide opportunities for the children to discuss and share their ideas when completing the worksheet.

Assessment opportunities
Discussions with the children as they are exploring the lengths of the pins' shadows on the tennis ball will enable you to assess how well they have understood the ideas presented to them.

Opportunities for IT
Children could use a word processor or desktop publisher to write a leaflet explaining about the different time zones in the world. A world map, taken from clipart or from a suitable CD-ROM, could be included in the leaflet.

Display ideas
Draw a Sun and an Earth with two people drawn on different parts of the Earth where they cast different-length shadows. Mount these on the wall and write an explanation of why the length of the shadow is different at each place. Ask the children to write about their observations of the tennis ball and pins, and add this to the display.

Other aspects of the Science PoS covered
Experimental and Investigative Science – 1a; 2b, c; 3b, c, e.

Reference to photocopiable sheet
The answers are as follows.

1. Some of the time zone lines are not straight because they follow country boundaries. This ensures that as far as possible, the time is the same throughout the two countries concerned. Some countries are so large that they have more than one time zone.

2. The Earth turns through 15 degrees in one hour.

3. It takes the Earth four minutes to turn one degree.

4. The times would be: Paris 12 noon; Rome 1 pm; Tokyo 9 pm; Sydney 10 pm.

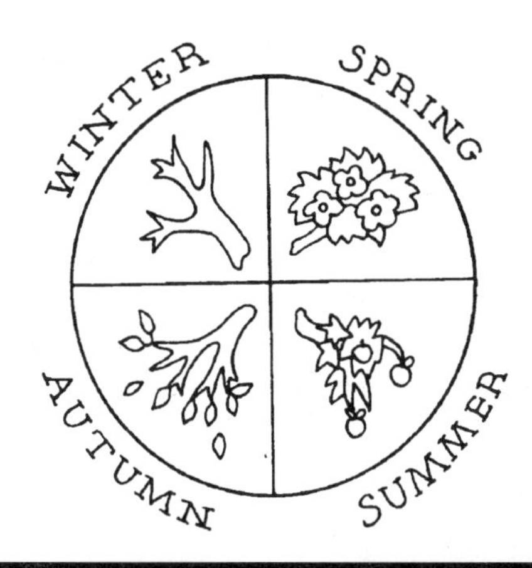

EARTH'S ORBIT

Day length varies according to the time of year and position on the Earth.

Whole class or small groups.

45–60 minutes.

Warn the children of the dangers of looking directly into a light source.

Previous skills/knowledge needed
The Earth and the Sun are separate, spherical bodies. The Earth spins on its axis.

Key background information
The Earth moves around the Sun in an almost circular orbit, taking 365 days to do so. A year is defined as the time taken for the Earth to make one complete orbit. The Earth's axis is tilted at an angle of 23.5 degrees. The axis always points in the same direction in space as the Earth follows its course around the Sun. This gives rise to the seasons and the associated variations in day length and height of the Sun in the sky. In December, the North Pole is tilted at its greatest angle away from the Sun, bringing winter to the northern hemisphere. In June, the North Pole is tilted at its least angle away from the Sun, bringing summer to the northern hemisphere. The reverse is true in the southern hemisphere. (See Figure 1.)

The *solstice* refers to either of the two days of the year when the Sun is furthest from the equator. The summer solstice (northern hemisphere) occurs when the Sun is furthest north from the equator on about June 21st. This marks the beginning of summer in the northern hemisphere (despite being also known as Midsummer's Day), and has the longest period of daylight of any day in the year. The winter solstice occurs when the Sun is furthest south from the equator on about December 22nd. This marks the beginning of winter in the northern hemisphere, and has the shortest period of daylight.

Preparation
Make a large diagram of the seasons illustration in Figure 1. Make the card figure (3cm tall) from the card.

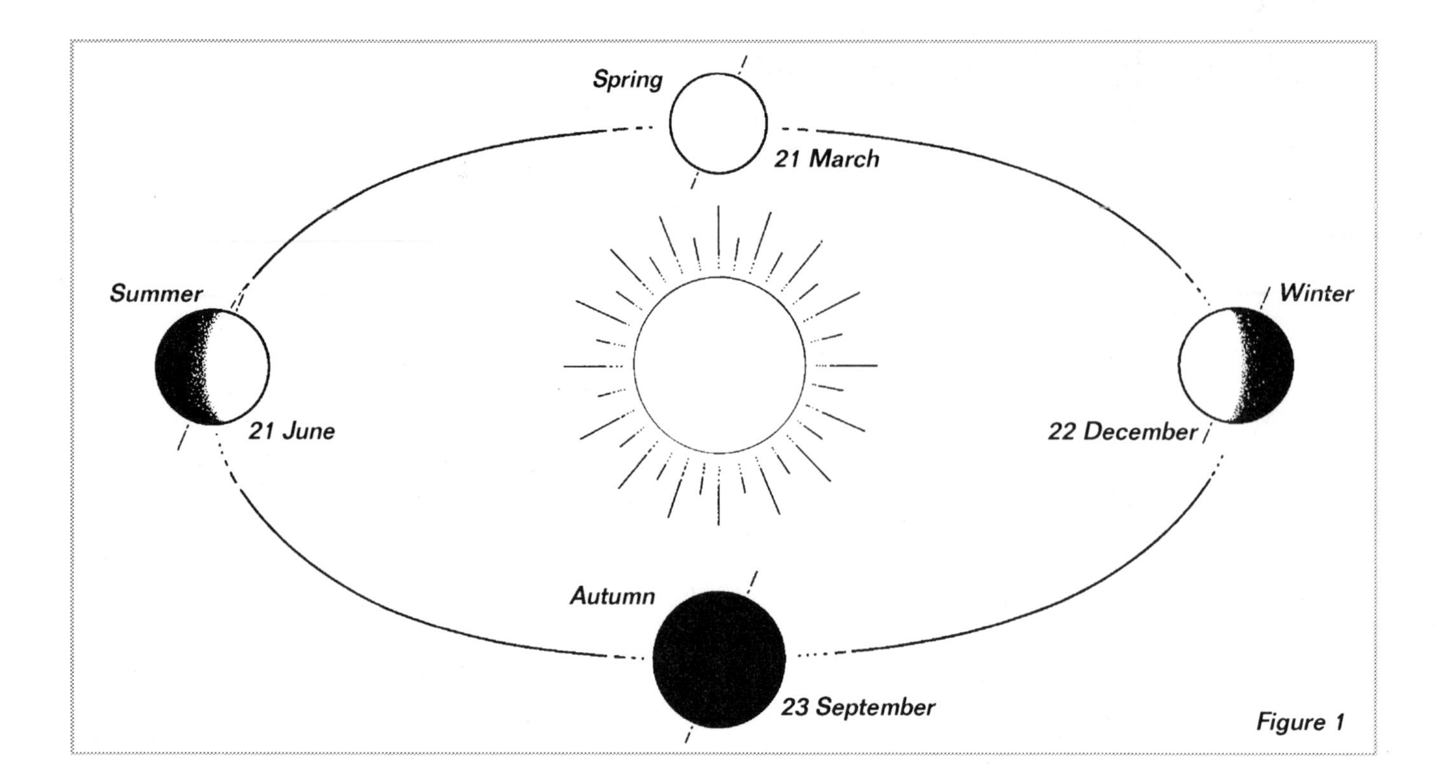

Figure 1

Resources needed
A globe, an electric lamp without a shade, Blu-Tack, a small card figure, a diagram of the seasons.

What to do
Ask the children to tell you at what time of year the daytime is longest. When is it shortest? Can the children suggest why this is? Tell them that they are going to use a globe to find out. Show the children the globe and remind them that the Earth spins on an axis which is tilted at the same angle all the time. Remind them that the Earth takes 24 hours to spin round once.

Place the globe on the floor, about a metre away from a lamp which is also on the floor. If the globe is not tilted, ask a child to tilt the globe gently away from the lamp. Call this direction *north*. The lamp's bulb needs to be about the same height as the middle of the globe. Which part of the globe is receiving light? (You may need to darken the room to see the light clearly.) Slowly turn the globe to observe what happens on different parts of the surface. Attach the card figure to the globe in the northern hemisphere using Blu-Tack. Look at the shadow cast. Turn the globe slowly to watch the changes in the shadow length during a 'day'.

Move the globe to each of the other three positions (as in Figure 1) around the lamp, keeping the tilt of the Earth in the same direction each time. Look at how much of the globe receives light each time. Look at the differences in the length of the card figure's shadow. Show the children the diagram of the seasons for the northern hemisphere. Explain how the tilt of the Earth's axis and the position of the Earth in its orbit around the Sun causes differences in day length.

Suggestion(s) for extension
Ask the children to use the globe and lamp to work out the time of year when the North Pole has daylight for 24 hours and the time when it has night for 24 hours. Work out the times of year of the seasons for the southern hemisphere. Discuss what life might be like in the Arctic Circle during the periods of 24 hours of darkness and light.

Suggestion(s) for support
Allow those children who need it to use the globe and lamp several more times to look at the position of the Earth in relation to the Sun as it moves in its orbit. Talk through what is happening in the northern hemisphere each time, so the children understand how the length of day and seasons change. If necessary, correct the misconception that summer is due to the Earth being closer to the Sun.

Assessment opportunities
You will be able to assess how well the children understand the ideas presented through individual and group discussions as the lesson progresses.

Display ideas
Mount the large diagram of the seasons on the wall. Ask the children to write about and draw how the seasons arise due to the Earth's orbit around the Sun. Add this work to the display, together with pictures or drawings showing the different seasons.

Other aspects of the Science PoS covered
Experimental and Investigative Science – 2a, b; 3b.

THE MOON

The Moon orbits the Earth.

Whole class.

45–60 minutes.

Warn the children of the dangers of looking directly into a light source.

Previous skills/knowledge needed
The Earth, Moon and Sun are separate, spherical bodies.

Key background information
The Moon is a satellite of the Earth – it is not a planet. The Moon is approximately 385,000km away from the Earth and has a diameter of 3,476km. It takes approximately 28 days to orbit the Earth, and always keeps the same face towards the Earth. The 'dark' side of the Moon has only been seen by orbiting and landing spacecraft. The Moon does not emit light itself; it reflects the light of the Sun. The amount of light reflected depends on where the Moon is in its orbit. The apparent movement of the Moon across the sky is caused by the rotation of the Earth on its axis. Humans first landed on the Moon in 1969. The phases of the Moon are shown in Figure 1.

Preparation
Prepare a large drawing of the illustration showing the phases of the Moon in Figure 1. The activity should be carried out in a darkened room.

Resources needed
A projector, a tennis ball, pictures of the Moor
of the phases of the Moon.

What to do
Ask the children to tell you what they know about the Moon. How have they found out this information? Do they know when humans first landed on the Moon? What is the surface of the Moon like? Show the children some pictures of the Moon. Explain that its surface has hills, mountains, flat areas called plains and circular features called craters. Tell them how far away the Moon is from Earth, and that the diameter of the Moon is roughly the same as the distance across Australia.

Discuss how the Moon's appearance changes. Do the children know why this happens? Explain that the Moon does not emit its own light, but that it reflects the light of the Sun back to the Earth. Tell the children that they are going to try out a demonstration showing how the Moon goes through the various phases.

In a darkened room, turn on the projector. Ask a child to stand a good distance in front of the projector and hold a tennis ball just above her head. Tell the child that her head represents the Earth, the ball the Moon and the projector the Sun. Explain to the children that the Moon takes about 28 days to go round the Earth. To represent this, the child can slowly turn anticlockwise on the spot. What happens to the amount of light falling on the Moon as she turns? Allow as many children as possible to view or try out this

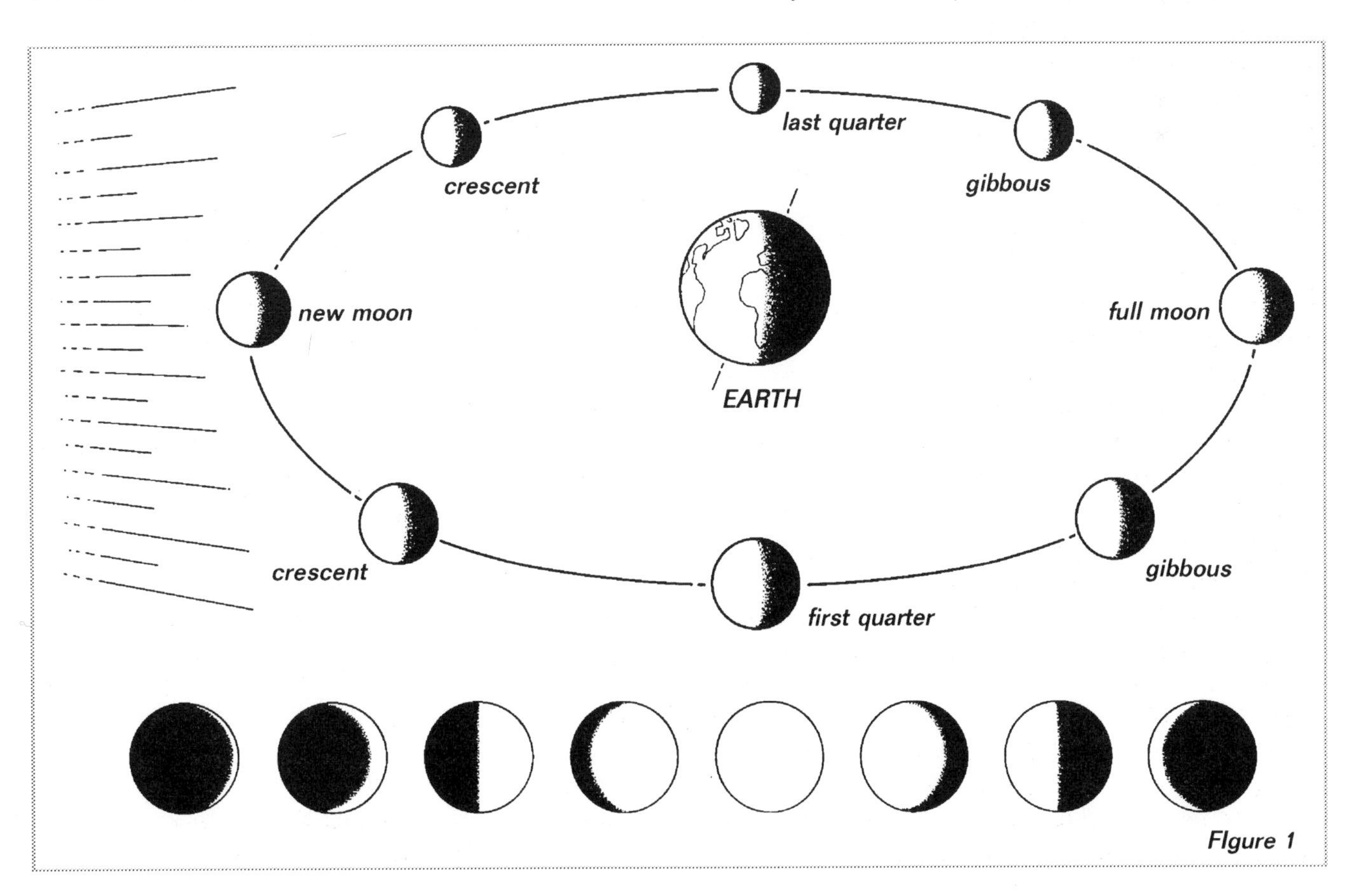

Figure 1

demonstration, so that they can all see the effect. Tell the children that the Moon always shows the same 'face' to the Earth. This can be represented by putting a mark on the ball.

Show the children the diagram of the phases of the Moon. Relate this to the demonstration. Go through each phase, asking a child to demonstrate using the ball and projector.

Suggestion(s) for extension
Ask the children to watch the Moon over several months and to keep a diary of their 'Moon watches'. What dates were noted for the start and end of each phase? How long did it take between one full moon and the next?

Suggestion(s) for support
Make sure those children who find the concept of the phases of the Moon difficult to understand have several chances to try out the demonstration. Talk them through each phase: Where is the light coming from? Why can it be seen from the Earth? At each quarter of a turn, ask: How much of the Moon can be seen now? How much is in shadow?

Assessment opportunities
You will be able to assess how well the children have grasped the idea of the Moon orbiting the Earth through discussions with individuals while they are carrying out or watching the demonstration.

Opportunities for IT
Children could use an encyclopaedic or space CD-ROM to find out more information about the Moon. If this is a new activity, they may need to be shown how to set up a search and move around the CD-ROM and how to print out their results or save them to a disk for use in a word processor.

If the children download text from the CD-ROM, it is important that they are shown how to put this text into a word processor and then to edit it in order to present the information they want in a form which is appropriate for them and their audience. The children may also need to be shown how to deal with pictures taken from the CD-ROM which they wish to use in their work.

This activity might be used to introduce the children to some of the editing and organising commands on the word processor, such as *cut and paste* or *drag and drop*, to move parts of the text around the screen. The children could then present their work for a classroom display or booklet, selecting appropriate fonts, styles and formats for their work.

The children could also create a multimedia display about the Moon, using suitable authoring software. They could divide the presentation up into different sections, such as Moon orbit, physical features, exploration of the Moon and phases of the Moon. The presentation could include text written by the children and pictures taken from clipart or CD-ROMs, drawn by the pupils and scanned into computer format, or created on a drawing or art package. If enough memory is available, children could even include short sequences of moving pictures taken from CD-ROMs or created using simple animation.

The teacher may want to set up the framework of the presentation in advance, creating a menu page and the links to the other sections. Children will need to be shown how to create new pages, create frames for their work, add text and pictures and then create the links to other pages.

Different groups could research and prepare information for their sections of the presentation. Each group could be given two or three pages and asked to design them on paper to show the information they have researched. They should then gather the resources together (pictures, text sounds, and so on) before starting work on the computer. Children will need support during this activity, especially if they are using facilities with which they are not familiar.

Display ideas
Mount some pictures of the Moon on the wall. Ask the children to write about and draw the phases of the Moon. Add this work to the wall display. Ask the children to make papier mâché models of the Earth and Moon to roughly the right scale. Hang these from the ceiling in front of the display.

Other aspects of the Science PoS covered
Experimental and Investigative Science – 1a; 2a, b, c; 3b, c, e.

Investigations

Scientific understanding involves knowledge of both the content of science and the methods by which that knowledge is obtained. Experimental and Investigative Science requires children to develop the intellectual and practical skills which will allow them to explore and investigate the world of science, and develop a fuller understanding of scientific phenomena, the nature of the theories explaining these phenomena and the procedures of scientific investigation. This should be achieved through activities that require a progressively more systematic and quantitative approach, developing and drawing on an increasing knowledge and understanding of science.

This section contains several activities which provide the children with an opportunity to plan and carry out investigations in which they:

▲ ask questions, predict and hypothesise;
▲ observe, measure and manipulate variables;
▲ interpret results and evaluate scientific evidence.

Within the context of their growing knowledge of physical processes, these activities will allow children to gain awareness both of the nature of scientific activity and of the basis on which scientific claims are made.

The activities here are necessarily more open-ended than those in other sections of the book, but guidance is given with regard to classroom management, the concepts likely to emerge and how you can use the activities for assessment purposes.

ELECTRICAL CIRCUITS

What could make a difference to the brightness of a bulb in a circuit?

Small groups or pairs.

60–120 minutes.

See safety guidelines on page 13.

Key background information

A complete circuit is needed to make electrical devices work. Electricity flows in one direction only. It flows from the negative end of a battery to the positive end. Initially, scientists thought that the flow was from positive to negative, and unfortunately this convention is still used when drawing circuit diagrams.

A *series circuit* is one in which electrical components such as light bulbs are connected in a line, one after the other. The amount of current in a series circuit is the same in both the outgoing and the returning wire. It can be measured using an ammeter. The brightness of the bulbs in a series circuit depends on the number of bulbs in the circuit (as well as the strength of the battery). This is because the bulbs offer resistance to the flow of electricity. The more bulbs there are in the circuit, the higher the resistance and the dimmer the bulbs will be. The same current goes through each bulb in turn, but two bulbs in a series circuit will be brighter than three or four bulbs in a series circuit because they offer less resistance. If one of the bulbs in a series circuit is unscrewed, all the bulbs will go out because the current cannot flow through the circuit.

Preparation

Ensure that all the electrical components to be used by the children are in working order before starting the investigation.

Resources needed

3.5V bulbs, 6V bulbs, bulb holders, 1.5V batteries, different sizes and lengths of insulated wire with the ends bare, adhesive tape, paper, pencils, small screwdrivers.

What to do

Provide each group/pair of children with a battery, a 3.5V bulb and holder, two pieces of insulated wire, a small screwdriver and some adhesive tape. Ask the children to tell you what the names of the items are. Do they know how to join them together to make the bulb light up? Allow the children time to do this. If they are finding it difficult to join the wires to the bulb holder, help them do this. Where do they think the bulb will go? Where do they think the wires will join on to the battery? Allow them time to try out things and eventually to make the bulb light up.

Ask the children to tell you what they have made (a circuit). Do they know how the electricity flows in the circuit? Where does it come from? Where does it go to? Discuss how the electricity flows in one direction only. Ask the children to tell you why they think the wire needs to be bare at the ends. Would the electricity flow if the plastic coating covered the ends? Try it and see. Explain that some materials allow electricity to flow through them and some do not. Which parts of the wire and bulb do the children think the electricity is flowing through in their circuit?

Now explain to the children that you want them to investigate what could make a difference to the brightness of a bulb in a circuit. Tell them that they can use circuits with more than one bulb in, and that they can use other batteries and wires if they need them.

Ask them to make some predictions first. Either ask the children to write down their ideas or act as scribe for the group. Which of their ideas do they want to test? If different children in the group want to test different things, perhaps the group could split into pairs for the investigation.

Discuss the investigation together as a group. How do they think they will do the investigation? What things will they need? How can they make it a fair test? What factors will need to be kept the same each time? What factor will change? How many times do they think they should test each idea? How will they record what they have done and their results? Are there any safety considerations to take into account? (Record sheets similar to those shown in Figure 1 could be used for this purpose.)

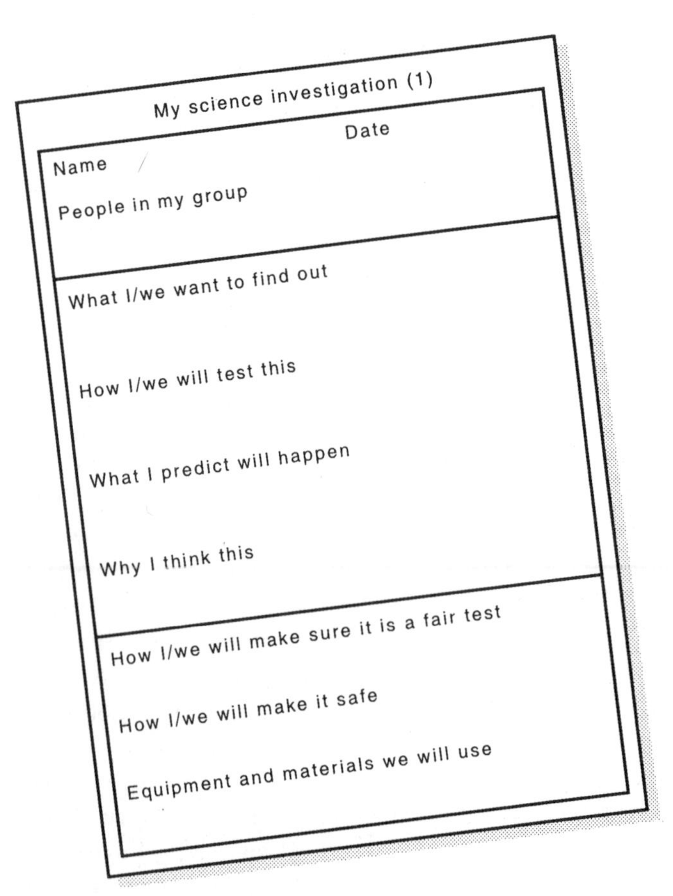

Figure 1

Ideas the children may decide to investigate could include:

- ▲ the number of bulbs in a circuit;
- ▲ the number of batteries in a circuit;
- ▲ the length of the wires;
- ▲ using different conductors in a circuit.

Observe the children as they carry out the investigation. Do they refer to their initial plan? Have they had to make any changes to their plan? Who decided on these changes? Are all members of the group participating? Have they remembered how to make it a fair test? How are they recording what happens?

After the investigation, talk to the children about what they have found out. Were the results what they had expected? Why/why not? What problems arose? How did they overcome them? Does their recording reflect what happened accurately? What factors have they found that affect the brightness of a bulb in a circuit? Why do they think these have an effect? Discuss this as a group.

Compare the results of all the groups in the class. How many different things were tried out? What conclusions can be drawn? What things could they try next?

Likely problems

Some children may have difficulty in deciding what to investigate. They may not have any ideas of their own what could affect the brightness of a bulb in a circuit. If this is the case, help them by joining up one bulb in a circuit and then joining up two bulbs in another circuit. What do they notice about the brightness of the bulbs in both circuits? Could the number of bulbs make a difference? Ask them to investigate this idea further.

If children are investigating the effect of the number of batteries, make sure the bulbs are of a high enough voltage to take the added current. 6V bulbs may be needed.

Sometimes one bulb in a series circuit may appear to be brighter than the others, which can cause great confusion. If this happens, swap the bright bulb with another bulb in the circuit: the normal result is that the brighter bulb has now moved position. This shows that the brighter bulb was not receiving more current than the others, but had a different resistance from the others. Check the metal thread on the bulbs for the specified voltage and current to make sure they are all the same. There may also be variations in the manufacture of the bulbs which can cause differences in brightness.

Sometimes a bulb may not be screwed very tightly into the bulb holder. This can create a dimmer bulb due to the poor connection. Make sure all the connections in the circuit are secure.

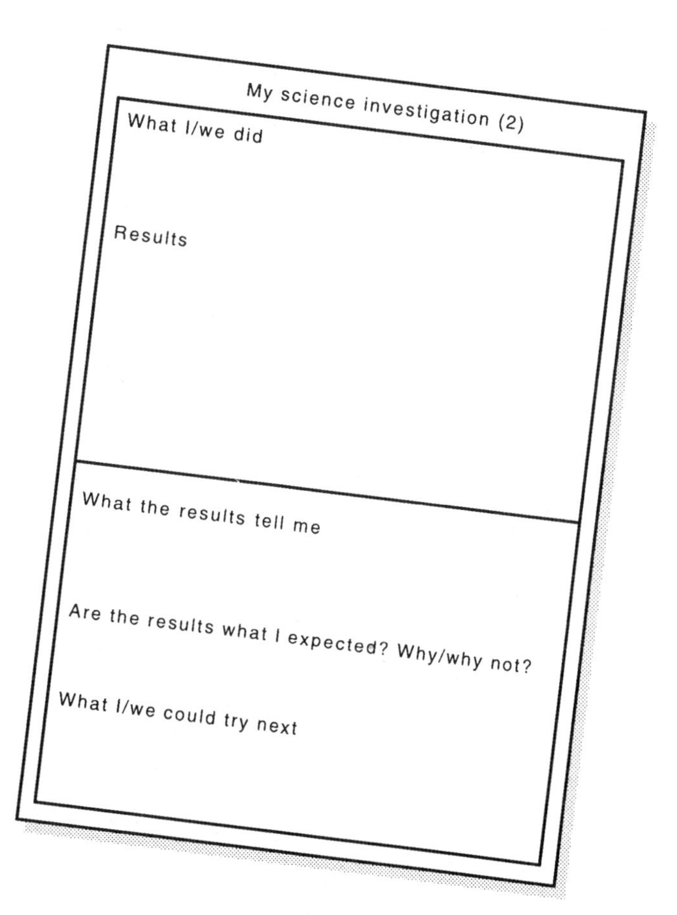

My science investigation (2)

What I/we did

Results

What the results tell me

Are the results what I expected? Why/why not?

What I/we could try next

Concepts likely to emerge

The more bulbs there are in line in a series circuit, the dimmer they will be. This is because each bulb offers resistance to the flow of electricity. The same current flows through each bulb in turn; but a series circuit with three bulbs has greater resistance than a series circuit with two bulbs, so the bulbs will be dimmer.

The greater the number of batteries in a series circuit, the brighter the bulbs will be. The bulbs in a series circuit with one 1.5V battery will be dimmer than those in a series circuit with two 1.5V batteries. The two batteries combine to increase the voltage (or charge). The more charge, the bigger the current. It is important to realise that it is not the physical size of the battery which is a factor. 1.5V batteries can come in all sizes and shapes, but they all produce only 1.5V.

The children may find that using very long wires or lots of conductors joined together produces a dimmer light than using shorter wires. This is because resistance increases as length increases so longer wires offer more resistance than shorter wires. Thick wires offer less resistance than thin wires. Thus the bulb in a series circuit using very thin wires will be dimmer than a bulb in a series circuit using normal leads.

The main point to remember is that the current in a series circuit depends on both the voltage and the resistance. If the resistance is increased, as when more bulbs are added to the circuit, then the current flow is reduced. The current is the same everywhere in the circuit, so any increase in resistance affects the whole circuit. This explains why two bulbs in a series circuit are dimmer than one bulb.

Using the activity for assessment

This investigation should enable you to assess all aspects of Experimental and Investigative Science. Record sheets like those shown in Figure 1 (see pages 94 and 95) can be used by the children to organise their investigation, and may also help you to assess different aspects of the children's learning such as using predictions, understanding fair testing and interpreting results. It is important to remember, however, that children do not always write or draw what they see or understand in an accurate way; so it is essential to talk to individuals about their written work, and to annotate their writing (if necessary) to include those ideas and concepts not recorded by the child.

An annotation sheet similar to the example shown in Figure 2 could be attached to each child's completed work. This can be useful for inclusion in pupil profiles and may assist with whole-school moderation of science work.

Other investigations which could be carried out

▲ How many different electrical components will work in a single series circuit?
▲ What could affect the strength of an electromagnet?
▲ What could affect the speed of a small motor?
▲ What could affect how well electricity is conducted?
▲ How does a dimmer switch differ from an ordinary switch?

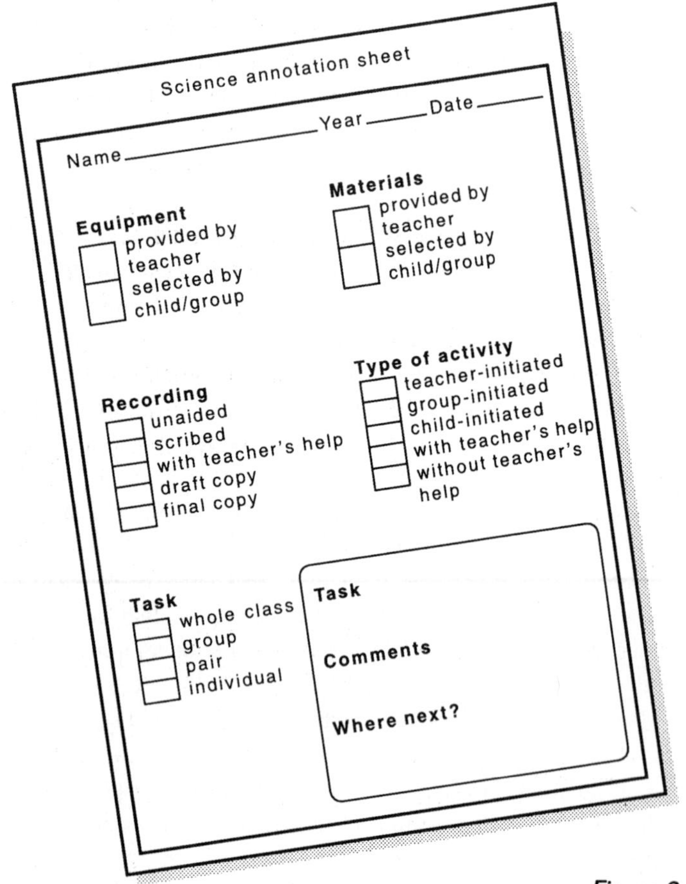

Science annotation sheet

Name ______ Year ______ Date ______

Equipment
☐ provided by teacher
☐ selected by child/group

Materials
☐ provided by teacher
☐ selected by child/group

Recording
☐ unaided
☐ scribed
☐ with teacher's help
☐ draft copy
☐ final copy

Type of activity
☐ teacher-initiated
☐ group-initiated
☐ child-initiated
☐ with teacher's help
☐ without teacher's help

Task
☐ whole class
☐ group
☐ pair
☐ individual

Task

Comments

Where next?

Figure 2

FORCES AND MOTION

What could make a difference to how fast a toy car moves across the floor?

Pairs or small groups.

60–120 minutes.

Key background information

Objects will stay at rest or continue to move in a straight line at a uniform speed until a force acts upon them (Newton's first law of motion). A force is a push or a pull. An object can be pushed to make it move. Once it is moving, other forces such as air resistance and friction act upon it to slow it down. The speed of an object can be described in terms of its going fast or slow, or scientifically by measuring the distance travelled divided by the time taken to travel that distance:

$$\text{speed} = \frac{\text{distance}}{\text{time}}$$

Preparation

Make sure the children have a large enough area in which to carry out the investigation safely.

Resources needed

A toy car, different floor surfaces (such as tiles and carpet), a measuring tape, a long piece of wood which could be used as a ramp, record sheets like those shown on pages 94 and 95 (if required), paper, pencil, stopwatch.

What to do

Provide the children with the toy car and ask them to push it so it moves gently across the floor, and to watch what happens. Ask them to do this several times. Does the car go the same distance in the same direction each time? What could affect these things? Explain to the children that you want them to find out more about how a toy car moves across the floor by carrying out an investigation. Tell them what the investigation is and ask them to make some predictions about factors which could affect how fast the car moves. Either ask the children to write down their own ideas individually, or act as scribe to write down all the ideas from the group.

Ideas the children may decide to investigate could include:

▲ the type of floor surface the car moves on;
▲ the amount of push the car receives;
▲ the weight or type of wheels on the car.

Which of these ideas would the children like to investigate? Help the children to plan the investigation as a group before they start. What things do they think they will need? How will they plan what to do? How will they ensure it will be a fair test? Which factors will need to stay the same? Which factor will they change? How many times should they test it? Are there any safety considerations? What will they be measuring and recording? How will they determine the speed of the car?

Once these things have been decided, observe the children during the investigation. Are they doing what they planned to do? Who is suggesting the ideas? Are they all participating? How are they ensuring it is a fair test? Are they recording what happens? Help the children with any measuring if necessary to ensure accuracy.

After the investigation, ask the children to discuss their results as a group. Were the results what they expected? Did they have any problems? How did they solve them? Do their recordings reflect accurately what happened? Could their recording methods be improved? What conclusions can be drawn? What forces were involved? How did these forces affect the movement of the car? How could the investigation be improved? What could they try next?

Likely problems

Children who decide to investigate the amount of push on the toy car may have trouble deciding how to measure this. They could design an elastic catapult which can be stretched to different lengths, and see how far the car travels. A ramp could also be used: it could be placed at different heights to alter the acceleration rate of the car. This would replace the need to measure the amount of push. It needs to be remembered that the ramp will have an optimum height before it ceases to work effectively. If the slope is too steep, the car will just hit the bottom of the ramp and go nowhere!

The children may need help in determining how fast the car is going. They could describe the movement in terms such as faster and slower, or you could show them how to measure speed by timing how long the car takes to travel over a certain distance. Some children may need assistance in measuring accurately.

If the children are investigating the effect of the floor surface on the speed of the car, it is probably enough to explore a smooth surface such as tiles or wooden floor and a rough surface such as carpet; but some children may wish to test other possibilities – in which case, the school playground, a grassy area and a pathway could be tried. Different materials could also be placed over the floor to create different textures, as long as they are large enough for the car to travel a sufficient distance.

Concepts likely to emerge

The type of floor surface will have an effect on the speed of the car. This is because the movement of the car is slowed down by friction. A rough or uneven surface creates more friction than a smooth, even surface. The toy car should therefore move more quickly over a smooth surface.

The stronger the force applied to an object, the faster it will accelerate. The children should discover that the harder they push the car, the faster it will travel. If a ramp is used then the larger the angle of slope (up to its optimum height), the more quickly the car will reach its maximum speed.

Some children may alter the car in some way to investigate how this affects its speed. If weights are added to the car, the children should discover that the heavier the car is, the harder it needs to be pushed to make it move. It will take a heavy car longer to reach a given speed than a lighter car using the same amount of push. (The children may also discover that a heavier car will take longer to slow down from a given speed, and will hit an obstacle with more force than a lighter car moving at the same speed.)

The size and type of wheels may have an effect on the speed of the car. Some children may try making different wheels to fit the car and comparing their effects. The size and shape of the wheels can alter the weight of the car, the friction created between the wheel and the floor, and the air resistance affecting the car as it travels along (due to changes in the car's shape).

Using the activity for assessment

This investigation should enable you to assess all aspects of Experimental and Investigative Science. Record sheets like those shown on pages 94 and 95 can be used by the children to organise their investigation, and may also help you to assess different aspects of the children's learning such as predicting, understanding fair testing and interpreting results. It is important to remember, however, that children do not always write or draw what they see or understand in an accurate way, so it is essential that you talk to individuals about their work and annotate it (if necessary) to include those ideas and concepts not recorded by the child.

An annotation sheet similar to that shown on pages 94 and 95 could be attached to each child's completed work. This can be useful for inclusion in pupil profiles, and may assist with whole-school moderation of science work.

Other investigations which could be carried out

- ▲ Are big elastic bands stronger than small elastic bands?
- ▲ What could make a ball bounce higher?
- ▲ What could make a marble roll further?
- ▲ What could have an effect on the strength of a tower?
- ▲ What affects how well an object floats?
- ▲ What could make a difference to how fast something falls?
- ▲ What could affect the strength of a magnet?

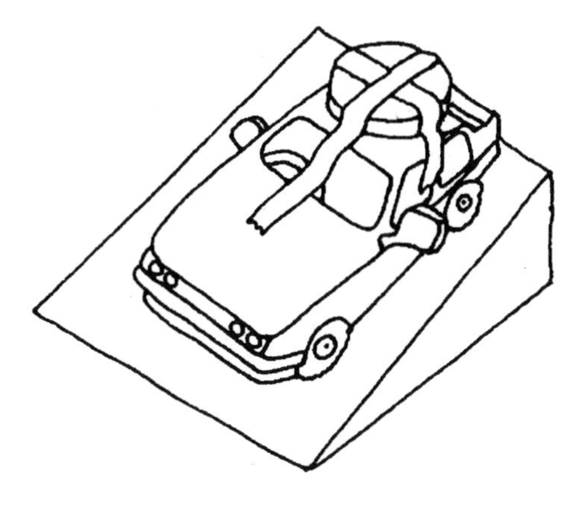

LIGHT

What could make a difference to how well light reflects off a material?

Pairs or small groups.

60–120 minutes.

Warn the children of the dangers of looking directly into a light source.

Key background information

When light rays hit an object, they bounce back off again. This is called *reflection*. All objects reflect light but some surfaces reflect light better than others. A white surface reflects most of the light falling on it, whereas a black surface reflects very little, especially if the surface is unpolished. Coloured surfaces reflect light to varying degrees. Flat, shiny surfaces reflect light the best. If the surface is highly polished, it will give a mirror-like reflection.

Preparation

Make sure the torches are working before the children begin the investigation. Make sure you have some spare batteries if torches fail during use.

Resources needed

Torches, paper, pencils, a collection of different papers, fabrics and objects which vary in colour and shininess.

What to do

Show the collection to the children and ask them to describe any differences and similarities between the items. Explain that you would like them to explore the collection further to find out what might make a difference to how well light reflects off a surface. Use the torch and a shiny material to discuss what is meant by reflection. Can an image of the torch be seen on the surface of the material? Can the children predict which other materials might reflect light well? Can they explain why? Which materials do they think will not reflect light so well? Why?

Discuss how the children will carry out the investigation. What things will they need? How do they think they will actually test each material? What things will they need to do to ensure that it will be a fair test? Are there any safety issues to be considered? How do they think they will record what happens?

As the children are carrying out the investigation, observe what they are doing. Are they following their plan? Have they remembered their ideas for making it a fair test? Are all the children taking part? Who is doing the recording? Have they had to make alterations to their plan? Who decided on these? Have they successfully carried out what they intended to do? You may need to refer the children back to their plan sometimes, if they seem to have lost their way. Remind them of their ideas for making it a fair test, and help them with their recording, if necessary.

When all the groups have completed the investigation, bring the whole class together to discuss and compare the results. Were their predictions correct? How did they decide on degrees of reflectiveness? What problems did they have? How did they overcome them? Did they need to make changes to the way they planned their investigation? Why? What recording methods did they use? What can they conclude from this activity? What could they try next?

Likely problems

The children will probably have most difficulty in determining the degrees of reflectiveness of different materials. Most materials will reflect light to a certain degree, so it may be a good idea for the children to agree on some sort of 'scale of reflectiveness'. For example, from 10 for very shiny surfaces, where a very clear image of the torch can be seen, down to 1 which might be an unpolished black surface where no image can be seen.

The children will probably also need guidance in exploring the factors which affect the degree of reflectiveness. Ask the children to consider the following points about the items: their colour, shininess, texture, hardness and shape (or degree of flatness). The amount of natural or artificial light in the room itself may also affect the results, so the children could try repeating their investigation in a darkened room. The children may also wish to explore the effect of how close the light source is to the item.

The children may find it simpler to consider one aspect at a time, for example to compare different colours first and then different degrees of shininess, so that they are not confused by too many different variables.

Some children may experience difficulties in deciding how to record the results. Help them to draw up a table which includes the name (or description) of each object/material, the variable to be considered (for example, colour) and the

agreed description or scale of reflectiveness. Another table could be drawn up if another variable is considered, and the results compared to see if, for example, white shiny objects have better reflective properties than black dull objects.

Concepts likely to emerge

White and pale colours such as pale green, cream and light yellow will reflect the most light. Dark colours such as red, maroon and black will reflect the least light. But colour alone does not determine reflectiveness. It will also depend greatly on the shininess of the surface. A shiny black object, for example, will reflect more light than a dull black object. Highly polished materials will create a mirror-like image on their surface.

Texture and shape also affect the amount of reflection. Smooth surfaces reflect light the best. The image which is formed on a shiny surface will depend on the shape of the surface. Curved mirrors, for example, can produce different images. Convex mirrors produce images which are upright and show a wide angle. Concave mirrors produce upright, magnified images, of near objects but for distant objects they produce images which are upside-down.

Other investigations which could be carried out

▲ What could affect the length of a shadow?
▲ How can mirrors be used to see round corners?
▲ What could affect the brightness of a torch beam?
▲ Does wall colour affect how distinct a shadow is?
▲ Which type of paper makes the best material for a shadow puppet?
▲ What effect does exposure to sunlight have on different-coloured papers?

SOUND

What could make a difference to the loudness of a sound?

Pairs or small groups.
60–120 minutes.

Key background information

Sounds are made when objects vibrate. The vibrations of the object cause air molecules to move. The vibrating air molecules cause a wave motion which carries the sound to our ears.

Sounds can be loud or soft. The loudness depends on the amount of energy in the sound wave. This is determined by how strongly the source of the sound compresses the air and how much air is made to vibrate. If an object is vibrated in a cavity, such as in a guitar, the sound is amplified and can last longer. This is because the sound waves inside the cavity hit the walls, bounce back and reinforce each other.

Sounds travel better through some materials than through others. Some materials (such as soft fabrics, curtains and carpets) can absorb sound and are used for soundproofing purposes. Loudness is also affected by distance from the sound source.

Preparation

Sensitive handling will be necessary for any child with impaired hearing.

Resources needed

May include: an alarm clock, cloth cardboard boxes of different sizes, elastic bands of different sizes, rice or pasta, different fabrics, paper, pencils, a tape recorder with microphone and sound level indicator, record sheets similar to those shown on pages 94 and 95 (if required).

What to do

Begin the investigation by talking to the children about the sounds they can hear around them. Ask them to listen carefully for a little while. What sounds can they hear? What is the loudest sound? Why do they think this is the loudest sound they can hear? What loud sounds do they dislike/like? What is the softest sound they can hear? What soft sounds do they like/dislike? How can a loud sound be made on a drum? How can a soft sound be made on a drum? How can we make loud and soft sounds on other instruments?

Discuss sounds which are near and those which are far away. How does distance affect sound? Show the children the alarm clock. Let them listen to the sound it makes. Then cover the clock with a cloth. What happens to the sound? Could all sounds be made softer by covering them in some way? Explain to the children that they may be able to find out the answers to some of these questions themselves. Tell them that you would like them to find out more about the things which can have an effect on the loudness of a sound. Ask the children to suggest some things they could investigate. Write down the suggestions as a group and discuss them. Which investigation do they think they could try out?

Ideas the children may decide to investigate could include: the size of chamber on a musical instrument;

- ▲ the distance you are away from a sound;
- ▲ the soundproofing qualities of different materials;
- ▲ the way an instrument is played;
- ▲ the amount of material used in an instrument (the amount of rice in a shaker, for example).

Once the children have decided what they would like to investigate, discuss how they plan to carry out the investigation. What things do they think they will need? What will they do? How will they ensure it will be a fair test? Which factors will need to change? Which factor will stay the same each time? How many times should they test each idea? Are there any safety considerations? What will they be measuring and recording? How will they decide on differences in loudness?

Allow the children time to write down their plans for the investigation (record sheets like those shown on pages 94 and 95 could be used for this), or act as scribe if necessary. Help the children gather the materials and equipment if necessary, and then observe them as they are carrying out the task. Are they following their plans? Have they remembered to make predictions? Are all the children participating? Are they recording what is happening? Have they remembered their ideas for making this a fair test? Help the children with measuring, if appropriate, to ensure accuracy.

Once the investigation is complete, bring the children together to discuss the results. Were the results as expected? Did they have any problems? How did they overcome them? Discuss their recording methods. Do their recordings reflect what happened accurately? What conclusions can be drawn from the investigation? What could they try out next?

Likely problems

Some children may have difficulty in deciding exactly what to investigate. If so, you could suggest a suitable investigation and help them plan what to do. They may experience difficulty in deciding how to distinguish between degrees of loudness. This can be overcome by relating each sound to one sound which is constant, such as the ticking of the alarm clock. Other sounds can then be defined as louder or softer than this sound. Alternatively, the children could grade the sounds on a scale from 1 to 10, or use a microphone attached to a tape recorder with a sound level indicator.

If the children are investigating the effect of the size of the chamber on an instrument they have made, they will need to ensure that the difference in size is great enough to have a marked effect on the loudness of the sounds produced.

If the children are testing how soundproofing and distance from the sound source affect the loudness of sounds, they will need to use something which makes a sound at a constant level. This could be achieved by playing the same sound on a tape recorder at the same sound level each time, or by using an alarm clock.

Concepts likely to emerge

A cavity or chamber in a musical instrument helps to amplify a sound. If elastic bands are stretched over boxes of different sizes, the size of the resonating chamber changes – but the amount of stretch on the elastic bands also changes. This will have an effect on the pitch of the sounds produced. Higher-pitched sounds often seem louder. For example, we can hear a high-pitched whistle over the noise of a crowd, while a low-pitched one might be difficult to hear.

The loudness of some musical instruments can depend on how they are played. A drum, for example, can be stroked lightly with the hand or banged heavily with a drumstick. The harder the drum is hit, the louder the sound will be. This is because loudness depends on how much air is made to vibrate.

Sounds travel away from sound sources and they get fainter as they do so. A sound will therefore be louder when we are closer to the source than when we are further away.

Sound will travel better through some materials than through others. Fabrics such as carpets and thick cloth can have a soundproofing effect, and will make the sound less audible if placed between the source of the sound and the person listening to it.

Other investigations which could be carried out

- ▲ What could have an effect on the pitch of a sound?
- ▲ Which material would be best to line a recording studio's walls?
- ▲ What could have an effect on the length of a sound?
- ▲ Would a low-pitched sound or a high-pitched sound be better for a warning device?

Assessment

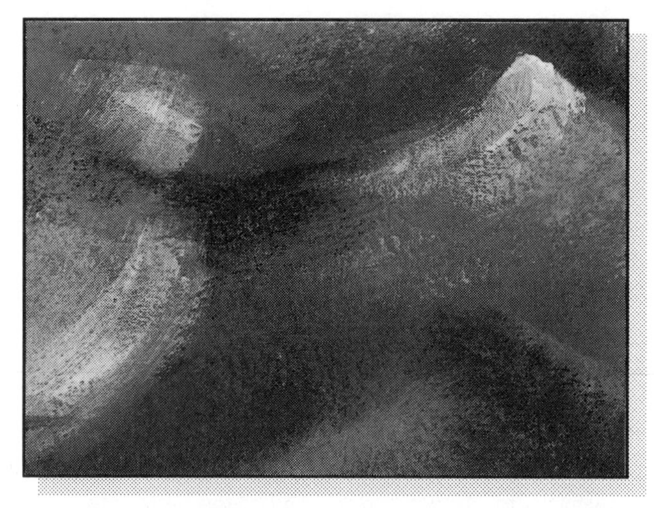

This section contains a selection of activities which you can use for summative assessment purposes. The activities have been designed to be used in two ways. Firstly, the individual tasks can provide you with ongoing feedback on children's progress. Secondly, all the activities could be presented together as a form of summative assessment at the end of a whole unit on one of the five topics covered, or at the end of Key Stage 2. The activities for each topic do not have to be attempted in any particular order. They are numbered only to aid cross-referencing.

All the activities presented in this section require similar classroom organisation, preparation, resources and information about what to do. Information about the PoS to be addressed, likely outcomes and reinforcement suggestions are provided separately for each activity. The activities provide a form of summative assessment which will assist in determining individual children's overall level of achievement. It will also enable you to assess those areas which may need reinforcement work, and will thus help to determine future planning requirements.

Used in conjunction with the formative assessment activities outlined in the main chapters, these activities will help you to provide feedback on progress to children and parents, as well as helping you to decide where to go next in planning for the children's learning. The completed activities could also be kept as part of a pupil profile to assist each child's current, or subsequent, teacher in determining starting-points for individual pupil planning.

ACTIVITY 1

PoS to be addressed

Many everyday appliances use electricity.

Likely outcome

B, C, D, E, G and H all use electricity.

Reinforcement suggestions

Ask the children to name all the things in the classroom which use electricity. Make sure they are aware that things which use batteries also use electricity. Ask them to conduct a survey of the appliances which use electricity in their homes.

ACTIVITY 2

PoS to be addressed

Recognise and assess the hazards and risks to themselves and to others when working with materials.

Likely outcome

A and C could be dangerous. Water can help to conduct electricity from the socket to the hand. The wires on a lead are no longer insulated if the lead is frayed.

Reinforcement suggestions

Discuss other dangerous ways of handling electricity, such as poking things into mains sockets, touching car batteries, flying kites near power lines, playing with electrical leads and overloading sockets. Ask the children to design a poster warning others about these dangers.

ACTIVITY 3

PoS to be addressed

A complete circuit is needed to make electrical devices work.

Likely outcome

See Figure 1.

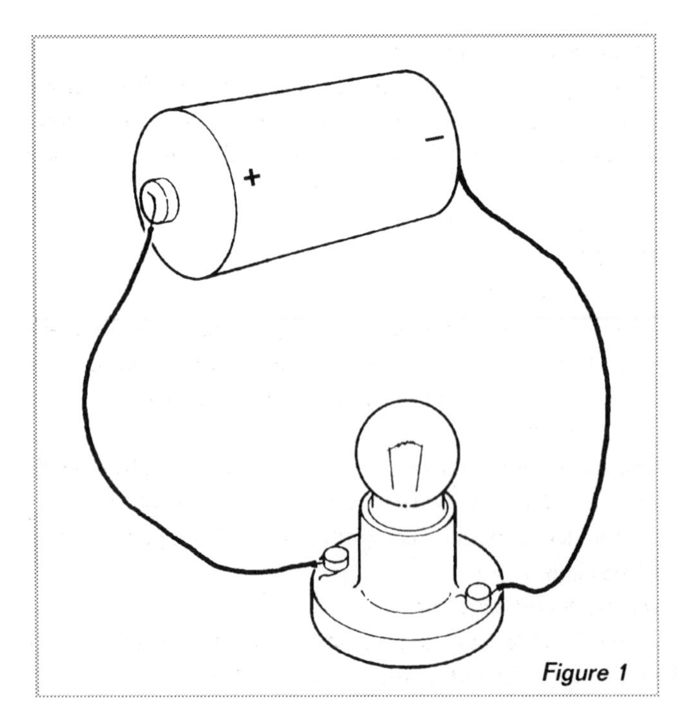

Figure 1

Reinforcement suggestions

Provide the children with the equipment shown in the illustration plus a small screwdriver, and ask them to make the bulb light up. They could then draw the circuit they have made.

ACTIVITY 4

PoS to be addressed

A complete circuit is needed to make electrical devices work.

Likely outcomes

In circuit A, there needs to be a wire going from the negative end of the battery to the base of the bulb. In circuit B, the wire from the base of the bulb should join the negative end of the battery, not the side of it.

Reinforcement suggestions

Allow the children an opportunity to make a circuit using a bulb without a bulb holder, so that they can find out where to attach the wires to the bulb. Look closely at a bulb holder to see where the metal tabs touch the bulb.

ACTIVITY 5

PoS to be addressed

Use knowledge and understanding to link cause and effect, such as when a bulb fails to light in a circuit.

Likely outcome

The bulb may not light for several reasons: the battery is flat, the bulb has blown, the wires are not attached to the battery or bulb holder securely enough, or the bulb is not screwed in tightly enough. The children do not need to mention all of these things, but they should show that they understand all the possible faults in the circuit.

Reinforcement suggestions

Ask the children to draw up a checklist for others to use if a bulb fails to light in an electrical circuit.

ACTIVITY 6

PoS to be addressed

How switches can be used to control electrical devices.

Likely outcome

The switch needs to be closed before the circuit will work.

Reinforcement suggestions
Allow the children the opportunity to make and use switches of their own in order to switch bulbs or buzzers on and off in a circuit.

ACTIVITY 7

PoS to be addressed
Some materials are better electrical conductors than others.
Likely outcome
The bulb in circuit A will light up. This is because all metals are good electrical conductors. They allow electricity to flow through them easily (they have a low resistance). Rubber is a good insulator. Electricity does not flow through it easily (it has a high resistance).
Reinforcement suggestions
Allow the children an opportunity to test the conductivity of a range of materials, using a circuit as shown in the activity.

ACTIVITY 8

PoS to be addressed
Use knowledge and understanding to link cause and effect in simple explanations of physical phenomena.
Likely outcome
As the electricity passes through a thinner, coiled wire in the filament, it meets more resistance than elsewhere in the circuit. Electrical energy is changed here to heat and light energy. The filament heats up, which causes it to glow. The filament is made of a special metal with a high melting point, and there is an inert gas in the bulb which prevents the filament from bursting into flames.
Reinforcement suggestions
Ask the children to look at a light bulb in close detail. What do they think all the parts are for? Why are the wires that hold the filament separated? Where do the wires go to inside the bulb's base? Why does the filament break sometimes?

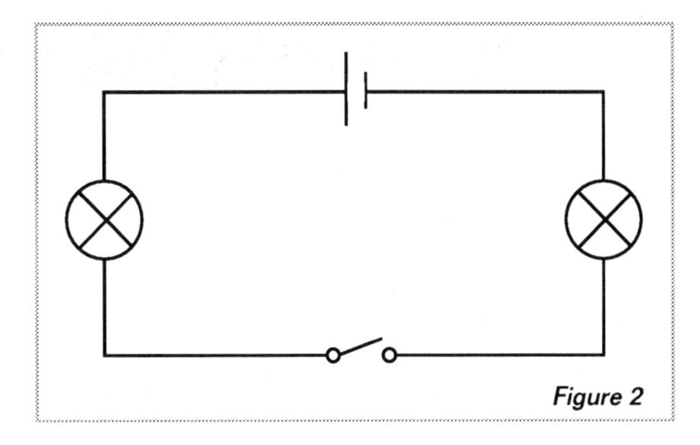

Figure 2

ACTIVITY 9

PoS to be addressed
Ways of varying the current in a circuit to make bulbs brighter or dimmer.
Likely outcome
B. This is because the more bulbs there are in a series circuit, the greater the resistance is in that circuit. Thus the current flow in a series circuit with two bulbs will be greater than the current flow in a series circuit with four bulbs due to the additional resistance of the extra bulbs.
Reinforcement suggestions
Provide the children with the equipment illustrated in the activity and allow them to try out the circuits for themselves to observe the differences. Then ask them to make series circuits with three bulbs and with five bulbs to observe the differences. What do they notice? Why?

ACTIVITY 10

PoS to be addressed
How to represent series circuits by drawings and diagrams.
Likely outcome
See Figure 2.
Reinforcement suggestions
Revise the symbols used in circuit diagrams with the children, and provide them with drawings of other circuits to redraw as diagrams. The children could then make the circuits they have drawn.

ACTIVITY 11

PoS to be addressed
How to represent series circuits by diagrams. A complete circuit is needed to make electrical devices work. How switches can be used to control electrical devices.
Likely outcome
B, D and F will not work. B will not work because the switch is open. D will not work because there is no battery. F will not work because no wire is attached to the negative end of the battery.
Reinforcement suggestions
Allow the children an opportunity to make the circuits shown in the diagrams to test the answers for themselves.

FORCES

ACTIVITY 1

PoS to be addressed

Both pushes and pulls are examples of forces.

Likely outcome

A – push, B – pull, C – pull, D – push.

Reinforcement suggestions

Ask the children to find ten objects in the classroom which they push to make them work and ten objects which they pull. Compare the children's responses. Discuss how some things can be pushed *and* pulled, such as a door.

ACTIVITY 2

PoS to be addressed

Forces can change the shape of objects.

Likely outcome

The children should draw or describe how the modelling clay can be pulled or pushed to change its shape. The pushes and/or pulls make the clay stretch and compress, which alters its original shape.

Reinforcement suggestions

Provide the children with some modelling clay. Ask them to change the shape of the clay in as many different ways as they can. Discuss what is happening to the clay and what causes this to happen.

ACTIVITY 3

PoS to be addressed

To describe the movement of familiar things.

Likely outcome

The toy car can be pushed to make it move. The push provides the initial force which starts the car moving.

Reinforcement suggestions

Provide the children with a variety of devices which can be pushed to make them work. Ask the children to watch what happens when each object is pushed. What causes the movement in response to the push? Does a larger/stronger push change what happens?

ACTIVITY 4

PoS to be addressed

Forces can make things speed up, slow down or change direction.

Likely outcome

The children should mention that they could cause the toy car to slow down by pushing it from the front in some way, or by pulling it from behind. The force of the push or pull slows the car down. Some children may also recognise that friction could cause the car to slow down, so a rough surface could be placed in the car's path.

Reinforcement suggestions

Provide the children with some toy cars and challenge them to find ways of making the cars move faster, move slower and/or change direction. What is happening in each case? What forces are involved?

ACTIVITY 5

PoS to be addressed

There are forces of attraction and repulsion between magnets.

Likely outcome

In A, the magnets are attracting each other because the unlike poles are facing each other. In B, the magnets are repelling each other because the like poles are facing each other.

Reinforcement suggestions

Provide the children with some magnets and ask them to find out which parts of the magnets attract each other. Do they attract along the full length of the magnet or only in certain parts? What is the pushing away of like poles called? Discuss the terms 'attraction' and 'repulsion' using the word 'force'.

ACTIVITY 6

PoS to be addressed

There are forces of attraction between magnets and magnetic materials.

Likely outcome

Paul and Ranji were investigating which materials are attracted to magnets. They predict that all metals are attracted to magnets, but their results show that this is not so for all metals. The results show that steel and iron are attracted, but that brass, aluminium and cupro-nickel (50p coin) are not.

Reinforcement suggestions

Allow the children to test a wide variety of metals to find out which ones are magnetic.

ACTIVITY 7

PoS to be addressed

Forces are pushes or pulls.

Likely outcome

The children should mention that forces are pushes or pulls. The example should indicate that a force can cause something to move, change shape, speed up, slow down or change direction.

Reinforcement suggestions

Use a tennis ball to discuss the forces used to make a ball move. How can it be made to move faster/slower? How can we make it change direction? What happens to the shape of the ball when it is bounced? How does this cause the ball to react?

ACTIVITY 8

PoS to be addressed

Forces act in particular directions.

Likely outcome

See Figure 3. There is a downward force on the book (gravity) and an upward force from the table (reaction force). The forces are equal to each other, therefore the book does not move.

Reinforcement suggestions

Provide the children with several examples of the use of force, such as hitting a ball with a racket, pushing a button on a calculator and rolling a ball along the floor. Ask the children to tell you the forces involved in each case. Compare and discuss the children's answers. Ask the children to draw the objects, showing at what points the forces are acting.

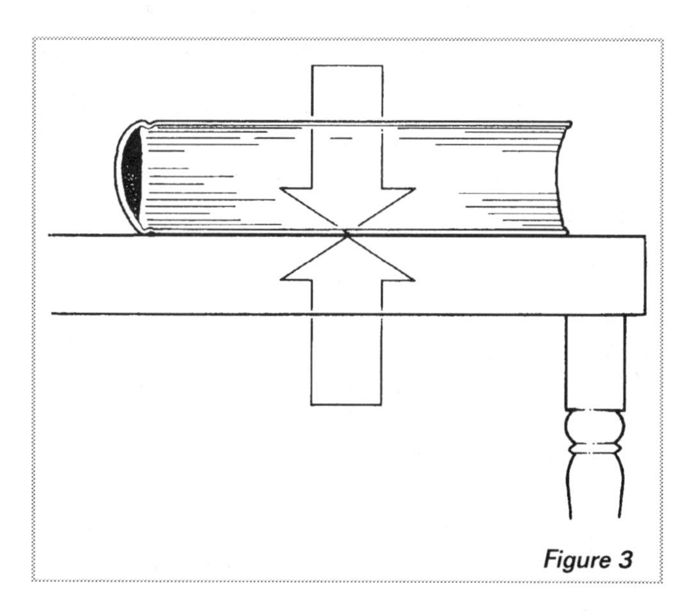

Figure 3

ACTIVITY 9

PoS to be addressed

Objects have weight because of the gravitational attraction between them and the Earth. Friction, including air resistance, is a force which slows moving objects.

Likely outcome

A. They will land together, because the downward force (gravity) acting on both is the same and the upward force (air resistance) is the same due to their being the same size and shape. They will fall at the same speed.

B. The paper made into a ball will land first, because it has less air resistance than the flat paper (which has a larger surface area).

C. They will land together, because there is no air resistance on the Moon and so the object's shape and area will make no difference. The force acting down on the two objects will be the same since their weight is the same.

Reinforcement suggestions

Ask the children to drop pieces of paper of the same size and shape and to compare this with the effect of dropping pieces of different sizes and shapes. Discuss the results, referring to gravity and air resistance. Compare these results with those which you would expect to occur on the Moon.

ACTIVITY 10

PoS to be addressed

When springs and elastic bands are stretched, they exert a force on whatever is stretching them.

Likely outcome

The plastic dart will be pushed forwards when the elastic band is let go. The stretched elastic band exerts a force on the plastic dart, and when the band is released this force pushes the dart forwards.

Reinforcement suggestions

Challenge the children to make a catapult. What happens if the elastic is stretched to various lengths? Compare the distances the dart travels for different degrees of stretch. Explain why this happens.

ACTIVITY 11

PoS to be addressed

When springs are compressed, they exert a force on whatever is compressing them.

Likely outcome

The toy should spring up into the air after the spring has been pushed down and released. This is because when the spring is compressed, it exerts a force on whatever is compressing it. When the spring is released, this force pushes upwards and the ladybird jumps up. The force of this released spring, pressing against the surface on which the toy is standing, makes the whole toy jump up into the air.

Reinforcement suggestions

Provide the children with a collection of toys which use springs to make them work. Challenge the children to find out how each toy works. What does the spring do? How does it make the toy work?

ACTIVITY 12

PoS to be addressed

Forces acting on an object can be balanced or unbalanced.

Likely outcome

The wood floats because the force acting downwards on the wood (gravity) equals the force acting upwards from the water (upthrust). The wood displaces an amount of water equal to what it weighs. Most woods are less dense than water.

The coin sinks because the force acting downwards (gravity) is greater than the force acting upwards (upthrust). The coin displaces a weight of water less than its own weight. The coin is made up of metals which are more dense than water.

Reinforcement suggestions

Ask the children to test a collection of objects to see whether they float or sink in water. Ask them to make predictions first. Discuss the results. Refer to the objects' shapes as well as discussing density and displacement.

LIGHT

ACTIVITY 1

PoS to be addressed

Light travels from a source.

Likely outcome

Light sources include the Sun, table lamp, portable television, torch, candle, fire.

Reinforcement suggestions

Ask the children to name light sources in the classroom and at home. Agree on a list. Discuss natural and artificial light sources.

ACTIVITY 2

PoS to be addressed

The brightness of lights can vary.

Likely outcome

D. The lamp without a shade will produce the brightest light.

Reinforcement suggestions

Use a darkened room to demonstrate how bright each of the lights in the activity is. Try each one, one at a time. Compare the number of objects that can be seen in the room, how clear the objects appear and how bright the light looks. (Do not allow children to look directly at a light source for more than a moment.)

ACTIVITY 3

PoS to be addressed

Light travels in a straight line from a source.

Likely outcome

John would be able to see the candle because the holes in front of him are all lined up. In Sarah's case, the second card will block the light coming from the candle.

Reinforcement suggestions

Try out the activity. Shine a torch to look at the shape and direction of the beam. This activity tells us that light travels in a straight line.

ACTIVITY 4

PoS to be addressed

Light cannot pass through some materials.

Likely outcome

B, E, F.

Reinforcement suggestions

Ask the children to test the materials pictured in the activity and record what happens. Get them to test other materials as well. Look at the materials which the light does shine through. What do they all have in common?

ACTIVITY 5

PoS to be addressed

Light cannot pass through some materials.

Likely outcome

The children need to define 'transparent' in terms of objects or materials which allow light to pass through them. They might also mention that we can see objects *clearly* through transparent things. Transparent objects include those made of clear glass and clear plastic.

Reinforcement suggestions

Ask the children to select ten objects, five of which they think are transparent and five of which they think are not. Provide them with a torch to see which objects will let the light through. Were they right in their predictions? How clearly can objects be seen through the transparent things?

ACTIVITY 6

PoS to be addressed

Light cannot pass through some materials, and this leads to the formation of shadows.

Likely outcome

The drawings of the shadows should look like the outlines of the objects.

Reinforcement suggestions

Ask the children to hold various objects in front of a torch. What shapes are outlined on the wall behind? Can they look at the objects and predict what the shapes of their shadows will be?

ACTIVITY 7

PoS to be addressed

Light cannot pass through some materials, and this leads to the formation of shadows.

Likely outcome

In A, the shadow will be to the right of the object (on the page). In B, the shadow will be around the base of the object.

Reinforcement suggestions

Provide the children with a small box and a torch to try out the activity. Ask them to try the torch at different heights and angles. What shapes do they see? Use another object. Ask the children to predict where the shadow will be before they try it out.

ACTIVITY 8

PoS to be addressed

Light cannot pass through some materials, and this leads to the formation of shadows. Light travels in a straight line from a source.

Likely outcome

A. Objects which are closer to the light source will have a larger shadow. This is because the object blocks out more light than if it is further away.

Reinforcement suggestions

Ask the children to draw a shape on card and cut it out. Fix the shape to a thin stick and then hold the shape in front of a torch, so that the shadow is projected on to a wall. Ask the children to move the shape closer to the torch, then further away from it. What happens to the size of the shadow? What happens to its outline? Design and make shadow puppets.

ACTIVITY 9

PoS to be addressed

Light is reflected from surfaces.

Likely outcome

B, C, E. Shiny surfaces produce reflections. Flat, shiny surfaces produce the best reflections.

Reinforcement suggestions

Provide the children with a collection of objects, some of which are shiny and some of which are not shiny. Ask them to sort the collection into those objects they can see themselves in and those which they cannot. What do the objects in each group have in common? Why can't we see our reflection in dull surfaces?

ACTIVITY 10

PoS to be addressed

Light is reflected from surfaces.

Likely outcome

The drawing should show the orange with the stick on the right-hand side. This is because the image in mirrors is the reverse of the real object.

Reinforcement suggestions

Ask the children to work in pairs, facing each other. One should act as the mirror while the other person slowly moves. Which hand does the 'mirror' move if the person moves her left hand? Discuss how the image is reversed.

ACTIVITY 11

PoS to be addressed

Light is reflected from surfaces.

Likely outcome

The drawing should show a line coming away from the mirror at roughly the same angle (to the mirror) as the beam hitting the mirror. This is because the angle of a light ray hitting a mirror is the same as the angle of the ray reflected from the mirror.

Reinforcement suggestions

Provide the children with a torch, a mirror and two tubes. Ask them to angle the torch in front of the mirror and shine it through one of the tubes so that the beam hits the mirror at an angle. At what angle do they have to place the other tube to 'catch' the beam as it leaves the mirror? Try different angles. Is there a pattern in the results?

ACTIVITY 12

PoS to be addressed

Light cannot pass through some materials, and this leads to the formation of shadows.

Likely outcome

Light cannot pass through some materials and so, because light travels in straight lines, the area behind the object does not receive any light. This is called the shadow.

Reinforcement suggestions

Ask the children to describe what happens when they make shadows with a torch and opaque objects. Why does the shadow form behind the object? How can they explain what is happening? Why do shadows not form behind transparent objects?

ACTIVITY 13

PoS to be addressed

We see light sources because the light from them enters our eyes.

Likely outcome

In A, the arrows should be drawn from the lamp to the book and from the book to the person's eyes. In B, the arrows should be drawn from the TV set to the person's eyes. This is because we see light sources when the light from them goes straight into our eyes, and we see other objects when light from a light source shines on to them and is then reflected into our eyes.

Reinforcement suggestions

Discuss how the children think we see things. Tell them that light is reflected off surfaces into our eyes. Try marking arrows on other drawings of people looking at objects or light sources. Discuss the answers.

ACTIVITY 14

PoS to be addressed

We see light sources because light from them enters our eyes.

Likely outcome

Light comes from light sources, either straight into our eyes or reflected from objects into our eyes. The children could also mention some of the following points about how the eyes work: The light rays enter the pupils of our eyes and travel to a lens. The lens focuses light on to the retina, where special receptors carry messages to the brain. The brain interprets these messages as an image.

Reinforcement suggestions

Discuss how light from light sources enters our eyes, and how light can be reflected off objects into our eyes. Ask the children to find out how the eye works using reference books. Discuss the names of the parts of the human eye.

SOUND

ACTIVITY 1

PoS to be addressed

Sound comes from a variety of sources.

Likely outcomes

The things in the picture which can make a sound include: car, people, aeroplane, ambulance, drill and traffic signals.

Reinforcement suggestions

Take the children out on a walk and ask them to write down (or record on tape) all the things which they can hear. Discuss the variety and sources of sounds heard.

ACTIVITY 2

PoS to be addressed

Sounds can be made in different ways.

Likely outcome

Sounds could be made in the following ways: shaking the rice inside the jar; banging the jar against something; tapping the balloon rubber with a finger or beater; plucking the balloon rubber; swirling the rice around on the balloon rubber; swirling the rice around in the jar.

Reinforcement suggestions

Challenge the children to make one instrument, and then to make as many different sounds as they can with that instrument. In how many different ways can sounds be made?

ACTIVITY 3

PoS to be addressed

Sounds can vary in loudness. Some sounds can be heard from a long way away.

Likely outcome

C. The air horn will usually make the loudest sound. The loudness of the other things will depend on how forcefully

they are used. The children need to explain that a loud sound is necessary to be heard over a long distance.

Reinforcement suggestions

Try out the sounds of the things in the activity. See which sound can be heard over the longest distance. Record the results.

ACTIVITY 4

PoS to be addressed

The loudness and pitch of a sound can be altered.

Likely outcome

Accept an answer which explains how the pitch or loudness of the sound could be changed. One solution might be to alter the distance between each pair of nails so that the elastic bands are stretched to different lengths. This would alter the pitch of the notes. Loudness could be changed by altering how forcefully the bands are plucked or stroked.

Reinforcement suggestions

Provide the children with the instrument shown in the illustration and allow them time to explore different ways of changing the sounds.

ACTIVITY 5

PoS to be addressed

Sounds can be loud or soft.

Likely outcome

Soft sounds could be made by using your hand instead of a beater. The drum could be tapped lightly or stroked. Louder sounds could be made by hitting the drum more forcefully and using the beater.

Reinforcement suggestions

Provide the children with a variety of musical instruments and challenge them to make loud and soft sounds with them. How many different soft/loud sounds can they make? Make up tunes with loud and soft sounds in them.

ACTIVITY 6

PoS to be addressed

The pitch of sounds produced by some vibrating objects can be changed.

Likely outcome

A will make a lower sound than C. The unfilled portion of the bottle is called the resonating chamber, and if this is large (little water in the bottle) then the vibrations in the chamber are slower than if the bottle is almost full. Larger resonating chambers make lower sounds.

Reinforcement suggestions

Allow the children an opportunity to make the bottle instrument and try out the different sounds it can make. Can they make other instruments with resonating chambers, such as a guitar?

ACTIVITY 7

PoS to be addressed

Know what pitch means when referring to sounds.

Likely outcome

Pitch refers to how low or high a sound is. The faster something vibrates, the higher the pitch of the sound it produces.

Reinforcement suggestions

Ask the children to listen to the sounds on a pitched instrument such as a xylophone. Can they tell the difference between the notes? Which ones are low? Which ones are high?

ACTIVITY 8

PoS to be addressed

Sounds become fainter the further away you are from the source.

Likely outcome

As Mary walks away from the band, the music will become fainter. This is because she is walking further away from the sound source.

Reinforcement suggestions

Ask the children to listen to a sound such as the clapping of your hands. Then ask them to move away by a measured distance each time, say five metres, and listen to the sound again. What do they notice about the sound the further they move from the source? Try out different sounds. Which sounds can be heard from the furthest away – high sounds or low sounds?

ACTIVITY 9

PoS to be addressed

Vibrations from sound sources can travel through a variety of materials to the ear.

Likely outcome

The children were testing how well a sound could be heard through different materials. Their results show that the sound could be heard best when the buzzer was in an otherwise empty shoe box. When the box had carpet inside it, the sound could no longer be heard a shorter distance away than when the box was unlined. This means that the sound could travel through the cardboard box better than through the box and the carpet together. The experiment shows that the loudness of a sound is affected by the material it travels through, and that this effect varies with different materials.

Reinforcement suggestions

Allow the children an opportunity to carry out this test for themselves. How do their results compare with the ones given in the activity?

ACTIVITY 10

PoS to be addressed

Musical instruments can vary in pitch.

Likely outcome

B and D. The other instruments could make loud and soft sounds but not sounds of a variable pitch.

Reinforcement suggestions

Provide the children with a variety of musical instruments and ask them to find out which ones can vary the pitch of a sound. How do they think this change in pitch is achieved?

ACTIVITY 11

PoS to be addressed

Begin to apply ideas about physical processes to suggest a variety of ways to alter the pitch or loudness of a sound.

Likely outcome

The pitch of a recorder can be varied by changing the positions of the fingers over the holes when the instrument is played. This alters the length of pipe through which air flows. A shorter pipe produces a higher pitch because the resonating chamber is smaller. Loudness can be altered by blowing gently or forcefully down the recorder. This alters the extent to which the air vibrates.

Reinforcement suggestions

Provide the children with a recorder to test what sounds it can make. How can they make lower/higher sounds? How can they make softer/louder sounds? Compare this with another instrument, such as a guitar.

ACTIVITY 12

PoS to be addressed

Sound is heard when objects vibrate and these vibrations travel through the air to the ear.

Likely outcome

The children should explain that the guitar makes a sound by someone plucking or stroking the strings. The strings vibrate, and these vibrations cause the air molecules around the guitar strings to vibrate. The sound moves in a wave to the ear, where it is channelled down the ear to the ear drum. The ear drum vibrates and the sound passes into the inner ear where nerve impulses travel to the brain, which interprets them as sound.

The children need not mention all these things, but they should refer to objects vibrating and the sound travelling from vibrating objects to the ear.

Reinforcement suggestions

Use reference books to find out about the human ear and how it works. Look at the vibrations made on a drum when it is struck. Relate this to the vibrations on the ear drum.

EARTH AND BEYOND

ACTIVITY 1

PoS to be addressed

The Sun, Earth and Moon are approximately spherical.

Likely outcome

The drawing should be labelled Sun, Earth, Moon from left to right.

Reinforcement suggestions

Show the children pictures in posters and books of the Sun, Earth and Moon so that they can learn to recognise each one. Cut out pictures of each one. Write Sun, Earth and Moon on pieces of card. Ask the children to match up the pictures with the correct labels.

ACTIVITY 2

PoS to be addressed

The Sun, Earth and Moon are approximately spherical.

Likely outcome

C. The children need to recognise that the Sun, Earth and Moon are spherical.

Reinforcement suggestions

Provide the children with opportunities to recognise spherical shapes. Make a collection of 2D and 3D shapes, asking the children to recognise the difference between them. What is the difference between 2D and 3D? What is the difference between a circle and a sphere? Ask the children to find spherical objects in the classroom.

ACTIVITY 3

PoS to be addressed

The position of the Sun appears to change during the day.

Likely outcome

The children should draw the Sun in the middle of the sky, higher up than the Sun already drawn.

Reinforcement suggestions

Ask the children to track the Sun by making hourly observations. Make sure that the children do not look directly at the Sun. Ask them to make comparisons. Where was the Sun before? Where is it now? Does it look lower/higher in the sky?

ACTIVITY 4

PoS to be addressed

The position of the Sun appears to change during the day, and shadows change as this happens.

Likely outcome

The children should draw a shorter shadow around the base of the right-hand stick. The shadow will be shorter at lunch-time. This is because the Sun is likely to be almost directly over the stick.

Reinforcement suggestions

Ask the children to use a torch and an object to study shadows. What does the shadow look like when the torch is directly overhead? To the left? To the right? Very low to the left? Very low to the right? Ask the children to tell you how this relates to shadows made by the Sun.

ACTIVITY 5

PoS to be addressed

The position of the Sun appears to change during the day, and shadows change as this happens.

Likely outcome

The children should mention that the position of the Sun has changed during the day. This alters the size and direction of the shadow. Some children may mention that the Sun only appears to move, and that it is the rotation of the Earth which makes the Sun look as if it is moving.

Reinforcement suggestions

Ask the children to select a tree or other suitable object in the school grounds which is likely to stay in sunshine all day. Allow the children to observe and draw the shadow each hour on a sunny day. Discuss how and why it changes.

ACTIVITY 6

PoS to be addressed

The position of the Sun appears to change during the day.

Likely outcome

The children should refer to the fact that it is the movement of the Earth which makes the Sun appear to move across the sky. Some children may mention that the Earth rotates from west to east, making the Sun appear to move from east to west.

Reinforcement suggestions
Ask the children to stand and revolve slowly in an anticlockwise direction. What happens to their surroundings? How do their surroundings appear to move? Relate this to the way the Earth moves on its axis, using a globe to demonstrate.

ACTIVITY 7

PoS to be addressed
The Earth spins round on its own axis, and day and night are related to this spin.
Likely outcome
The children should suggest that Ahmed and Anna are trying to demonstrate how night and day are caused by the Earth spinning on its axis. Half of the globe has light from the torch shining on it. This represents day. Half of the globe has no light shining on it. This represents night.
Reinforcement suggestions
Allow the children to try out the experiment. Ask the children how it represents day and night. Choose a point on the globe which is in the light and is therefore experiencing daytime. What happens to this place as the globe spins round? Now choose a point which is in darkness. What happens to this place?

ACTIVITY 8

PoS to be addressed
The Earth spins round on its own axis, and day and night are related to this spin.
Likely outcome
The children should mention that the Earth spins round on its axis, and that at any point in time part of the world will receive light from the Sun and part of the world will not. The part in the light is experiencing daytime and the part in the dark is experiencing night-time.
Reinforcement suggestions
Use a globe and a torch to represent the Earth and the Sun. Show the children how part of the Earth is in light (day) and part of the Earth is in dark (night). Spin the globe slowly and ask the children to observe what happens. What changes occur? Why?

ACTIVITY 9

PoS to be addressed
The Earth spins round on its own axis.
Likely outcome
The arrow should be drawn pointing from west to east. The Earth takes 24 hours (one day) to spin once around its own axis.
Reinforcement suggestions
Use a globe to demonstrate the direction in which the Earth spins. Reinforce the points of the compass. Ask the children to play games where they move to the west, east, north and south, either on the globe or in real space.

ACTIVITY 10

PoS to be addressed
The Earth orbits the Sun once every year, and the Moon takes approximately 28 days to orbit the Earth.
Likely outcome
The sentences should read:
The Earth orbits the *Sun*. It takes *a year* (or 365¼ days) to make this orbit. The Moon orbits the *Earth*. It takes approximately *28* days to make this orbit.
Reinforcement suggestions
Ask the children to use reference books to find out about the orbits of the Earth and the Moon. Ask them to prepare a short talk about what they find out.

ACTIVITY 11

PoS to be addressed
The Earth orbits the Sun once each year.
Likely outcome
The model is showing how the Earth orbits the Sun. Some children may also mention that the orbit around the Sun gives rise to changes in day length and the seasons on the Earth.
Reinforcement suggestions
Use a lamp and globe to recreate the model shown in the activity. Use this to discuss how the Earth's orbit around the Sun results in changes in day length throughout the year.

ACTIVITY 12

PoS to be addressed
The Moon takes approximately 28 days to orbit the Earth.
Likely outcome
The children should mention how the Moon orbits the Earth. The Moon reflects the light of the Sun back to the Earth. The amount of light reflected depends on the position of the Moon in its orbit around the Earth. This means that different proportions of the Moon can be seen from the Earth at different times of the month.
Reinforcement suggestions
Ask the children to keep a diary of their Moon watches over several months. What changes do they notice in the shape of the Moon? Discuss why this happens.

Photocopiables

The pages in this section can be photocopied for use in the classroom or school which has purchased this book, and do not need to be declared in any return in respect of any photocopying licence.

They comprise a varied selection of both pupil and teacher resources, including pupil worksheets, resource material and record sheets to be completed by the teacher or children. Most of the photocopiable pages are related to individual activities in the book; the name of the activity is indicated at the top of the sheet, together with a page reference indicating where the lesson plan for that activity can be found.

Individual pages are discussed in detail within each lesson plan, accompanied by ideas for adaptation where appropriate – of course, each sheet can be adapted to suit your own needs and those of your class. Sheets can also be coloured, laminated, mounted on to card, enlarged, and so on where appropriate.

Pupil worksheets and record sheets have spaces provided for children's names and for noting the date on which each sheet was used. This means that, if so required, they can be included easily within any pupil assessment portfolio.

The activities on pages 138 to 157 can be used for the purposes of summative assessment. Background notes for these activities are provided in the Assessment chapter.

Uses of electricity

Name ______________________________ Date ______________

▲ Tick the objects below which use electricity.

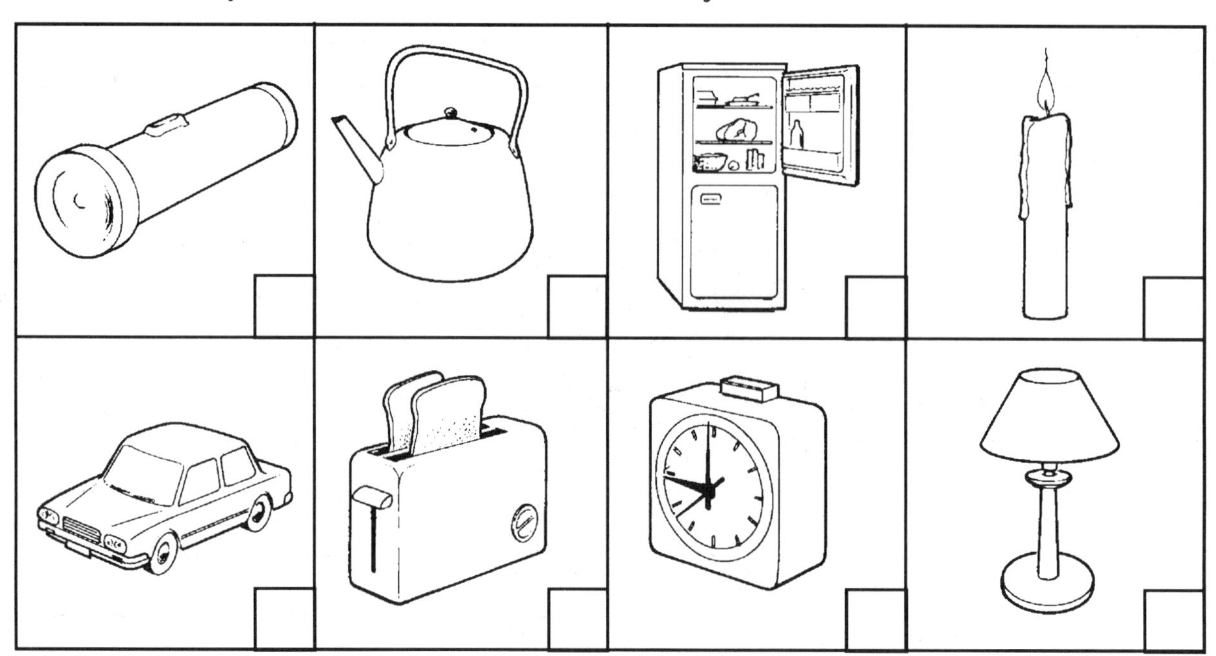

▲ Put ticks to indicate whether these statements are true or false:

Statement	True	False
Many everyday appliances use electricity.		
Electricity can be used to make heat.		
Electricity is used in every home in the world.		
Electricity can be used to make light.		
Electricity can be produced by water.		
Electricity can be produced by wind.		
Batteries are one source of electricity.		
Electricity can be produced from stone.		
We cannot live without electricity.		
A car needs electricity to work.		
Electricity disappears when a switch is off.		
Electricity can flow or move.		

Electrical safety (see page 15)

Electrical safety

Name ______________________________ Date ______________

▲ Look at each picture below. Write down what is dangerous about each situation. Give a reason why.

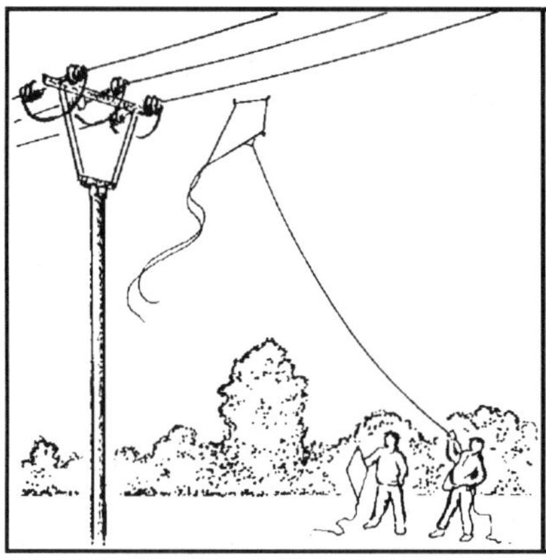

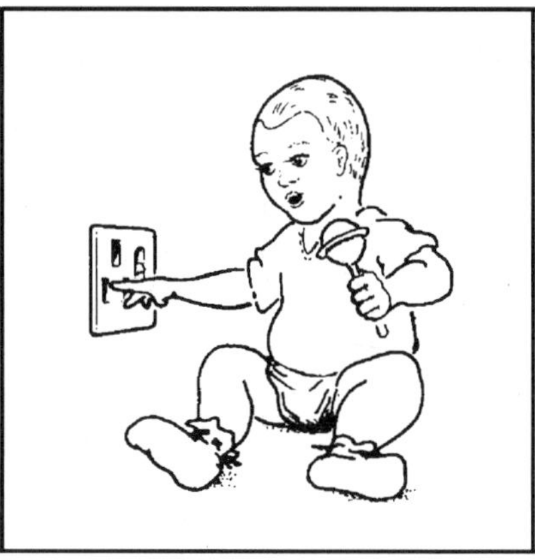

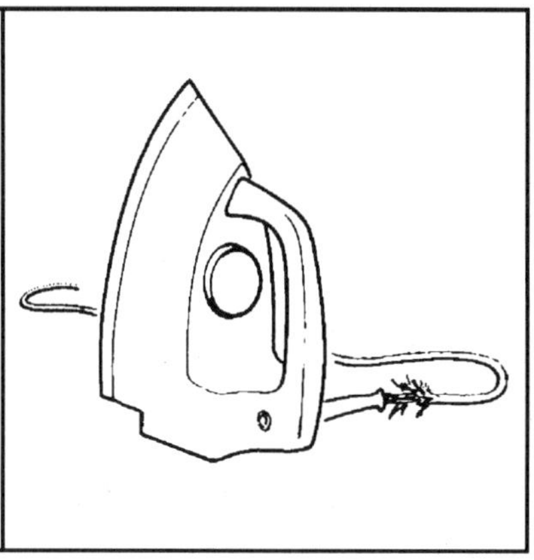

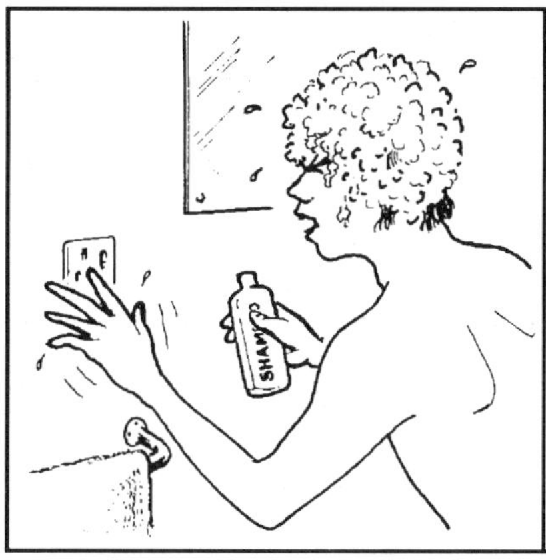

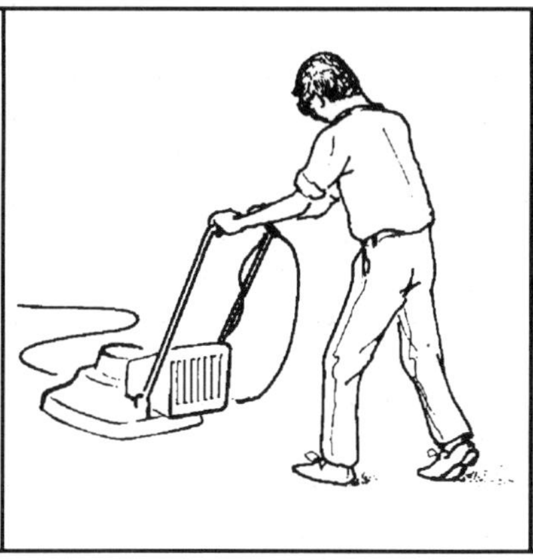

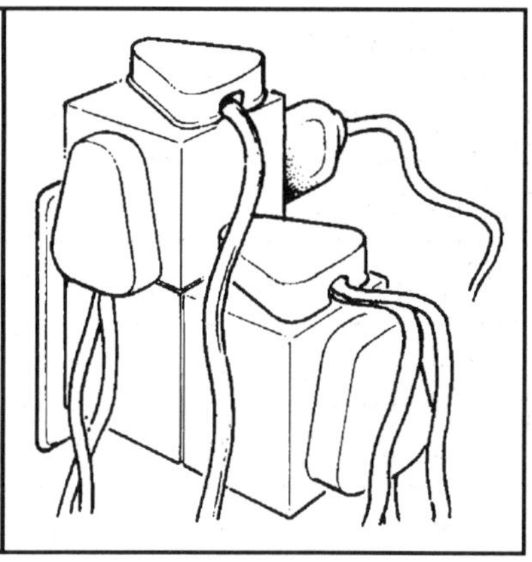

▲ Use the back of this sheet to make a list of other things which can be dangerous when using electricity. Share your ideas with others. Do they agree?

Making a circuit (see page 16)

Lighting the bulb

Name ______________________________ Date ______________

There is something wrong in each of these pictures.

▲ Draw or write what is needed to make the bulb light up.

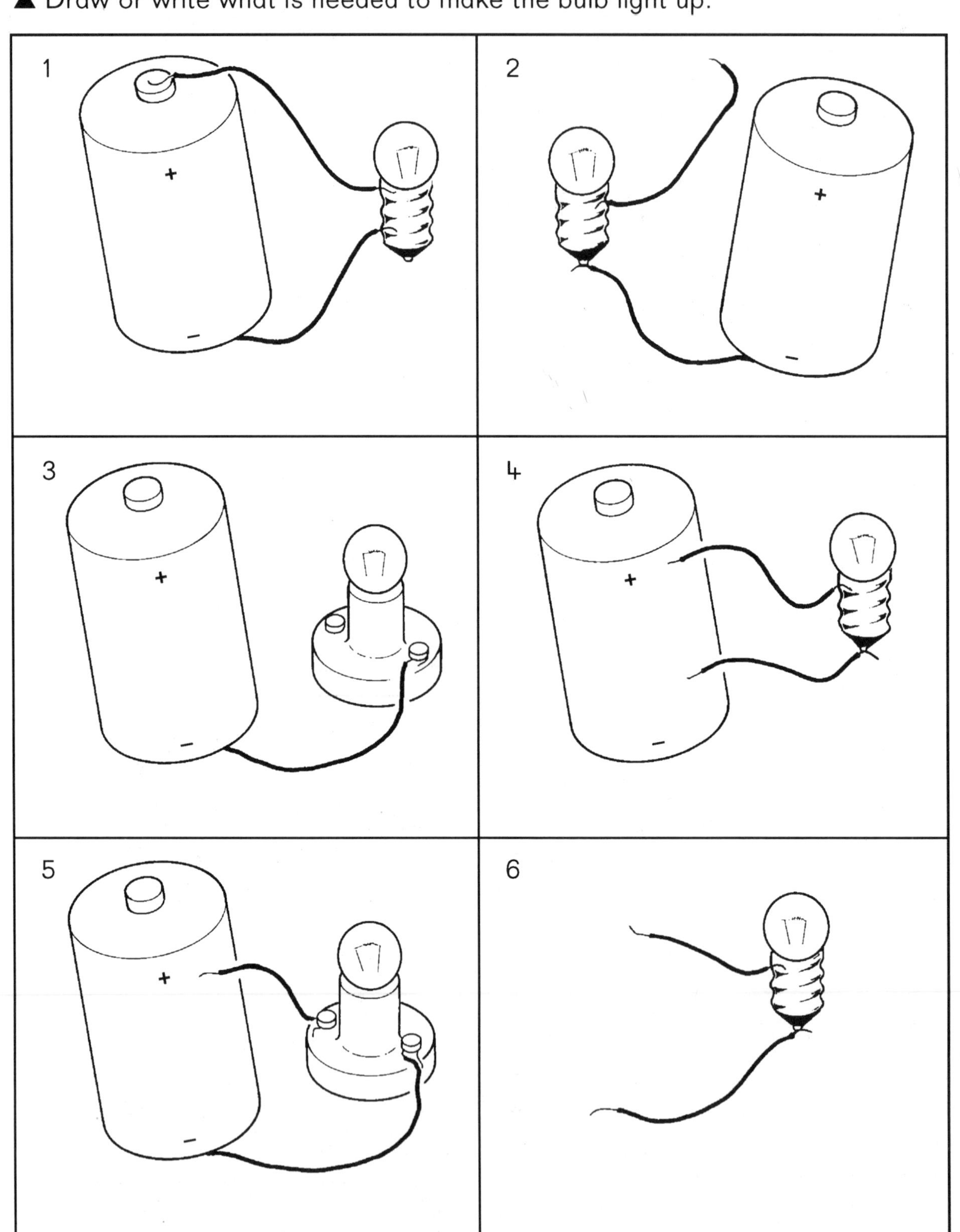

Using switches

Name ______________________________ Date ______________

You will need: a 1.5V battery, a 1.5V bulb, a bulb holder, a small screwdriver, seven pieces of insulated wire with the ends bare, two pieces of card (7cm × 3cm), four paper fasteners, four paper-clips, adhesive tape.

▲ Use the diagram below to make a circuit with two switches.

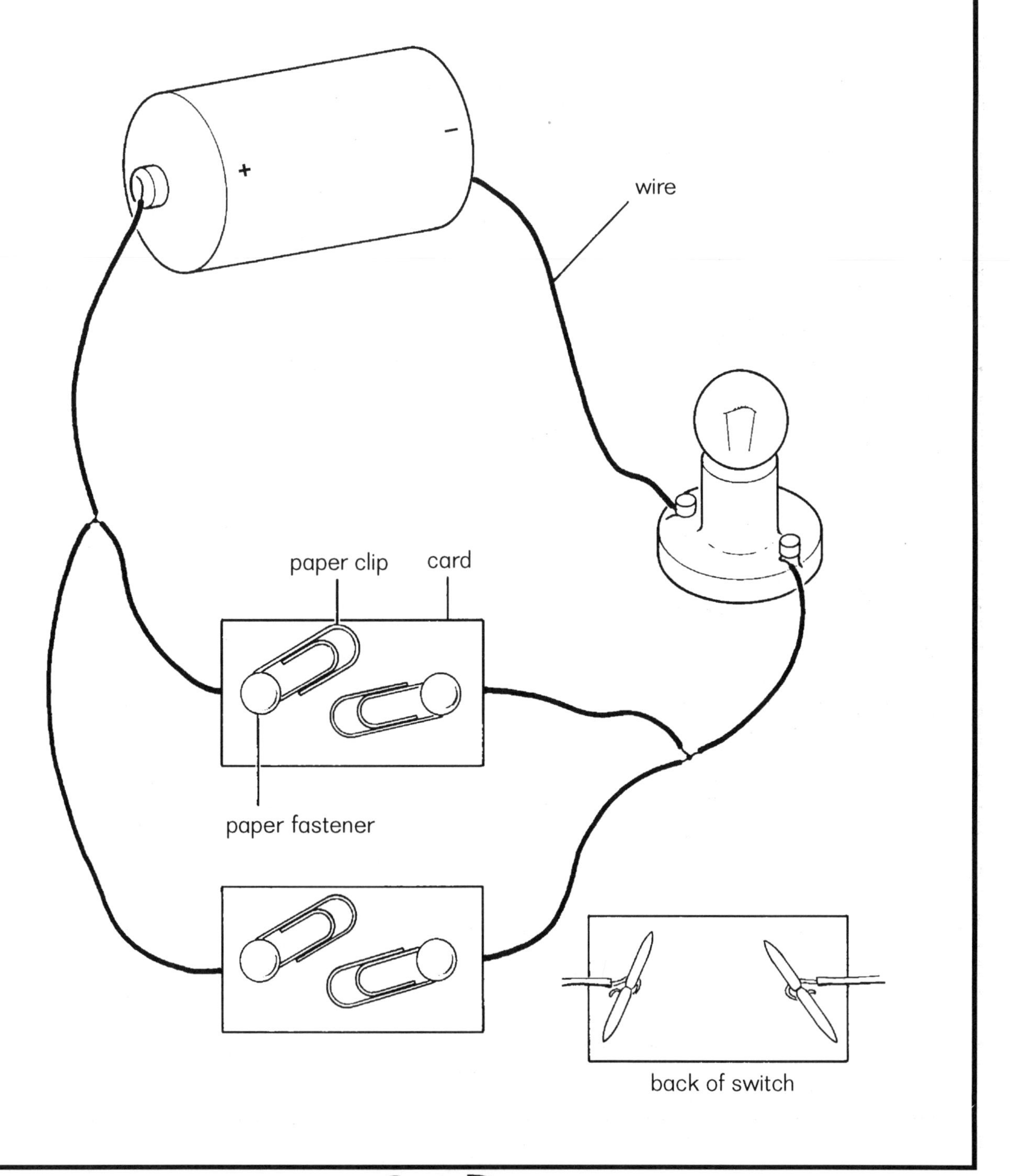

Will it conduct electricity?

Name ________________________ Date ____________

▲ Set up a circuit as shown.

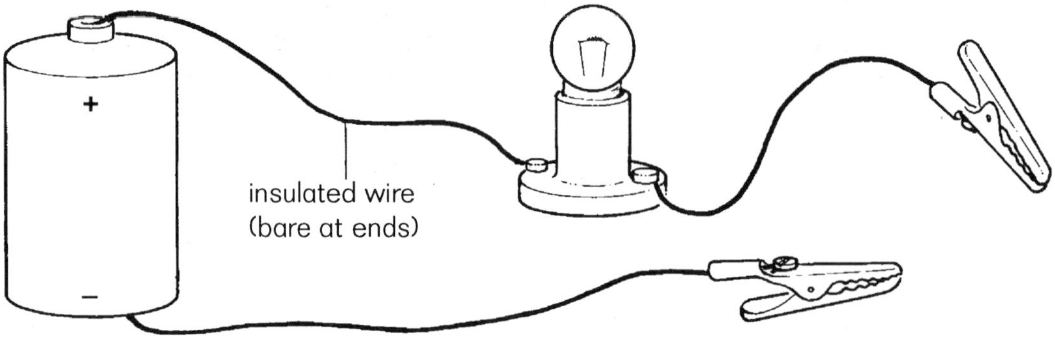

▲ Test each object listed below to find out which ones conduct electricity. Try out some other objects of your own.

Object	My prediction: Will it conduct?	Result: Does it conduct?
plastic spoon		
metal spoon		
wooden ruler		
paper		
cotton fabric		
glass		
brass weight		

What my results tell me: ________________________

____

____

____

Making a winch

Name____________________________ Date____________

You will need: two 1.5V batteries, three pieces of insulated wire with the ends bare, a small electric motor, a motor pulley, cotton thread, a toy car, a shoe box, a large book or wooden board, adhesive tape, scissors.

1 Attach pulley to arm of motor (by pushing it on).

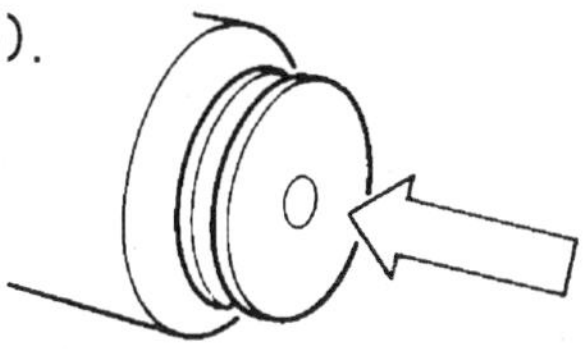

2 Attach wires to motor (by twisting wires around motor terminals).

3 Tie a length of cotton thread (about 50cm) to the pulley and secure it with a small piece of adhesive tape.

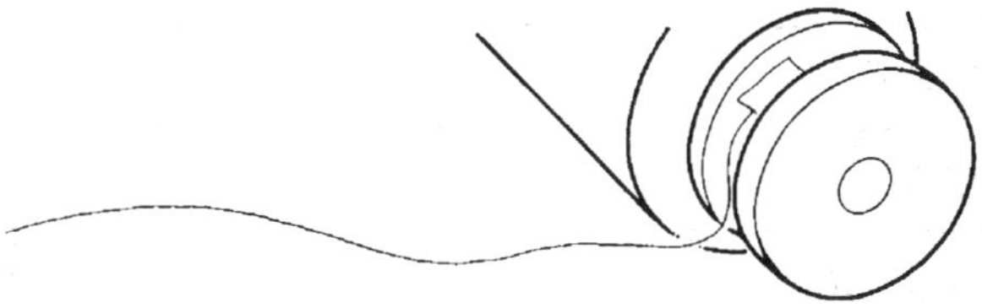

4 Attach motor to shoe box as shown. Keep one wire free from the battery.

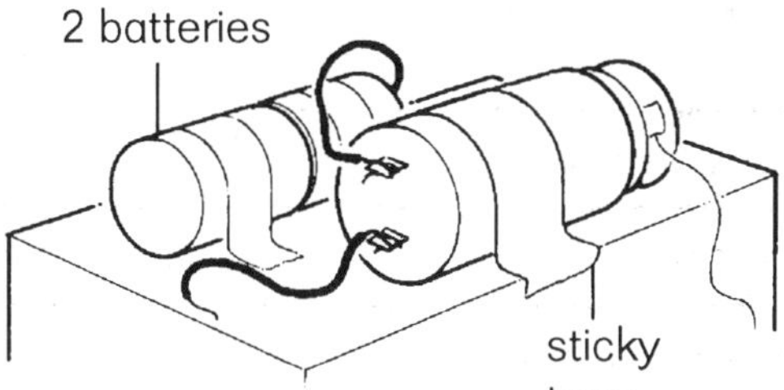

2 batteries

sticky tape

5 Fix a toy car to the free end of thread and place a book or piece of wood against the shoe box like a ramp.

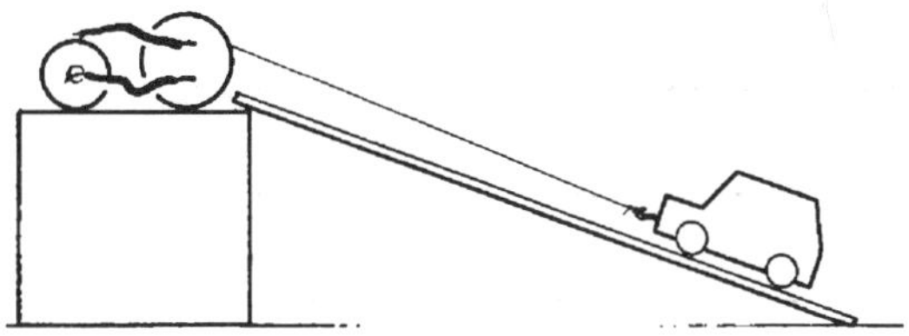

6 Touch the battery with the free wire. What happens?

____

____

____

Drawing circuits (see page 28)

Drawing circuits

Name ____________________ Date ____________

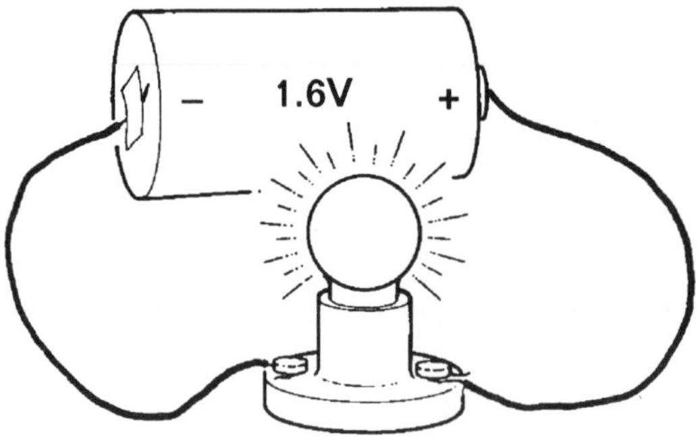

1.6V

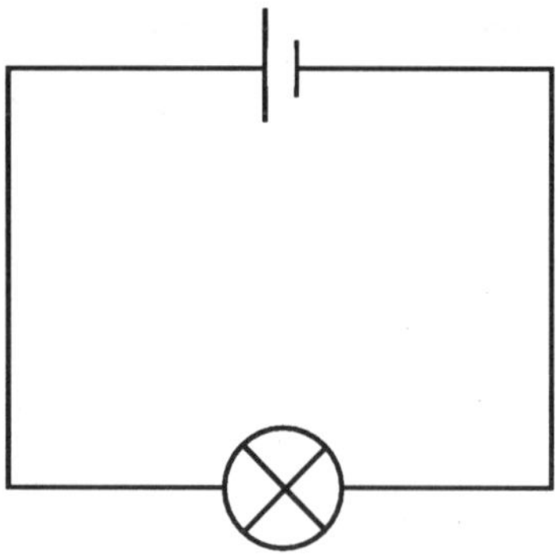

This is a drawing of a circuit. This is a diagram of the same circuit.

Circuit symbols

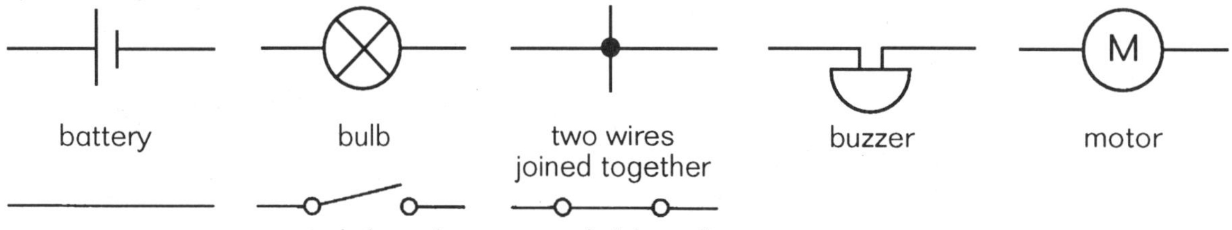

battery

bulb

two wires joined together

buzzer

M

motor

wire

switch (open)

switch (closed)

▲ Use the circuit symbols to redraw these circuits:

1	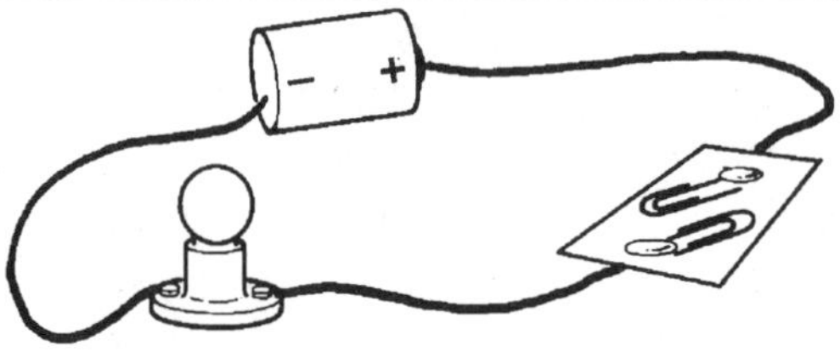
2	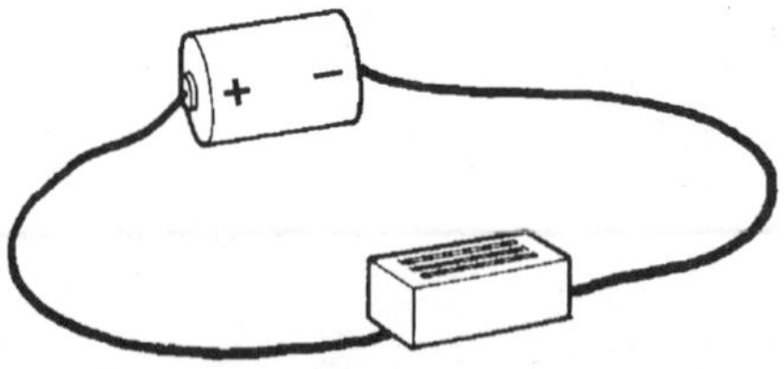
3	

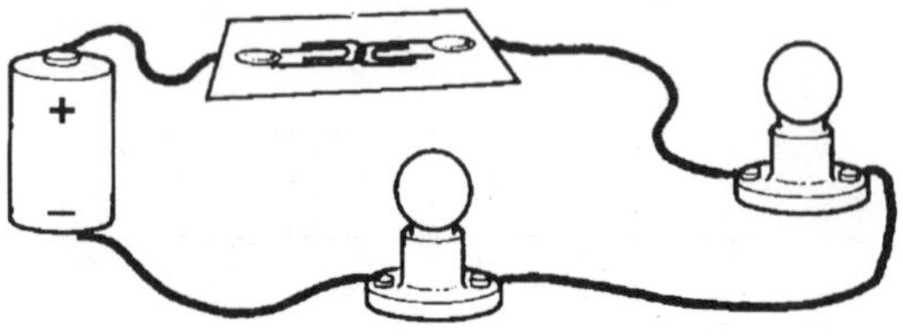

Constructing circuits from diagrams

Name ______________________ Date ____________

Circuit symbols

battery | bulb | switch | buzzer

▲ Which of these circuits will work when the switch is closed?

1

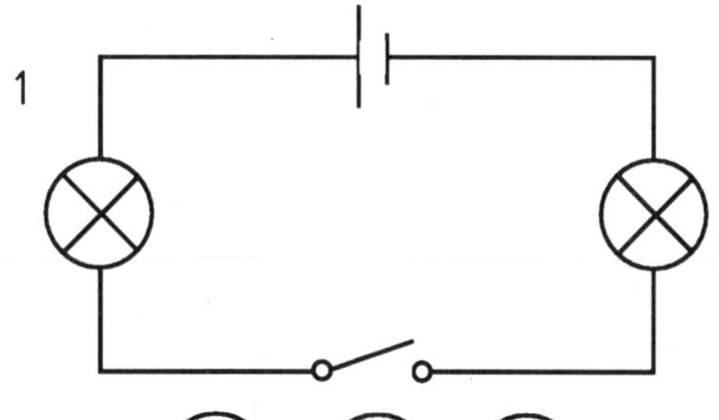

2

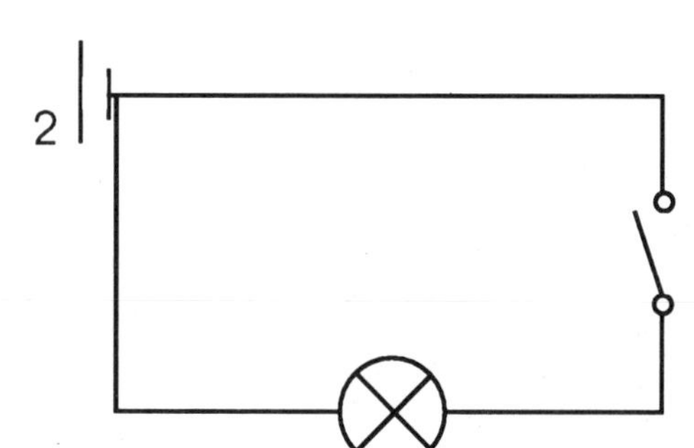

3

4

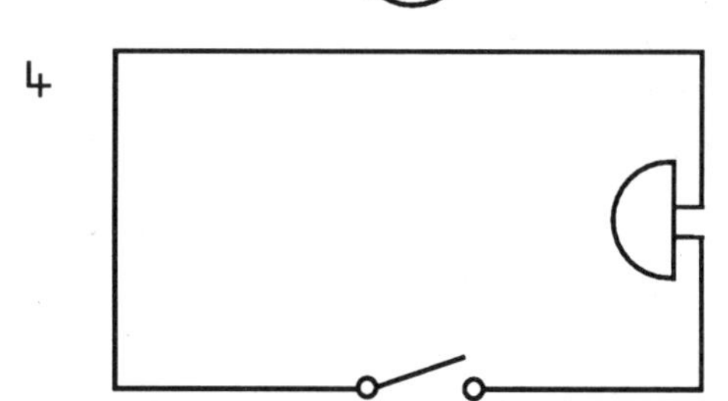

5

6

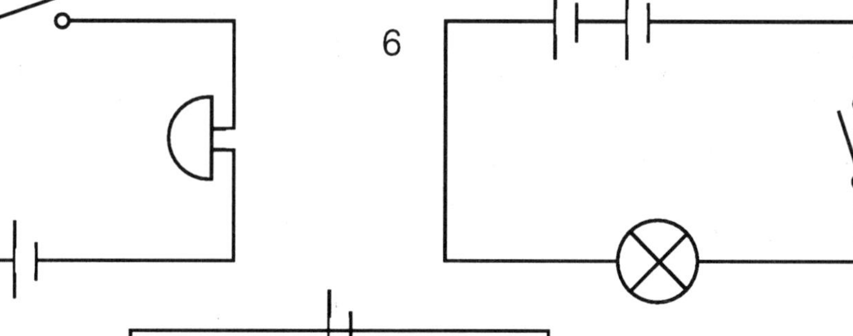

7

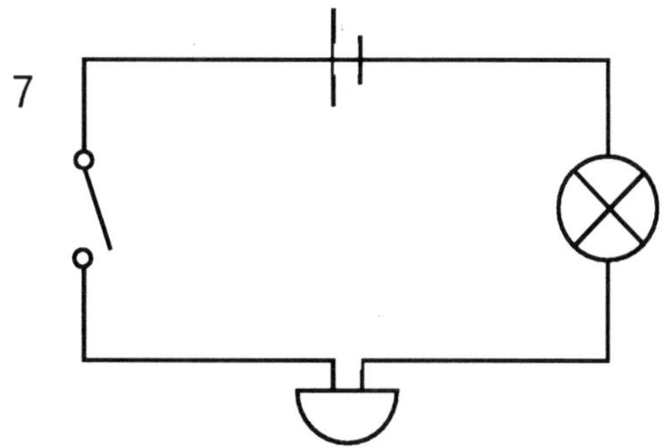

▲ Construct the circuits to see if you were right.

What are forces? (see page 33)

Push or pull?

Name ______________________________ Date ______________

▲ Look at the objects below. Decide whether you need to push or pull them to make them work. Write *push* or *pull* underneath each object.

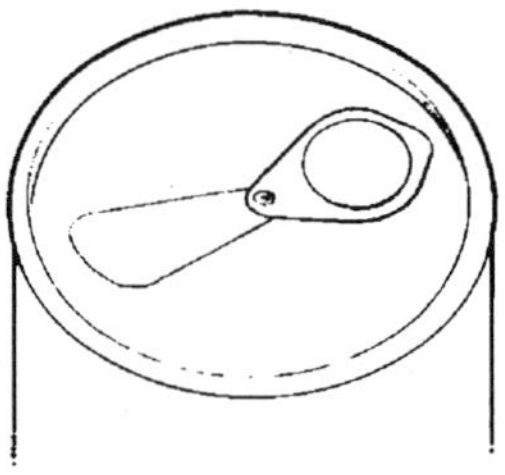

_______________ _______________ _______________

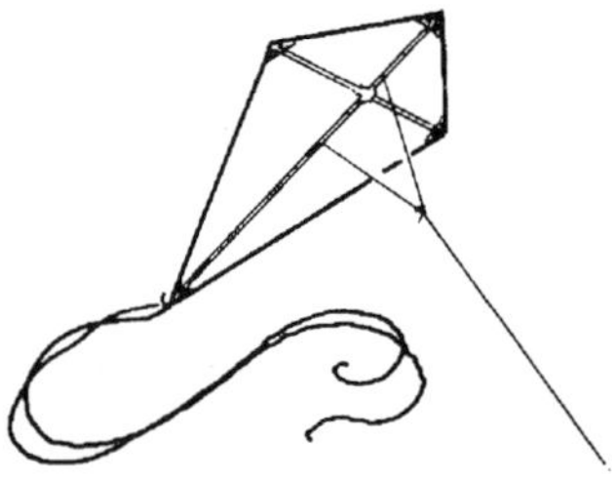

_______________ _______________ _______________

▲ Now look around your classroom. Make a list of things which you have to push or pull to make them work.

Push	Pull

Strength of shapes (see page 35)

Strength of shapes

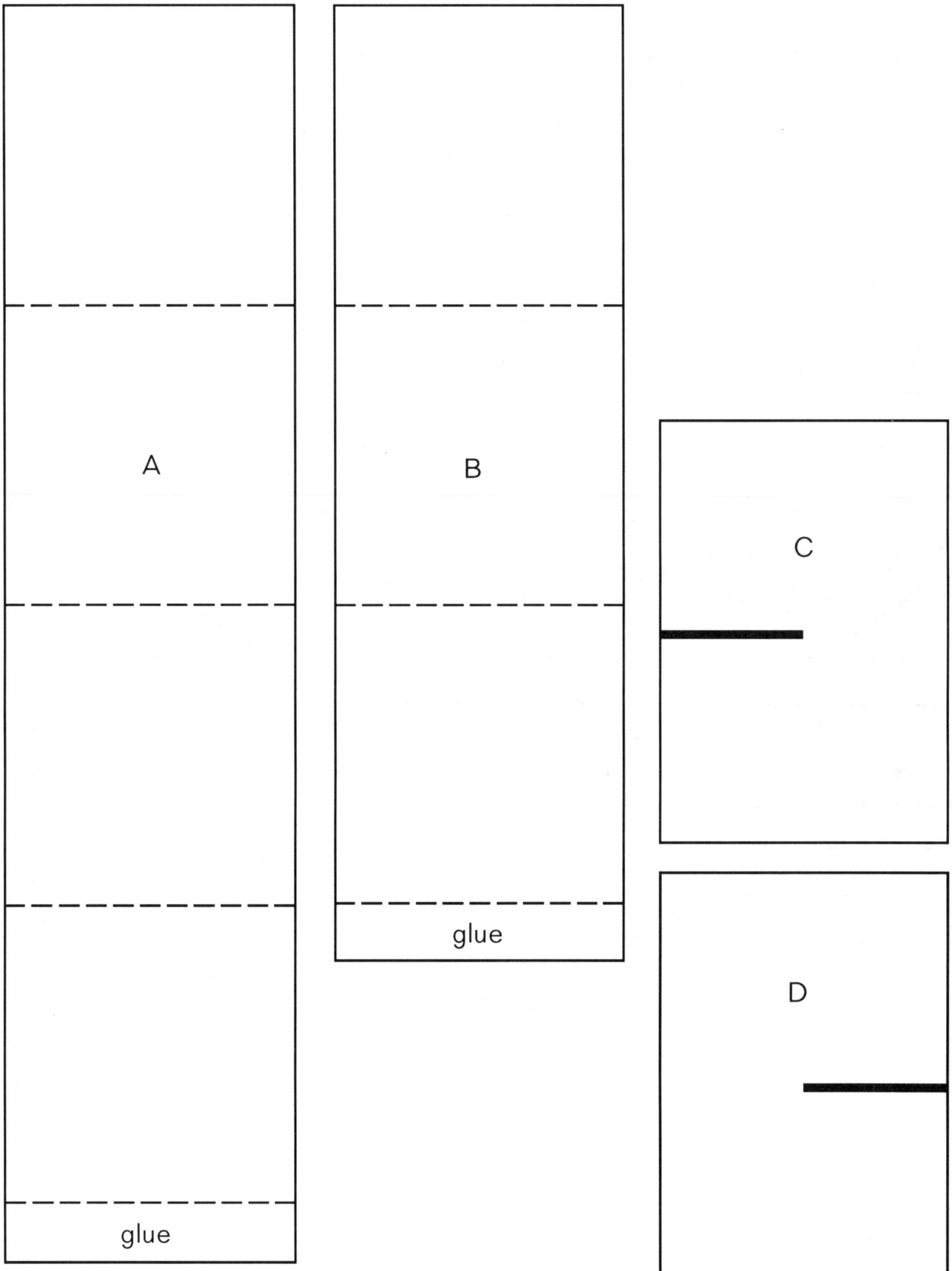

A

glue

B

glue

C

D

cut out shaded slits

Are all metals magnetic?

Name ______________________ Date ____________

▲ Which of these objects do you think will be magnetic? Predict first, then use a magnet to find out.
▲ Record your results in the chart.

Object	Prediction: Will it be magnetic?	Result: Is it magnetic?
1p coin		
10p coin		
£1 coin		
aluminium can		
foil		
steel can		
spoon		
brass weight		
paper-clip		
copper wire		
tin-plate lid		

▲ What did you find out from this activity? ______________________

Testing magnetism (see page 40)

Testing magnetism

Name ______________________________ Date ______________

▲ Use your largest magnet to find out if a paper-clip is attracted through these objects.

Object	Prediction: Will it work through this?	Result: Did it work through this?	Object	Prediction: Will it work through this?	Result: Did it work through this?
paper			tin-plate lid		
fabric			plastic lid		
wooden ruler			steel can		
plastic ruler			aluminium can		
silver spoon			glass jar		
stainless steel spoon			cardboard		
foil			thin book		

▲ What have you found out? ______________________________

____

____

▲ Now find out how strong your magnets are. Find out whether a paper-clip is attracted through books of different thicknesses. Complete the chart, using a tick if the magnet works through the book.

Book	Thickness of book	Magnet size		
		small	medium	large
A	2/3mm			
B	5mm			
C	7mm			
D	10mm			
E	15mm			
F	20mm			
G	25mm			
H	30mm			

Moving objects

Name ______________________ Date ____________

My prediction:

The marble/ping-pong ball will move fastest along the ____________ surface because ______________________

Type of surface	Distance travelled		
	1st try	2nd try	3rd try
plain cardboard			
glue ridges			
bubble wrap			
fabric			

What these results tell me: ______________________

Type of surface	Time taken to travel fixed distance		
	1st try	2nd try	3rd try
plain cardboard			
glue ridges			
bubble wrap			
fabric			

What these results tell me: ______________________

Parachutes

Name ______________________ Date ____________

▲ Follow the instructions to make these two parachutes.

1 Cut out both shapes.

2 Cut eight lengths of cotton thread, each 10cm long.

3 Attach the thread to each corner of the shapes with adhesive tape.

4 Join the four threads together with adhesive tape.

5 Attach a paper-clip using adhesive tape.

Elastic power (see page 48)

Make a buggy

Name ________________________________ Date ________________

▲ Use the ideas shown here to make a buggy. Make sure the buggy is high enough to use the launcher. Do not use axles, as these will stop the launcher working correctly.

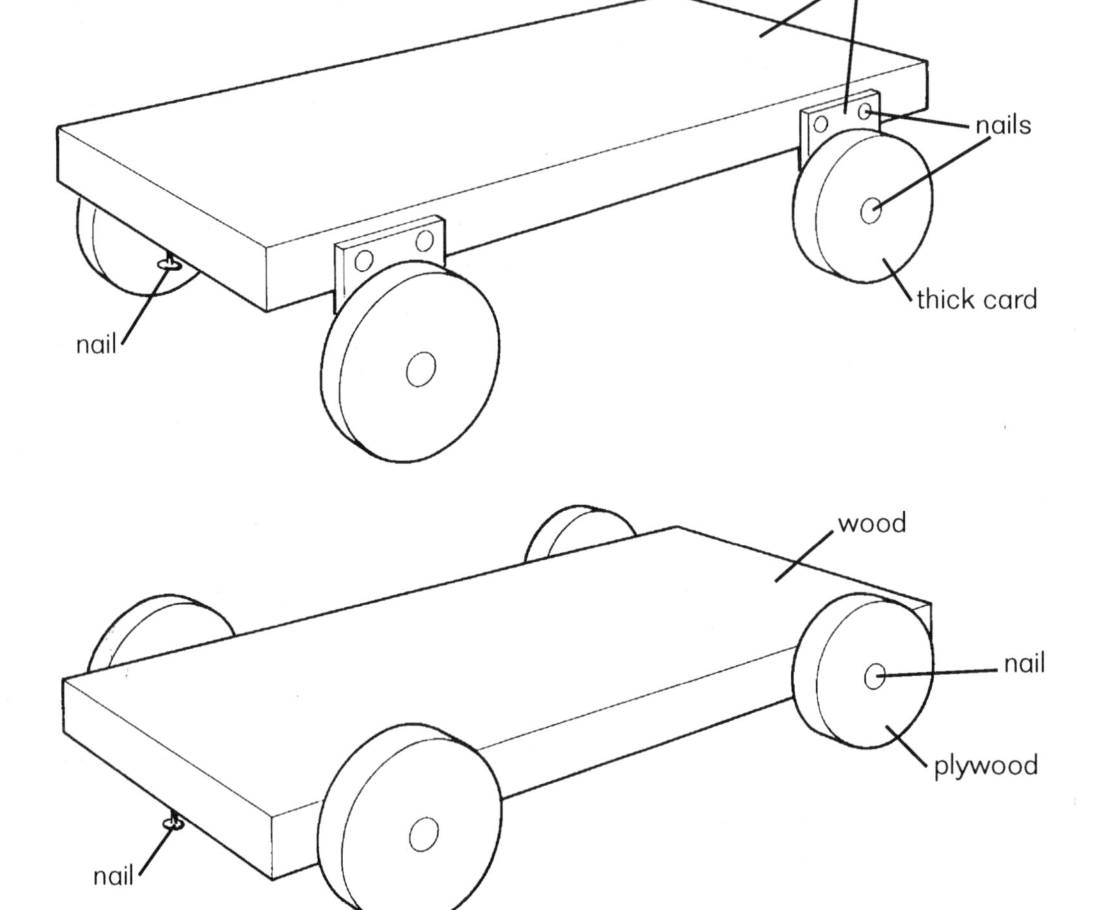

Buggy launcher: a long piece of wood with a nail at one end.

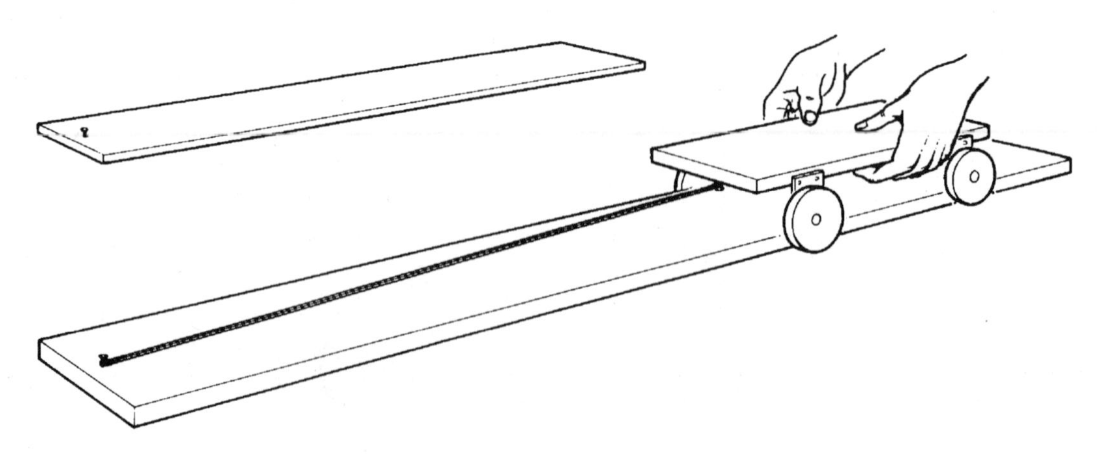

Direction of forces

Name ______________________ Date ____________

▲ Look at each example below. Decide what forces are acting in each case. Draw an arrow showing the size and direction of each force. Write about how the forces act in each example.

1 Kicking a football

2 Football moving in the air

3 Catching the football

4 Wood floating on water

5 Heavy toy truck on a paper bridge

Light sources (see page 56)

Sources of light

Name ______________________________ Date ____________

▲ Look at the picture below. Write down the names of all the sources of light that you can see.

____

____

____

____

▲ List other sources of light you can think of that are not in this picture.

____

____

____

____

Shadows (see page 59)

Making shadows

Name ______________________________ Date ______________

▲ What shadows do you think these objects will cast?
Draw your prediction first, then draw the actual result.
Try another object of your own choice.

Object	Prediction: What I think the shadow will look like	Result: What the shadow looked like
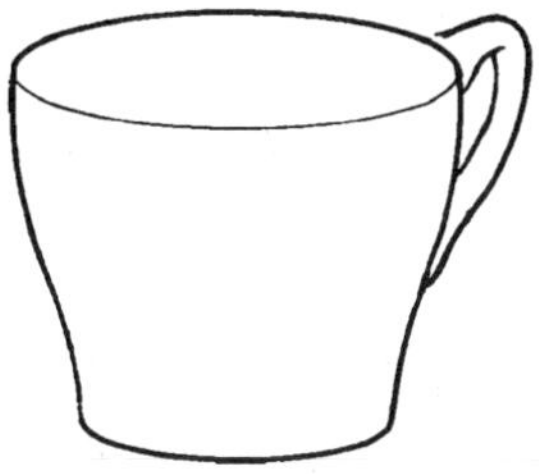		
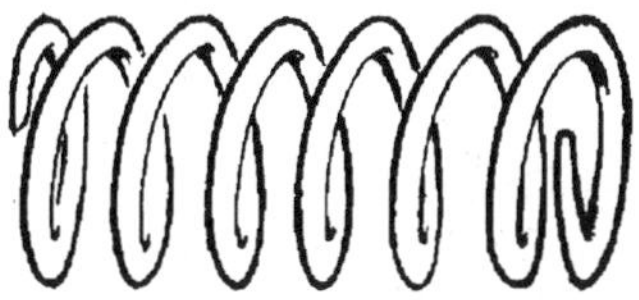		
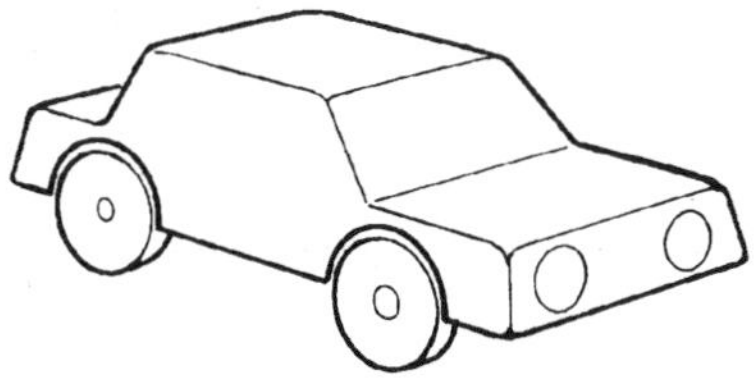		
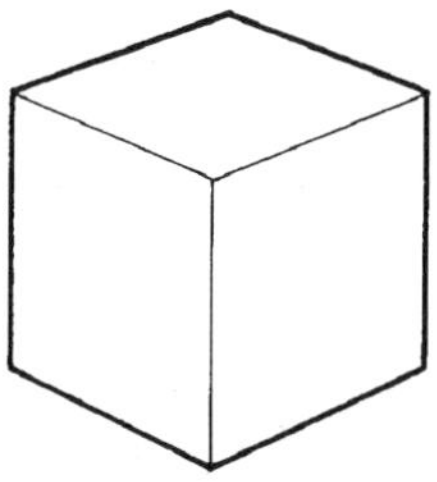		

Mirrors (see page 64)

Using mirrors

Name ______________________ Date ____________

1	2	3
4	5	6
7	8	9
10	11	12 lob

Sounds in school (see page 70)

Sounds in our school

Name ______________________ Date ____________

▲ At each place, stop and listen to the sounds you can hear. Write down the sounds. Decide on the loudest sound and underline its name. Measure the distance you need to walk away before you can no longer hear the loudest sound.

Place	Sounds heard	Distance away when loudest sound no longer heard
classroom time:		
corridor time:		
school office time:		
playground time:		
in front of school time:		

Pitch (see page 76)

Make a drum set

You will need: 6 glass bottles of different heights and sizes, 6 balloons, scissors, elastic bands.

▲ **What to do:** Cut off the necks of the balloons. Stretch the balloon rubber over the open ends of the bottles, making sure it is very tight. If necessary, place an elastic band around the balloon rubber to hold it in place.

▲ Flick the balloon rubber with your fingernail, or tap it with a pencil. What do you notice about the sounds? Pull the balloon rubber tighter. How does this change the sound?

Make a sliding instrument

You will need: a cardboard container with a plastic lid, scissors, a pencil.

▲ **What to do:** Carefully cut the small rim off the plastic lid. Make a small hole in the centre of the lid with the scissors. Push the pencil into the hole. Push the lid inside the container.

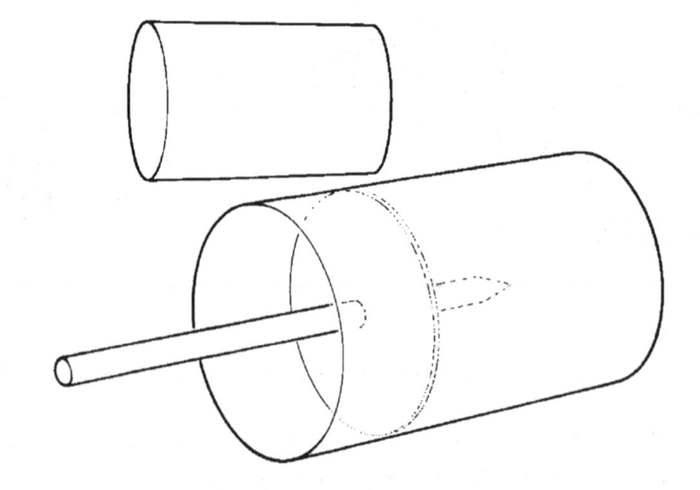

▲ Hold the pencil and push the lid into and out of the tube. At the same time, tap the base of the tin with your fingers. What do you notice about the sound?

Pitch (see page 76)

Make a set of pipes

You will need: 6 plastic straws, scissors.
▲ **What to do:** Flatten the end of each straw and then cut off the corners to make a point, as shown below.
Cut each straw to a different length.

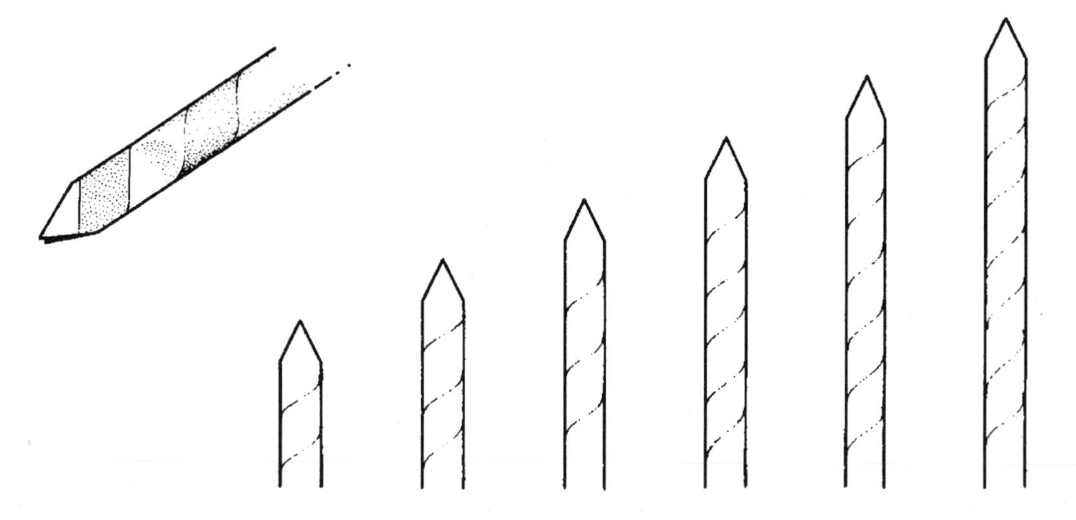

▲ Put the trimmed end in your mouth and blow. What do you notice about the sounds?

Make a guitar

You will need: a tissue box, elastic bands of different thicknesses, card scraps.
▲ **What to do:** Place the elastic bands around the tissue box as shown below.

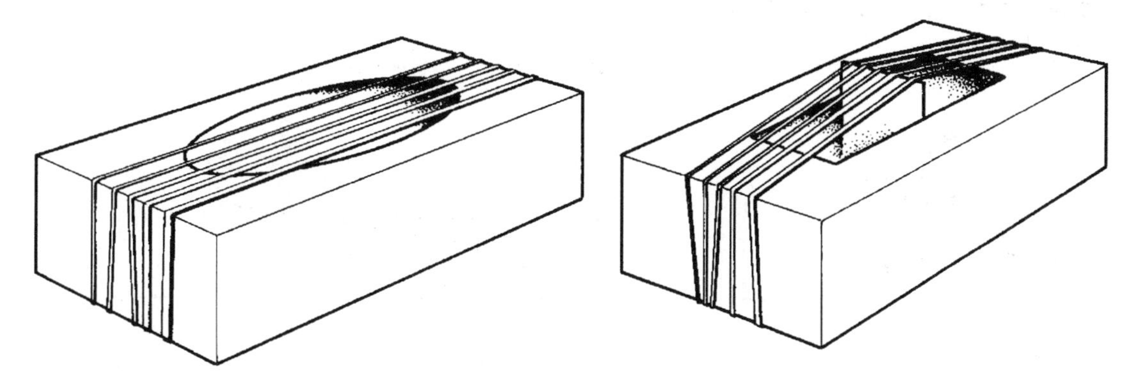

▲ Pluck each band. How can you make different sounds?

▲ Put your finger on a band as you pluck it. Move your finger up and down the band. What happens to the sound?

▲ Place some card underneath the bands. What happens to the sound?

▲ Pluck a thin band and a thick band. What is the difference in sound?

Day and night (see page 86)

Day and night

Name _______________________________ Date _______________

1 Which way does the Earth turn? Draw an arrow to show the direction.

N

S

2 Shade in the dark side of the Earth on this diagram. Write 'day' and 'night' on the correct sides of the Earth.

N

S

3 Draw where the Sun would be at the middle of the day.

East

West

4 Describe how day and night are caused. _______________________________

____

____

____

____

World time (see page 88)

World time zones

Name ______________________ Date ____________

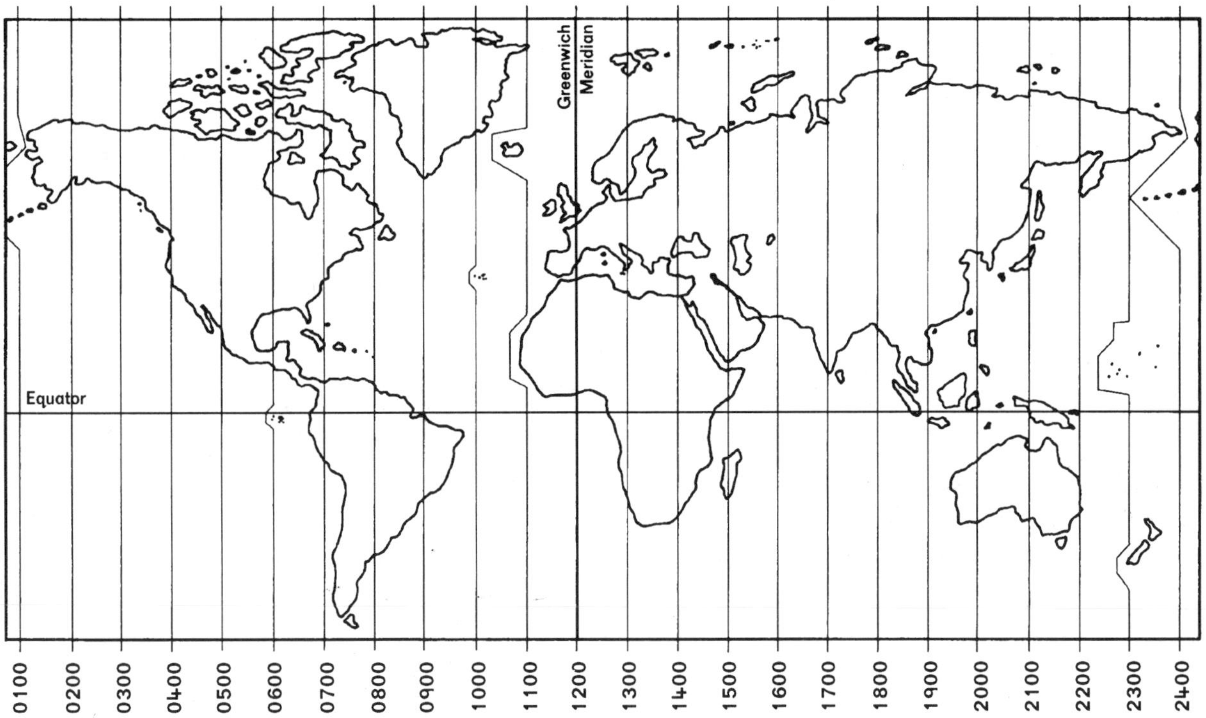
Greenwich Meridian
Equator
0100
0200
0300
0400
0500
0600
0700
0800
0900
1000
1100
1200
1300
1400
1500
1600
1700
1800
1900
2000
2100
2200
2300
2400

1 Why do you think some of the time zone lines are not straight?

____

____

____

____

2 How many degrees does the Earth turn in one hour?

____

3 How long does it take for the Earth to turn one degree?

____

4 If it is noon in Greenwich, what time is it in these places?

Paris ____________ Rome ____________

Tokyo ____________ Sydney ____________

Assessment activities – Electricity

1

▲ Tick the objects below which use electricity.

2

▲ Tick the pictures showing things which would be dangerous.

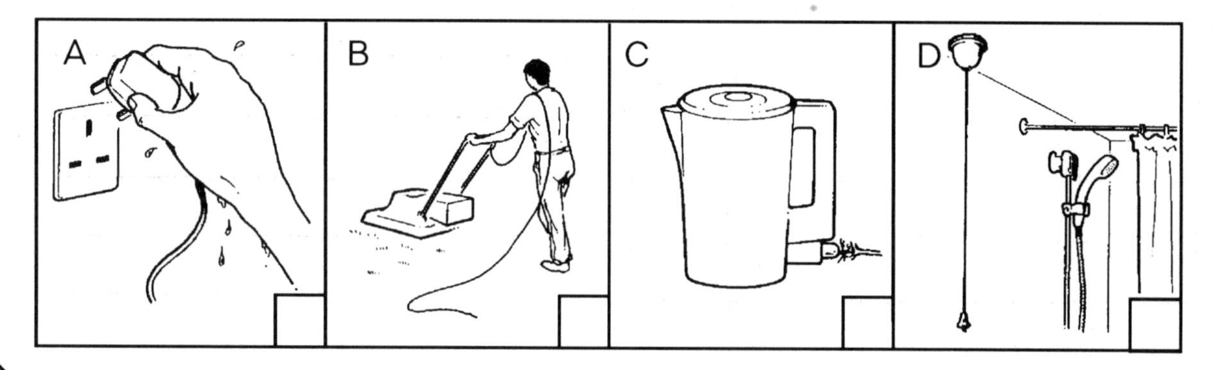

3

▲ Draw a circuit in which the bulb would light up using these components.

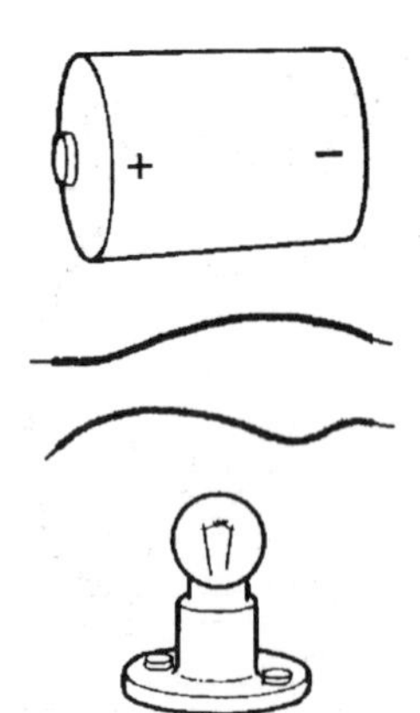

Assessment activities – Electricity

4

There is something wrong in each of these circuits.

▲ Draw or write the correct answer so the bulb will light up.

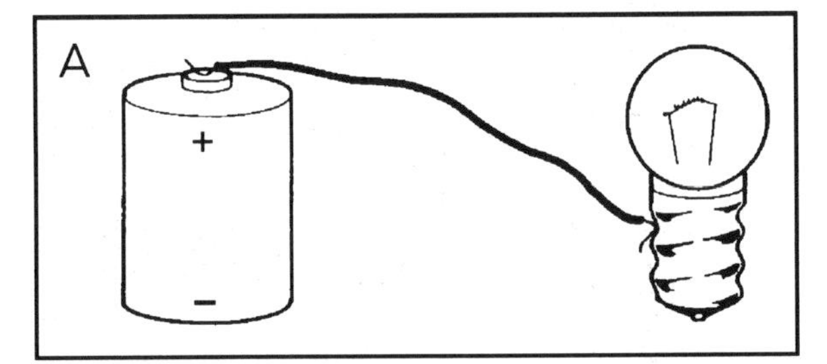

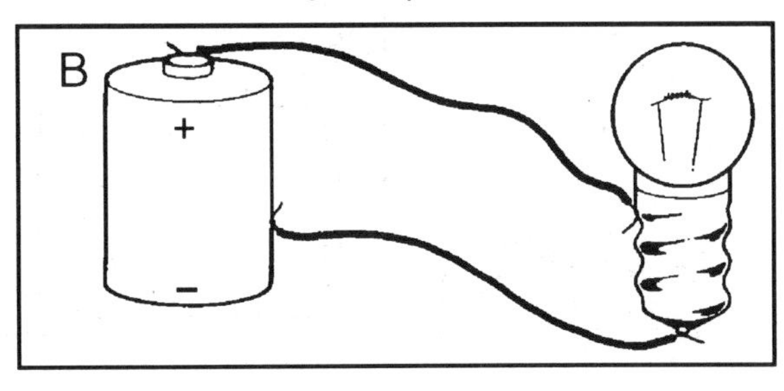

5

▲ Look at this circuit. The bulb will not light up for some reason. Can you suggest what might be wrong?

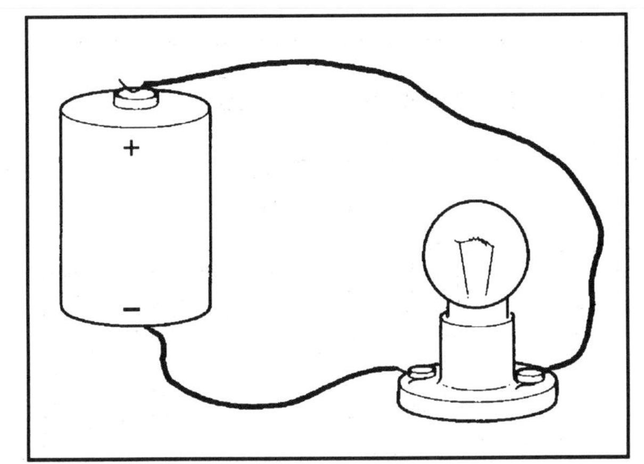

6

▲ Draw or write what needs to be done to make the bulb light up in this circuit.

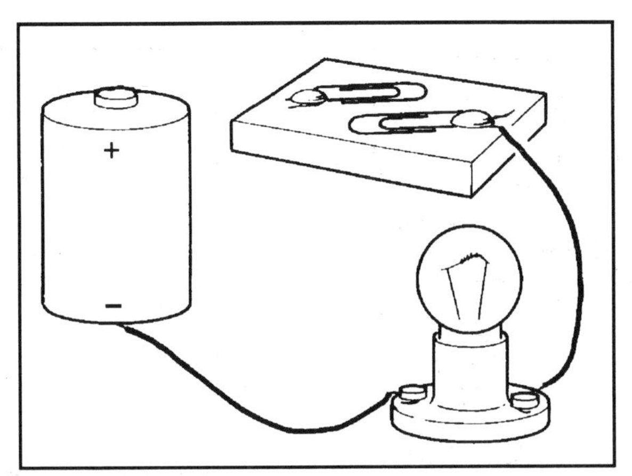

Assessment activities – Electricity

7

▲ Tick which bulb will light up – the one in picture A or the one in picture B. Can you say why?

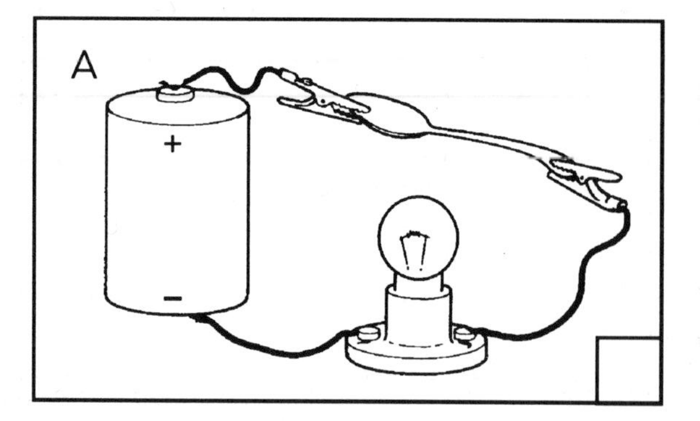

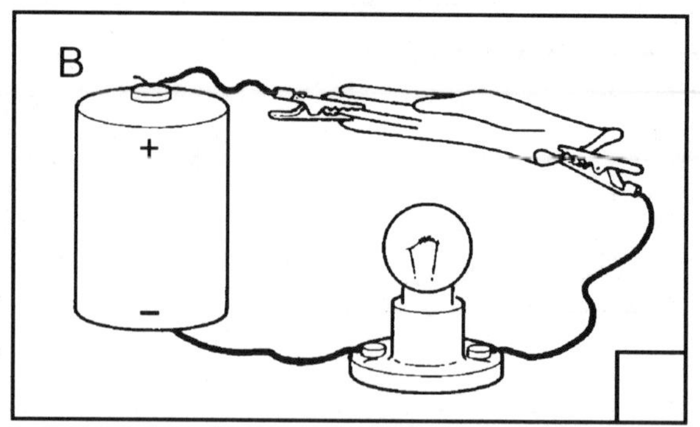

8

▲ Explain why the filament in a bulb lights up.

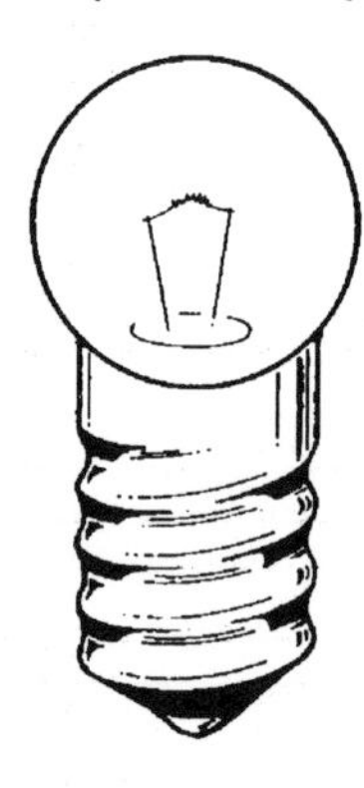

9

▲ Tick which of these two circuits will have brighter bulbs. Can you explain why?

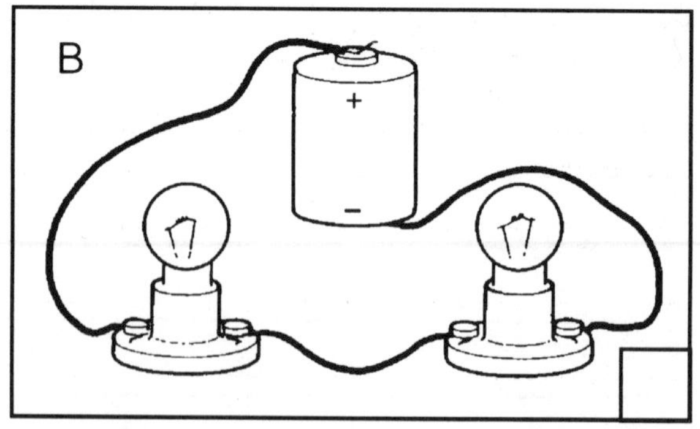

10 Assessment activities – Electricity

▲ Redraw this circuit drawing using symbols in a diagram.

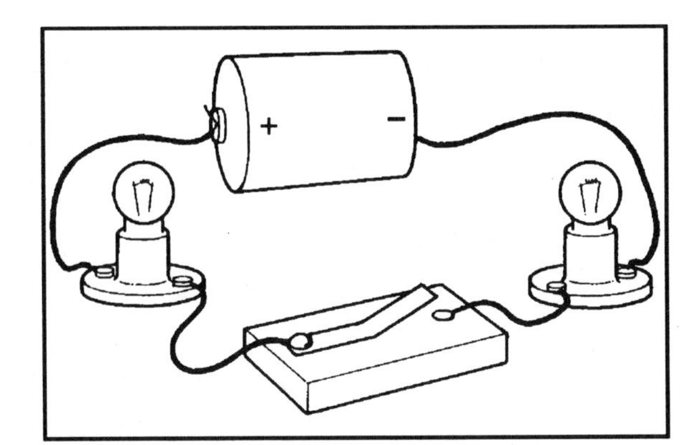

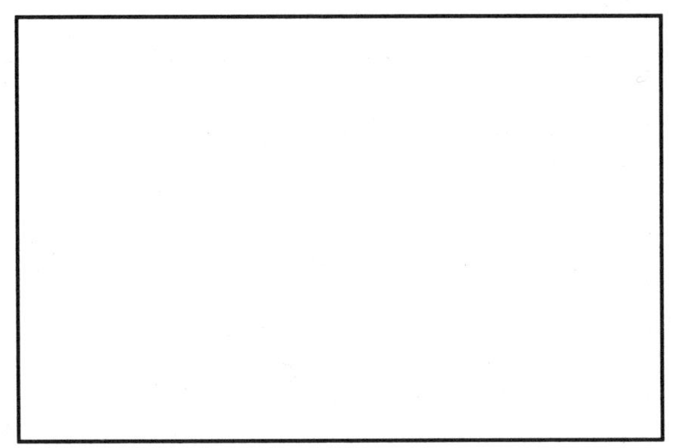

11

▲ Tick which of these circuits will not work. Give your reasons why.

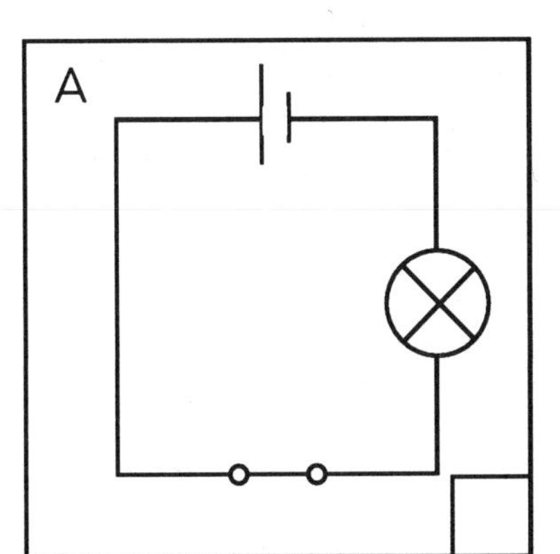

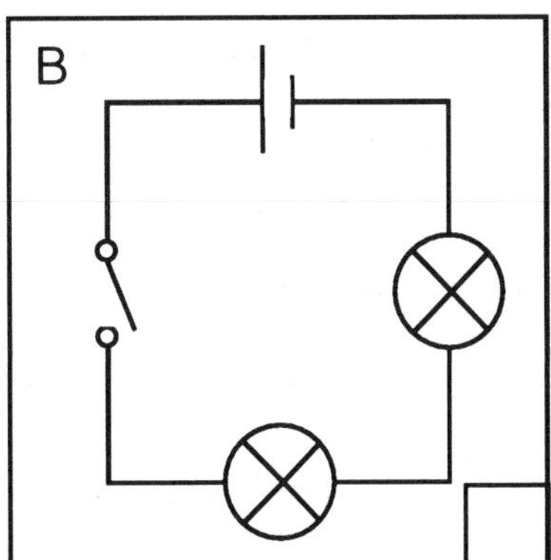

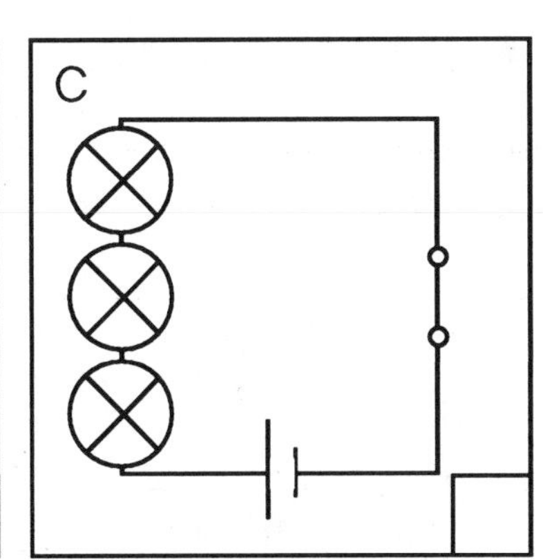

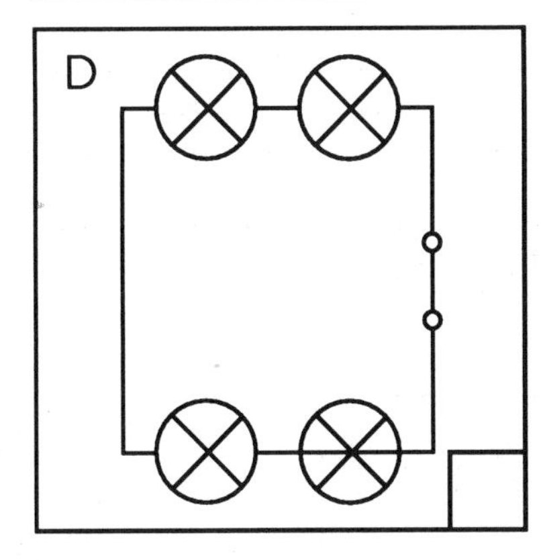

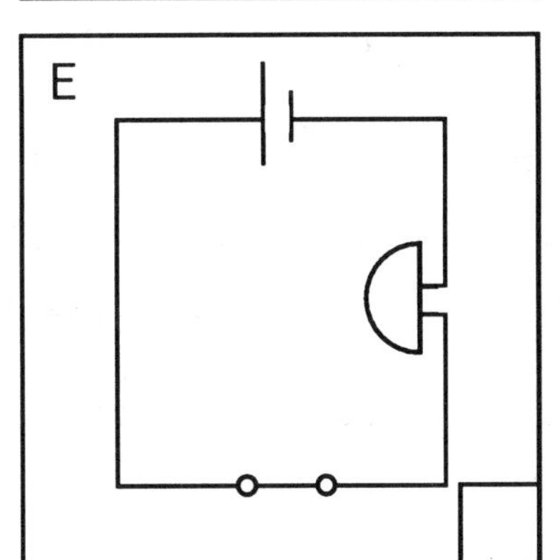

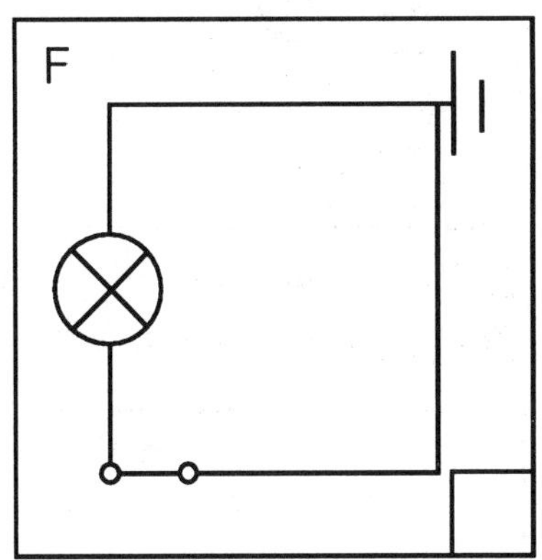

Assessment activities – Forces and motion

▲ Look at these objects. Decide whether you need to push or pull them to make them work. Write **push** or **pull** underneath each object.

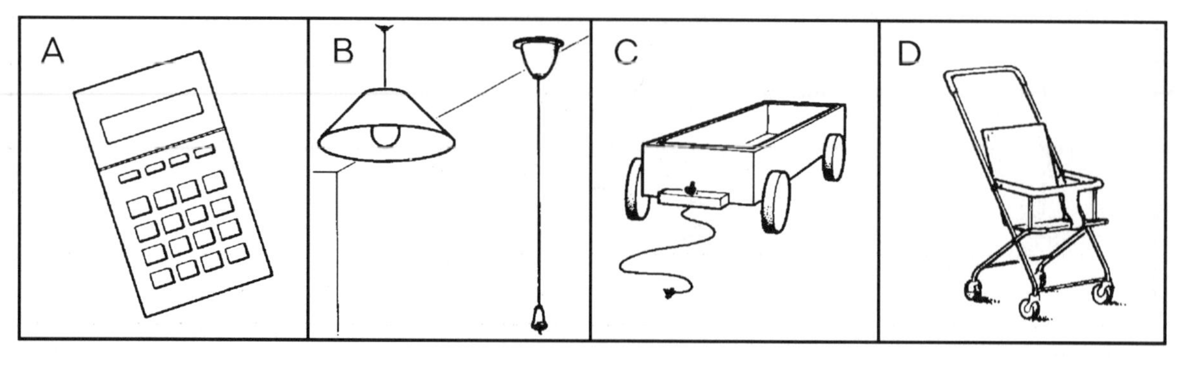

▲ Write down or draw how you could change the shape of this modelling clay. Explain what is happening.

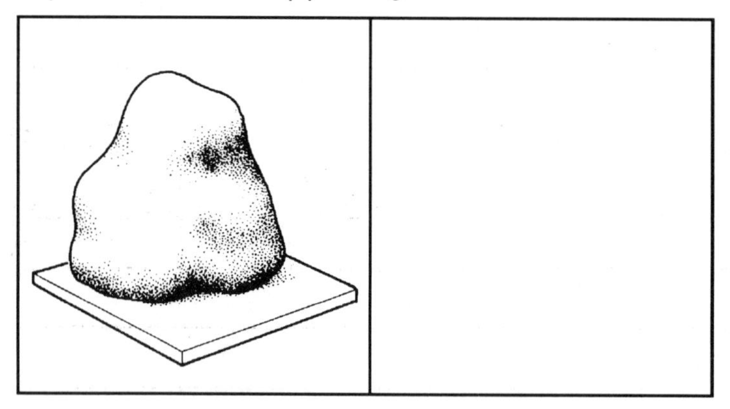

▲ Write down or draw how you could make this toy car move. Explain what is happening.

4

▲ Write down or draw how you could make this toy car slow down. Explain what you are doing.

5

The two magnets in picture A are joined together.
The two magnets in picture B will not join together.
▲ Suggest what is happening in each picture.

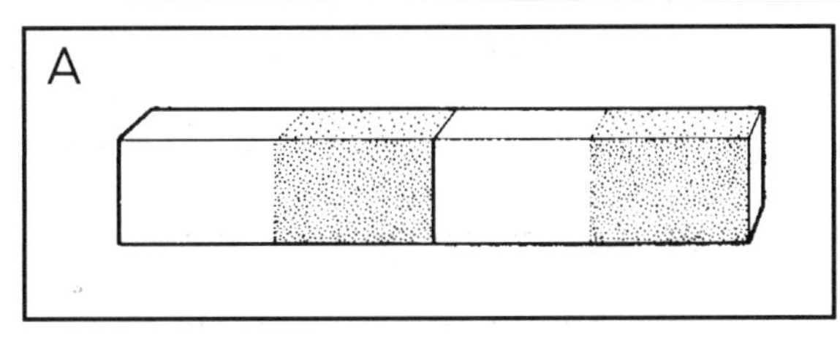

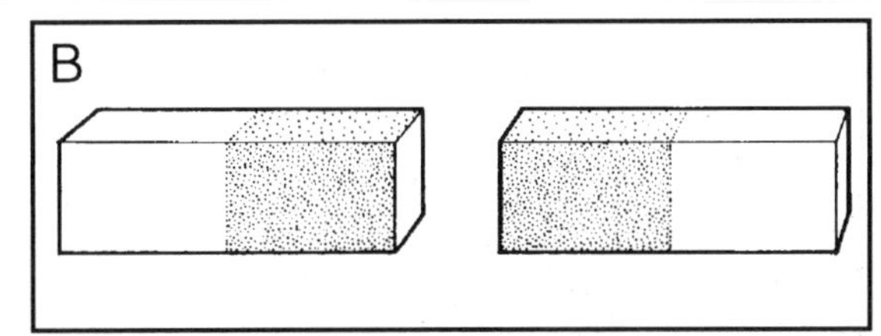

6

▲ Paul and Ranji have completed an investigation with magnets. Here are their results. Can you explain what the results tell us?

Object	Prediction: Is it magnetic?	Result: Is it magnetic?
paper	No	No
aluminium drink can	Yes	No
steel drink can	Yes	Yes
50p coin	Yes	No
fabric	No	No
brass weight	Yes	No
iron nail	Yes	Yes

Assessment activities – Forces and motion

7

▲ Can you explain what a force is? Give an example of what a force can do.

____

____

____

____

____

8

▲ Draw arrows on the diagram to show the forces acting on this book (if any).

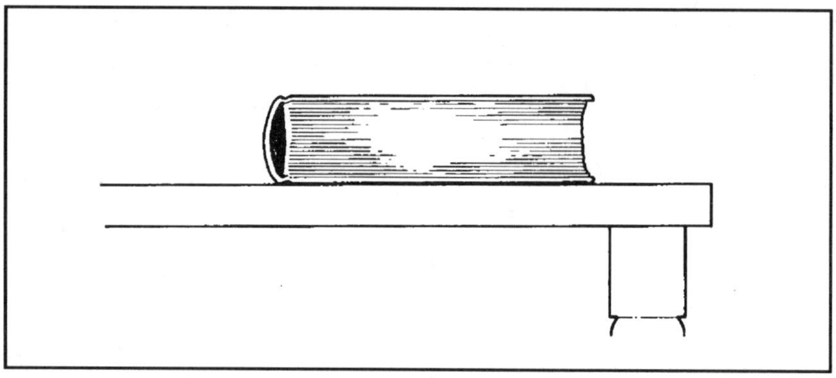

9

▲ Look at the pictures below. In each case, say which object will hit the ground first. Explain why.

A Earth	B Earth	C Moon
objects same size and shape, one is lighter	pieces of paper same size and weight, one flat, one in a ball	objects same weight, different shapes

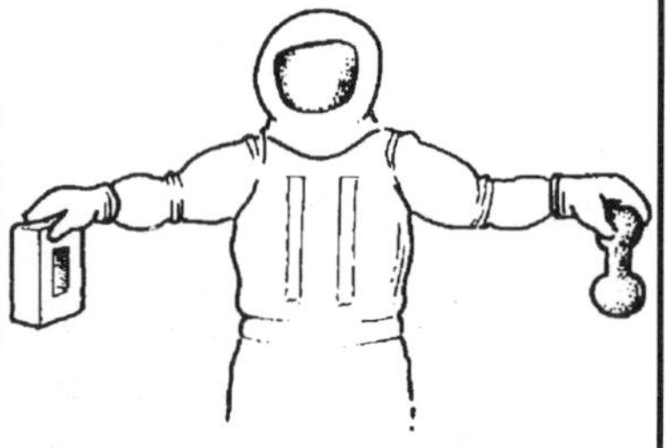

Which will land first?	Which will land first?	Which will land first?
____________	____________	____________
Why? ____________	Why? ____________	Why? ____________
____________	____________	____________
____________	____________	____________

Assessment activities – Forces and motion

10

▲ What will happen to the plastic dart when the elastic is let go?
Explain what is happening.

11

▲ What will happen to this toy if it is pushed down and then let go?
Explain what is happening.

12

▲ Explain why the wood floats and the coin sinks.

The wood floats because

The coin sinks because

Assessment activities – Light

1

▲ Name five things in this picture which can give us light.

1 ____________ 2 ____________ 3 ____________

4 ____________ 5 ____________

2

▲ Tick which light would be the brightest in a dark room.

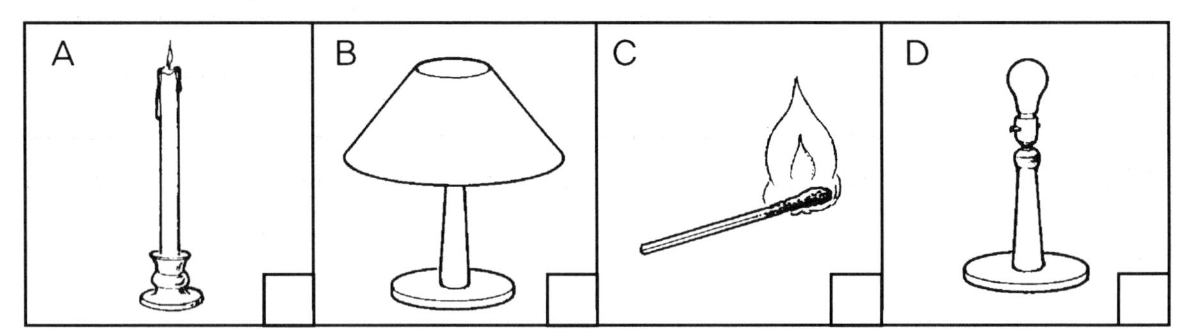

3

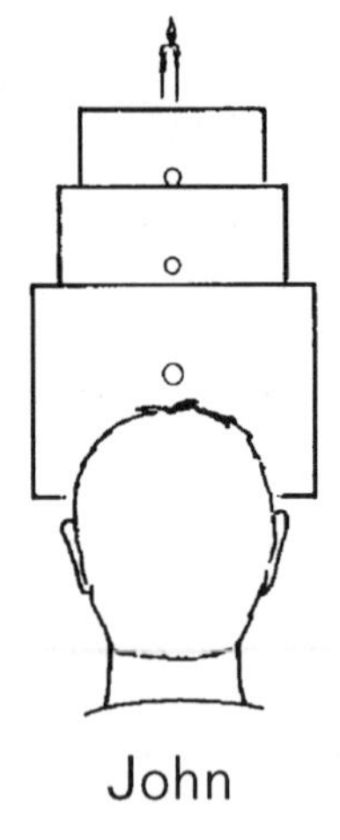

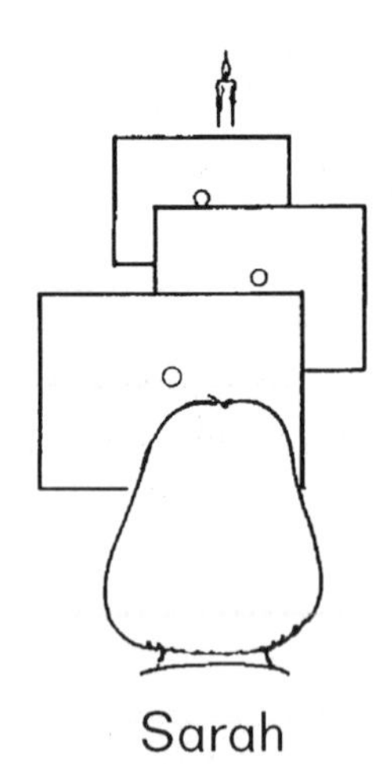

▲ Which person would be able to see the candle if they looked through the holes in the cards? ____________

Can you say why? ____________

____

Assessment activities – Light

4

▲ Tick the objects you think a torch light will shine through.

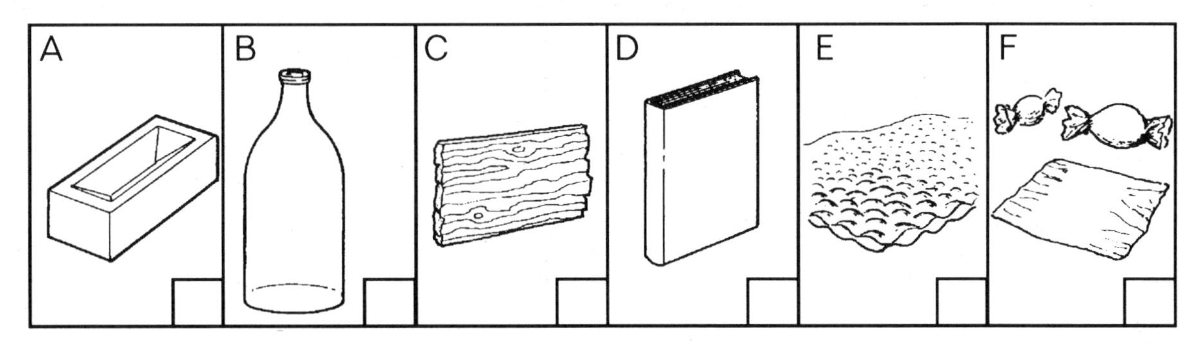

5

▲ What does transparent mean? ______________________________

____

____

____

Name a transparent object. ______________________________

6

▲ Draw the shape of the shadow made on the wall behind each object.

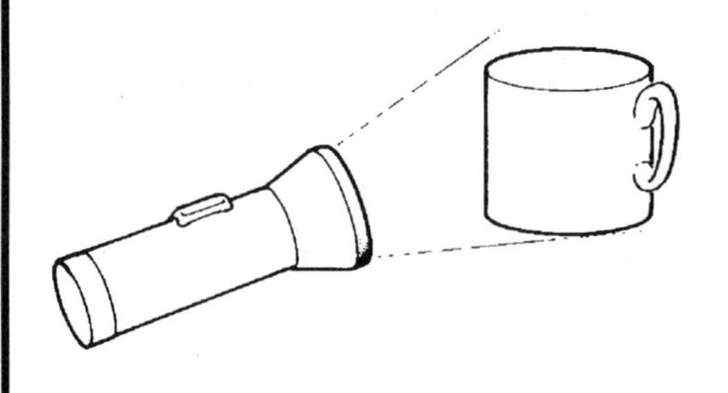

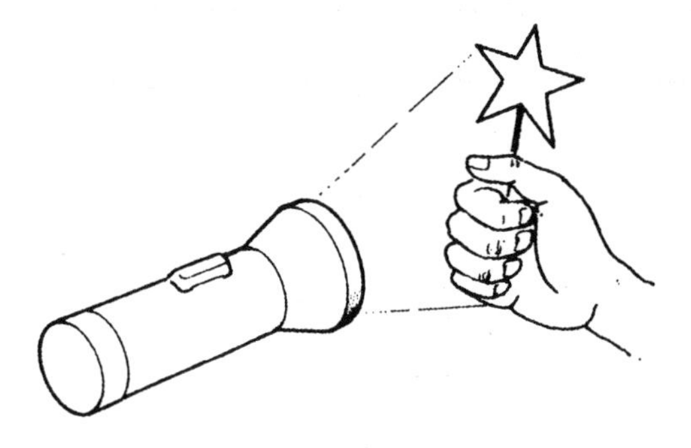

7

▲ Draw where you think the shadow will be.

A

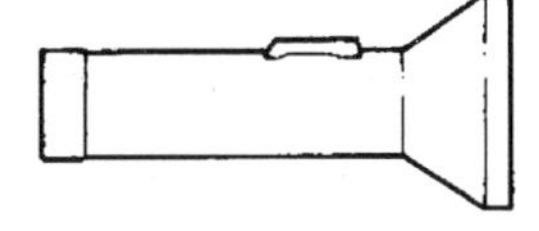

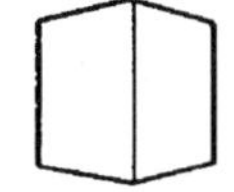

B

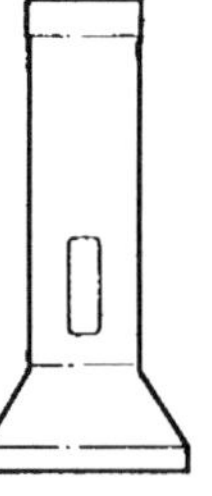

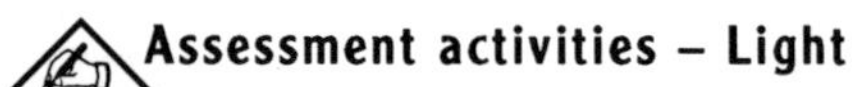

Assessment activities – Light

8

▲ Which shadow will be the larger? Tick the box.

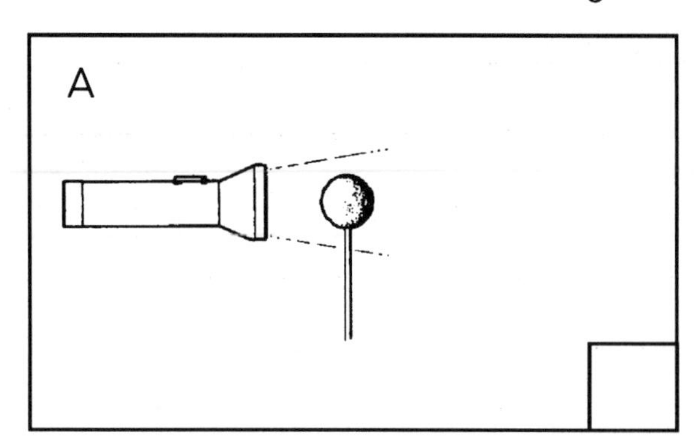

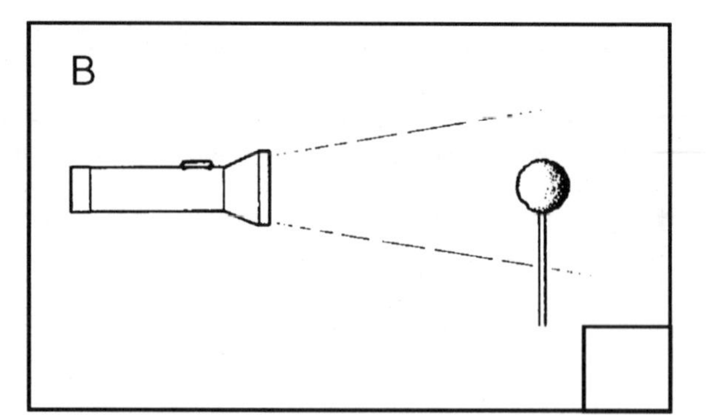

9

▲ Tick which of these objects you could see your reflection in.

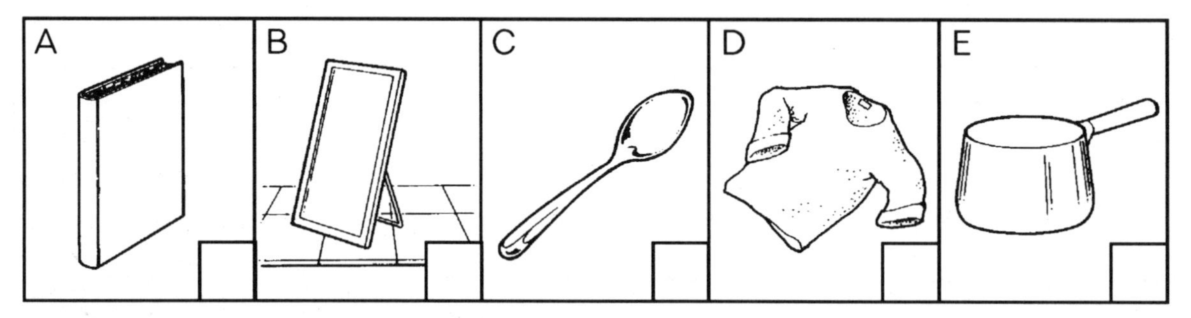

Which object gives the best reflection? ____________________

10

▲ Draw the image which would be seen in the mirror.

11

▲ Draw the beam of light reflected off the mirror.

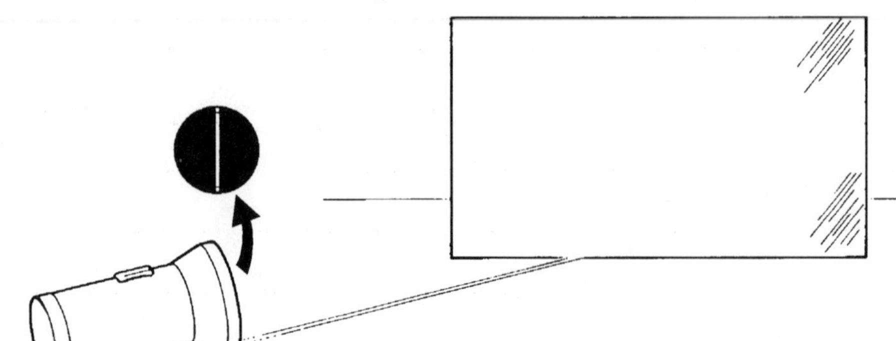

Assessment activities – Light

12

▲ Describe how shadows are formed.

13

▲ In each picture, draw arrows to show how you think the person sees the object.

A

B

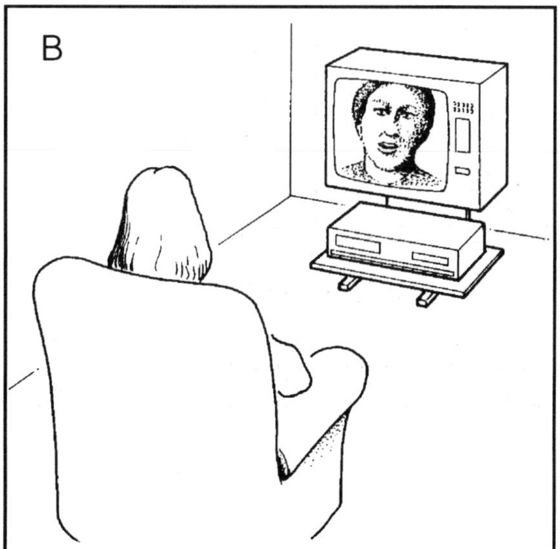

14

▲ Describe how we see objects.

Assessment activities – Sound

1

▲ Name five things in this picture which can make a sound.

1________________ 2________________ 3________________

4________________ 5________________

2

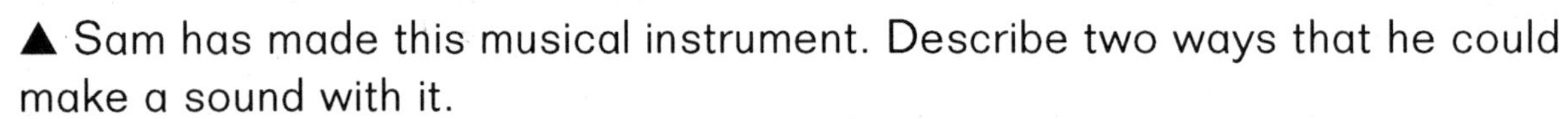

▲ Sam has made this musical instrument. Describe two ways that he could make a sound with it.

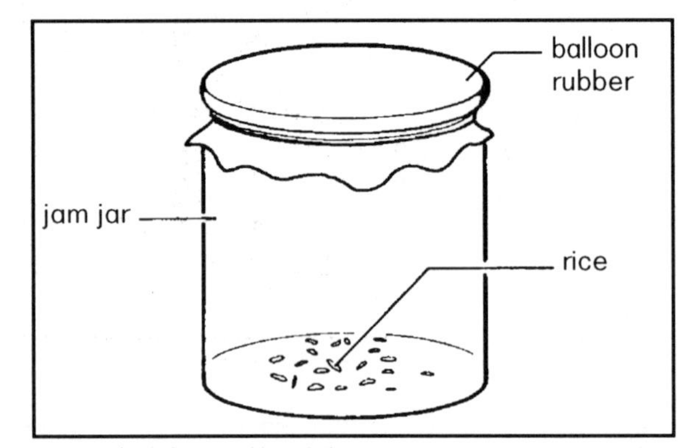

1 ____________________________

____

____

2 ____________________________

____

____

3

▲ If you wanted to attract someone's attention and they were a long way away, which of the following would you use? Tick the correct box.

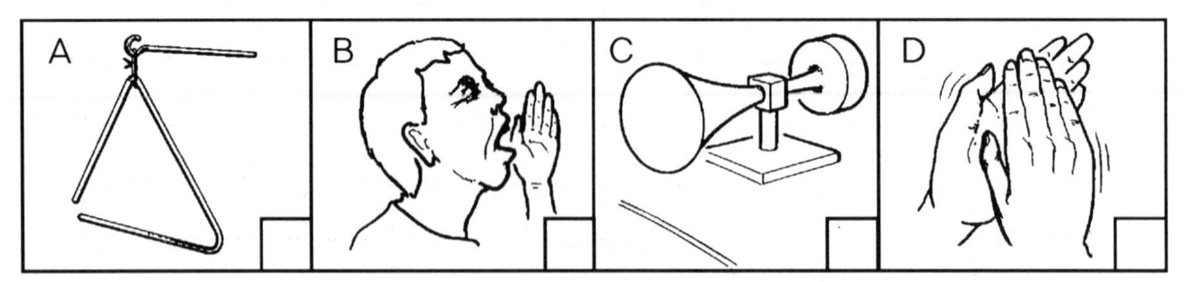

Why would you choose this? ______________________________

____

4

▲ How could you change the sound made with this musical instrument?

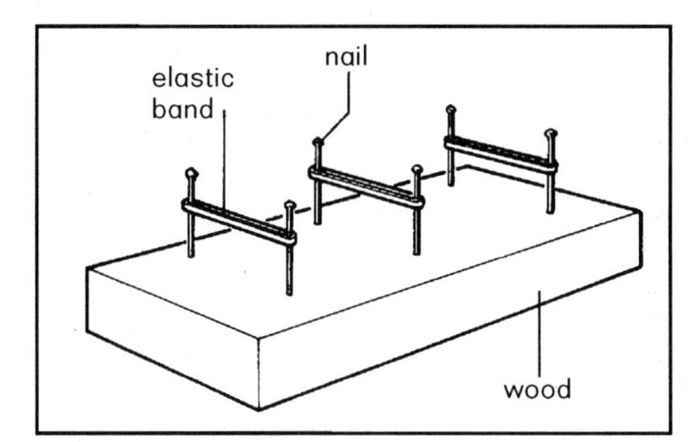

5

▲ How could you make loud and soft sounds with this instrument?

Soft ______________________

Loud ______________________

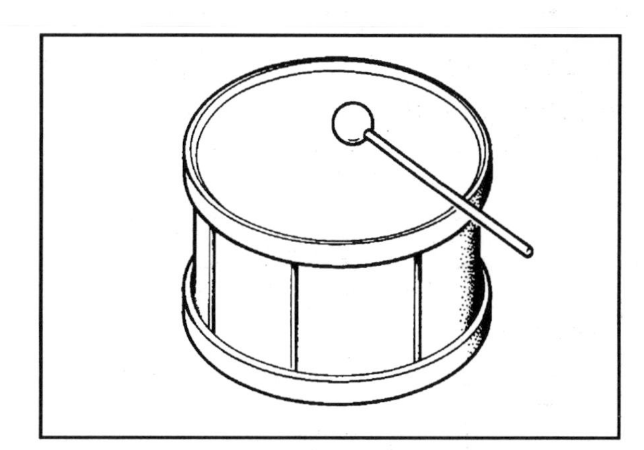

6

▲ Which bottle instrument will make a lower sound than B when blown across?

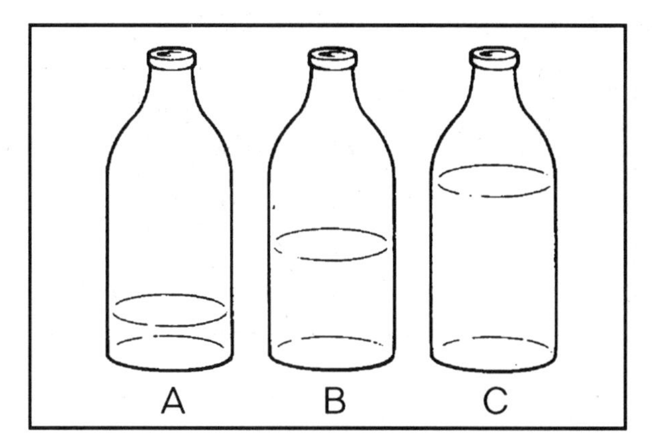

I think ______ will make a lower sound than B, because ______________

7

▲ Describe what *pitch* means when we talk about sounds.

____

____

____

____

____

8

▲ Mary is listening to a band playing in the park. What will happen to the sound of the music as she walks further away from the band?

____

____

____

____

____

____

9

This is a science experiment completed by Ranji and Sarah.

Things we used:

Shoe box, buzzer, battery, wires, bubble wrap, carpet scraps, newspaper, metre stick

What we did:

We put the buzzer inside the shoe box, turned it on and walked away until we couldn't hear the sound any more. We lined the box with different fabrics and tested the buzzer again.

Our Results:

Material	Distance away - sound no longer heard
empty shoe box	15 metres
lined with newspaper	12 metres
lined with carpet	7 metres
lined with bubble wrap	10 metres

▲ What do you think they were testing? _______________

____

▲ What do their results tell you? _______________

____

Assessment activities – Sound

10

▲ Tick which of these instruments makes a sound which can vary in pitch.

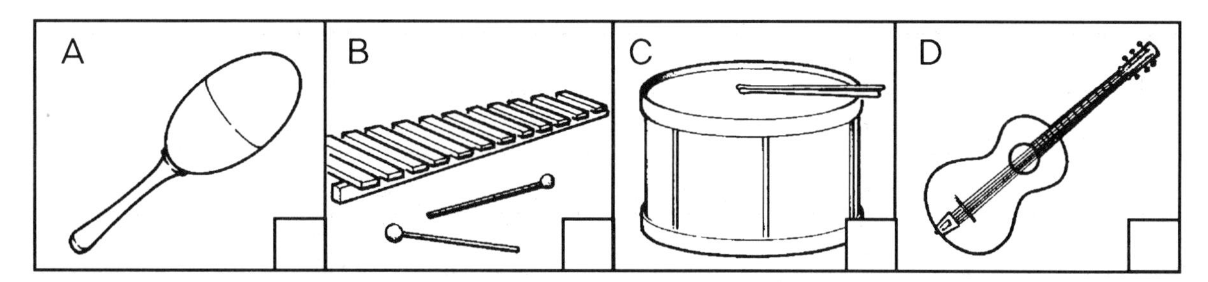

11

▲ Describe how you could change the pitch and the loudness of sounds made with this instrument.

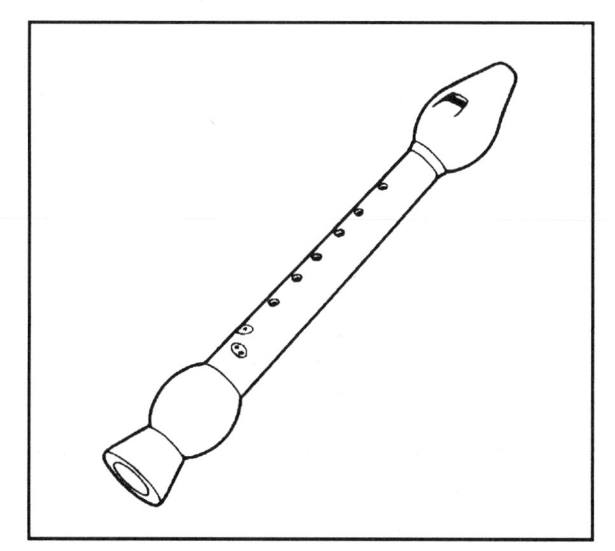

12

▲ Explain how the sound from this instrument is made and how it travels to our ears.

Assessment activities – The Earth and beyond

1

▲ Label the Sun, Moon and Earth in the picture below.

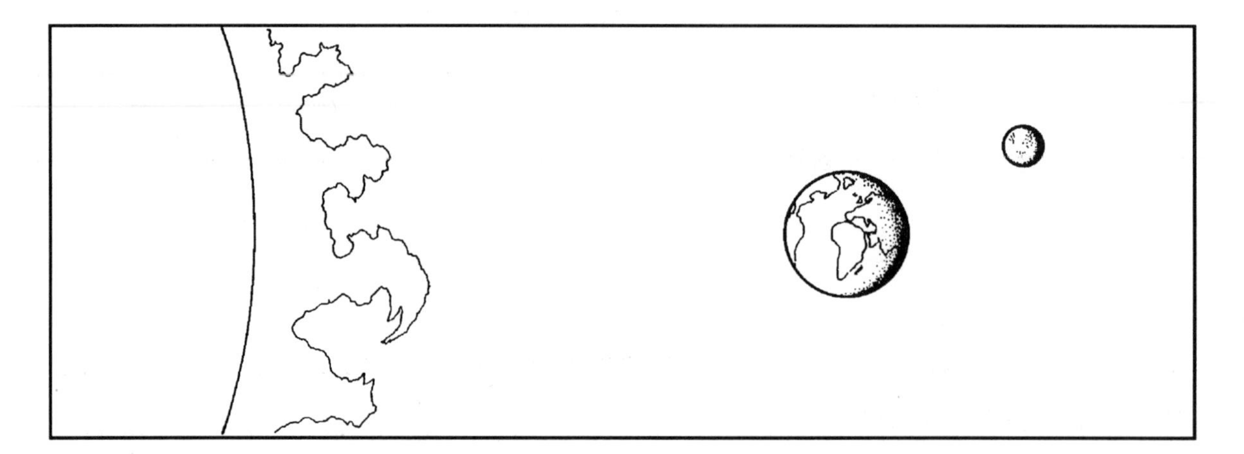

2

▲ Tick which shape the Sun, Moon and Earth are like.

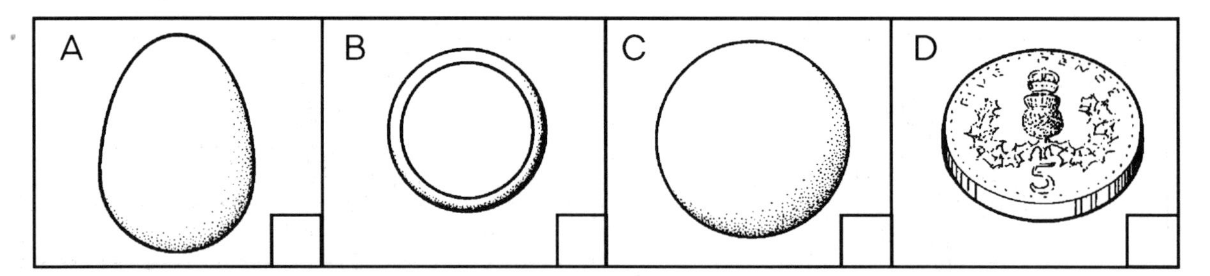

3

▲ Look at the picture below. It is morning. Draw in where you think the Sun will be at lunchtime.

Assessment activities – The Earth and beyond

4

▲ This is a stick and its shadow. It is 9 o'clock in the morning. Draw what you think the shadow will look like at lunchtime.

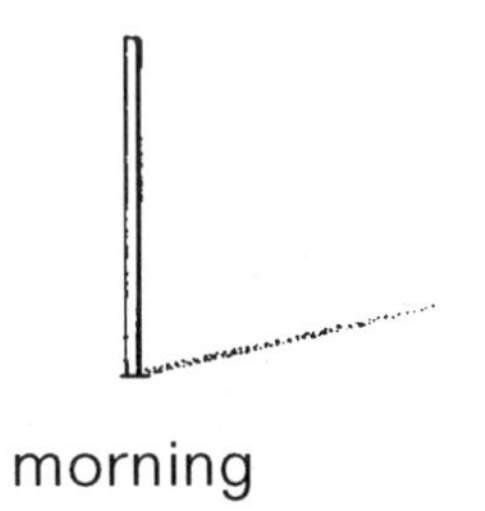

morning lunchtime

▲ Will the shadow be longer or shorter at lunchtime? ____________

Can you explain why? ____________

____

5

▲ The shadow from this scarecrow has changed during the day. Can you explain why? ____________

____

____

6

▲ Why does the Sun appear to move during the day?

____

____

____

____

____

7

▲ Ahmed and Anna are doing an experiment. What do you think they are trying to show?

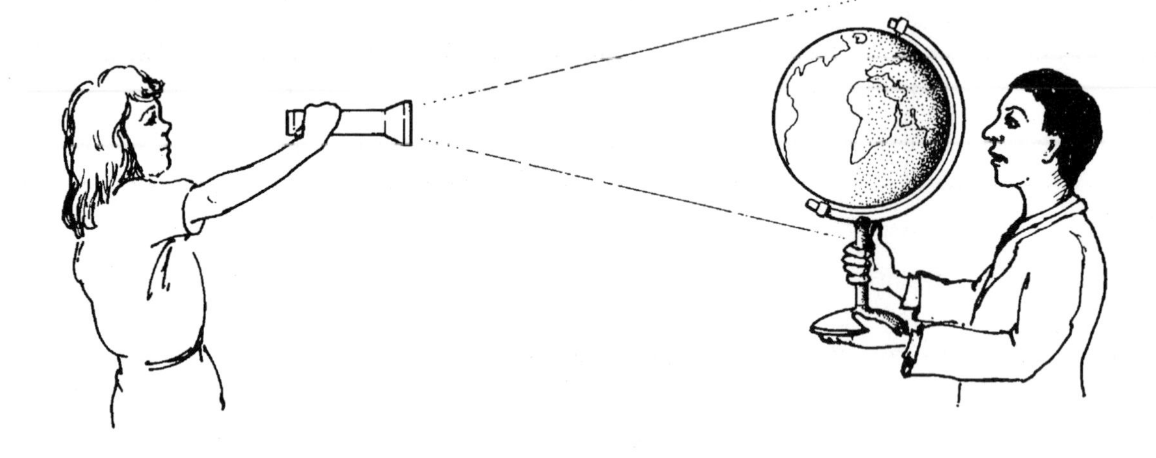

____

____

____

8

▲ Explain how night and day arise on the Earth.

____

____

____

____

9

▲ The Earth spins on its axis. Draw an arrow showing the direction in which it spins.

How long does the Earth take to spin round once? ______________________

10

▲ Fill in the missing spaces with the correct answers.

The Earth orbits the ______. It takes ____________ to make this orbit.

The Moon orbits the ______. It takes approximately ______ days to make this orbit.

11

▲ Explain what this model is showing.

____

____

____

____

12

▲ Explain why the shape of the Moon appears to change in the course of each month.

____

____

____

____

____

INFORMATION TECHNOLOGY WITHIN SCIENCE

The information technology activities outlined in this book can be used to develop and assess children's IT capability as outlined in the National Curriculum. Types of software rather than names of specific programs have been mentioned to enable teachers to use the ideas regardless of the type of computer they have access to.

Main IT focus

The main emphasis for the development of IT capability within these activities is on data handling and monitoring and control. The activities in this book are practically based and give children opportunities to use concrete materials and resources to develop scientific understanding. Content-specific software should not be used to replace such experiences, and should be used to develop or reinforce understanding only after initial practical work. Teachers should be aware that although such software may assist pupils in their learning of science, it may add little to the development of their pupils' IT capability.

Spreadsheets

The spreadsheet is a versatile and powerful tool which can be used in a variety of ways in science activities. A little time spent in exploring its potential will pay dividends for pupils and teachers alike. Spreadsheets have also become much easier to use with a mouse.

A spreadsheet is like a large set of pigeonholes. Any pigeonhole (or cell) can contain data in the form of text and numbers (and in some, even pictures) – or formulae which use the numbers to calculate an answer which appears in the same cell as the formula. The different cells are referenced by a co-ordinate system with letters on the *x* axis and numbers on the *y* axis.

Most spreadsheets contain a set of predetermined formulae which will, for example, add up the numbers in a set of cells or average a set of data. There are also quick ways of replicating a formula down or across the spreadsheet, so that the cell references are automatically updated as well. The numbers can be formatted to lie within the centre of a cell, on the right or lined up by the decimal point; the widths of the columns can be changed and text styles added to make the results more attractive.

One of the spreadsheet uses in this book allows children to record their investigative science work as on a printed table. The matrix arrangement of the spreadsheets suits many recording tasks, and is particularly useful where children are collecting a series of results and then finding the average. A formula can be set up to do this directly. The spreadsheet can be used in this way for a series of measurements from a single group of children, or for a class record where each row contains the results from a different group of children.

Most spreadsheets now also contain simple graphing facilities which allow children to plot graphs of one set of data against another. These are easy to set up, and mean that children have only to type their data once and can then present it in a range of formats.

Monitoring and measuring

The computer is an ideal tool for monitoring, in a scientific way, a range of physical changes over a period of time. The most common monitoring tasks in primary science involve sensing changes in light, heat, sound, movement and pressure. There is no requirement at Key Stage 2 to *measure* these changes, but many children will automatically want to record actual measurements (for example, when taking temperatures).

To use the computer for this type of work, schools will need to have access to an interface which links the various sensors to the computer and protects the computer. These can either be fitted inside the computer or be in a separate box linked to the computer through one of the connectors at the back. You will need to find out which type is the most suitable for your computer. Many interface cards come as a complete kit and include a range of simple sensors for classroom use.

The second part of the equipment is some suitable software which can interpret and display the results from the sensor. This is often shown in the form of a graph which can be printed out or saved to disk. The software can usually be configured to alter the frequency of the sensing: every minute, half-hour, hour, day, and so on. The equipment can be left running for long periods of time, so that (for example) temperature can be recorded over a full day to show daytime and night-time temperature changes.

More recently, a range of hand-held sensors have been introduced which are ideal for working out of doors or in places where it is difficult to reach a computer. The information is saved to an internal memory inside the sensor. This can be 'downloaded' into the computer and the results displayed on the screen. Schools can also make use of specific sensing equipment designed for a single purpose – such as electronic thermometers which can take readings from a sensor at the end of a wire (this is useful for recording external temperatures), or more common instruments such as simple photographic light meters.

A recent addition to many computers is the capacity to link a standard microphone to the computer, often through a small interface plugged into the printer port (parallel port). The equipment is often purchased as part of a multimedia pack, but the waveform pictures of the recorded sounds can also be used to give children an understanding of sound waves, pitch and loudness. In this way, it can also be used as a simple sound sensor.

The grids below relate the activities in this book to specific areas of IT and to relevant software resources. Activities are referenced by page number. (Bold page numbers indicate activities which have expanded IT content.) The software listed in the second grid is a selection of programs generally available to primary schools, and is not intended as a recommended list. The software featured should be available from most good educational software retailers.

AREA OF IT	TYPE OF SOFTWARE	ACTIVITIES (PAGE NOS.)				
		CHAPTER 1	CHAPTER 2	CHAPTER 3	CHAPTER 4	CHAPTER 5
Communicating Information	Word Processor	15, 26	46, 53	56, 57	71, **72**, 76	82, 88, **91**
Communicating Information	DTP	15				88
Communicating Information	Art software	15	35, 37			
Communicating Information	Graphics software	15, 28				83
Communicating Information	Authoring software				**72**	**91**
Communicating/ Handling Information	CD-ROM			67	79	82, **91**
Information Handling	Database	**14**				
Information Handling	Graphing software		40	**58**, 62		84
Information Handling	Spreadsheet		40, 44, 46, 48, 50, 53	**58**		
Measurement	Measuring	24, 26	45	57	74, 76, 77	
Control	Control	18, 20, 26	45			

SOFTWARE TYPE	BBC/MASTER	RISCOS	NIMBUS/186	WINDOWS	MACINTOSH
Word Processor	*Pendown* *Folio*	*Desk Top Folio* *Write On*	*All Write* *Kid Works 2*	*Creative Writer* *Easy Works* *Creative Writer*	*Kid Works 2*
DTP	*Typesetter* *Front Page Extra*	*Impression Style* *Desk Top Folio* *1st Page*	*Caxton Press* *Newspaper*	*Microsoft Publisher*	
Authoring		*Magpie* *Genesis* *Key Author*		*Genesis* *MMBox2*	*Hyperstudio*
Database	*Datashow* *Find IT, Grass* *Pinpoint Junior*	*DataSweet* *Sparks*	*Grass* *Claris Works* *Pinpoint Junior*	*Sparks* *Easy Works*	*Claris Works*
Graphing Software	*Datashow*	*Pictogram* *DataSweet*	*Datagraph*	*Datagraph* *Easy Works*	*Easy Works*
Spreadsheet	*Grasshopper* *Pigeonhole*	*DataSweet* *Grasshopper* *Advantage*	*Grasshopper*	*Sparks* *Claris Works* *Excel Starting Grids*	*Claris Works*
Measurement	*Sense-it*	*ReSound* *Junior Insight*	*Investigate*	*Insight* *Investigate*	
Control	*Control-IT* *Control Logo*	*Control IT* *Control Logo*	*Controller* *Control*	*Logicator*	

Cross-curricular links

	ENGLISH	MATHS	HISTORY	GEOGRAPHY	D&T	ART	MUSIC	RE
ELECTRICITY	Writing/discussing how electricity helps us. Debate – nuclear power should be stopped. Writing poems about electrical appliances. Electrical words – crosswords, word searches.	Data collection – number of electrical appliances at home. Survey – how to save electricity in our school.	Study of history of electricity – inventors, important dates. Development of electricity in British homes and industry since 1930. Its impact on daily lives.	Environmental changes – impact on environment due to production of electricity. Natural sources, pollution aspects, use of resources.	Designing, making and evaluating a battery-powered toy. Designing and making a badge or T-shirt telling people how to save electricity.	Making detailed observational drawings of electrical appliances. Paintings of electrical storms.	Pulses, beats, metronome. Making up sounds of an electrical storm. Making up songs about the uses of electricity.	Moral issues – nuclear power, dumping of wastes, uses of natural resources, responsibility of West, exploitations of developing countries.
FORCES AND MOTION	Writing/discussing favourite or most useful machines. Stories about machines, e.g. *The Trouble With Dad*. Writing action poems.	Working out speed of moving toy cars. Function machines. Data collection – number of machines at home. Angles, degrees of turn.	Impact of new technology – cars, machinery, factories. Victorian railways. Victorian toys. Buildings/ structures – Ancient Greece, pyramids of Ancient Egypt.	Forces of river erosion – resulting landscapes. Landslips and landslides.	Using construction kits to make working models of machines such as a crane. Designing and making a moving toy such as a string puppet.	Making observational drawings of machinery. Collage, murals of things which move. Mobiles.	Making machine sounds. Listening to electronic music, e.g. techno. Movement/dance to music.	Discussing people working together, helping each other, team work. Religious celebrations and processions. Violence/war – the use of force/ weapons.
SOUND	Discussing and writing about favourite sounds. Which sounds we dislike. Making words sound like their meaning. Writing sound poems. Finding out about deafness.	Data handling – favourite sounds/music.	Developing musical instruments. Radio, telephone. Music in Tudor, Victorian and modern times.	Environmental change – noise pollution. Causes and effects, prevention.	Designing, making and evaluating musical instruments. Designing a T-shirt telling people how to reduce noise pollution.	Paintings of things which make loud sounds. Mural of things which make soft sounds. Making wind chimes.	Listening to music which changes in speed, loudness, pitch, timbre. Working out the instruments in musical extracts, e.g. *Peter and the Wolf.* Making instruments.	Religious music – instruments used. Types of songs/ hymns used in different religions. Calls to prayer – bells, muezzin.
LIGHT	Writing about the dark – scary stories. Discussing fears – darkness. Debate – are street lights good? Stories about light, e.g. *The Lighthouse Keeper's Lunch.*	Mirror images – reflective symmetry. Shadow shapes.	Florence Nightingale. Development of candles and lamps.	Seasons/ weather – changes in daylight hours. Comparing sunshine conditions in different parts of world.	Designing and making a model candelabra. Designing a T-shirt with a sun motif. Designing and making a working lighthouse.	Making candles. Study artists influenced by use of light, e.g. paintings of sunrises, sunsets. Drawing candles/ lamps. Shadow puppets.	Making sounds to represent day and night. Listening to/making up songs about sunshine, shadows, light.	Festivals of light – Diwali. Importance of candles in religious ceremonies. Jesus – the light of the World. Hanukah.
THE EARTH AND BEYOND	Writing/discussing possibilities of life on other planets. Reading space stories/ poems. Writing space poems, crosswords.	Exploring large numbers, planet sizes, distances, scale, shapes, compass points, circumference. Data handling – information about time.	Study of history of astronomy, space travel. Local history – aspects of land change.	Environmental change – pollution, effects of humans on landscape. Weather studies. River studies.	Designing, making and evaluating a space rocket or moon buggy. Solar system mobiles. Scale models of planets.	Night sky paintings. Moonscapes. Collages, mobiles. Imaginary paintings of spaceships, aliens.	Devising space soundscapes. Holst: *The Planet Suite.* Jeff Wayne: *War of the Worlds.* Making up songs about space travel.	Creation stories – comparing different religions. Significance of stars – birth of Jesus.